This selection is taken from the Elizabe
version of Philemon Holland, the so-call
"translator-general in his age." Holland
translation was almost certainly read and used
by Shakespeare, and combines the splendid
rhythms of the King James Bible with the
exuberant vitality that we associate with
Elizabethan drama.

Southern Illinois University Press

THE HISTORY OF THE WORLD

COMMONLY CALLED

THE NATURAL HISTORY

OF C. PLINIUS SECUNDUS

or PLINY

TRANSLATED BY PHILEMON HOLLAND

SELECTED AND INTRODUCED BY PAUL TURNER

MCGRAW-HILL BOOK COMPANY
NEW YORK   TORONTO   LONDON

CONTENTS

Contents—*continued*   *Page*

INTRODUCTION

I

ACCORDING TO Bacon, Pliny's *Natural History* is not worth reading. It is "fraught with much fabulous matter, a great part not only untried, but notoriously untrue, to the great derogation of the credit of natural history with the grave and sober kind of wits." As thinkers, Pliny and Bacon were certainly poles apart, but as men they had quite a lot in common. Both were martyrs to experimental science. Bacon died of a chill that he caught while stuffing a chicken with snow, to test the preservative effects of refrigeration; and Pliny was asphyxiated by volcanic gases while investigating at close quarters the great eruption of Vesuvius in A.D. 79.

Another point of resemblance is that both men had distinguished public careers, and did all their writing in their spare time—though Bacon managed to increase his allowance of leisure by getting himself sacked from his last job. Pliny, by contrast, was an Admiral in command of a fleet when he died, yet his literary output was quite as large as Bacon's. Besides the *Natural History,* he wrote two long histories, a biography, and three technical handbooks, one on rhetoric, one on grammar, and one on the technique of throwing a javelin while riding a horse.

The secret of his amazing productivity was that he never wasted a second. In the intervals of his official duties he worked from early morning till late at night. Apparently he needed very little sleep, and was able to take it in small doses throughout the day, without seriously interrupting his train of thought. When not reading or writing himself, during meals, for instance, or while sunbathing, he always had something read aloud to him. In fact, he was as highly organized as any modern business executive, except that he had no dictaphone. At Rome he invariably travelled by sedan-chair, so that he could read or write *en route* (hence perhaps his fatness in later life); and on longer journeys he interrupted his reading only to dictate notes to a secretary, who was provided with gloves in winter, for fear the cold might affect the speed of his shorthand.

Among the by-products of all this study were a hundred and sixty volumes of closely written extracts, for which he was once offered something like £3,200. He refused the money, and left the precious volumes to his nephew, who may or may not have read them. By that time they had served their purpose and been written up into the thirty-seven books of the *Natural History*.

II

As a source of scientific information, the *Natural History* is not wholly reliable. In this function it has been largely superseded by the *Encyclopaedia Britannica*. But that was inevitable. Works of science are bound to be superseded, and will continue to do so, until what Peacock liked to call "the march of mind" eventually comes to a halt. So far, Pliny has merely suffered the same fate as Newton.

However, Pliny's importance as a scientist has been questioned on other grounds. He has been criticized, not for giving wrong or inadequate information, but for being unscientific in his methods. Certainly he relies too blindly on his written authorities, seldom bothering to check their statements by practical experiment, even when this could be done quite easily. For instance, he says that no amount of force or weight will break an eggshell standing vertically on end, though all the equipment needed to prove the contrary is a hammer and an egg (and a certain amount of water to clean up afterwards).

In his defence it must be pointed out that he is not wholly uncritical. He frequently shows how experiment or experience contradicts traditional theory; he is always mocking at Greek. credulity, and the absurd claims of magic; and he gets quite cross with Sophocles for talking such nonsense about amber. He is, in fact, quite as "scientific" as any scientist of his period; to expect him to be more so, when his whole object was to sum up the state of human knowledge in his day, is a little unreasonable.

In the history of science, then, the *Natural History* is a major document. It also gives valuable information, unobtainable elsewhere, about Greek and Roman painting, sculpture, architecture and other fine arts. Moreover, through its various unkind comments on contemporary life, it virtually develops into a sociological survey of the early Roman Empire. For such reasons it has been rightly called "perhaps the most important single source for the history of civilization."*

Such are Pliny's claims to the attention of the serious student. What has he to offer the more frivolous majority? He offers them a work which has been described by a Classical scholar of this century as "one of the half-dozen most interesting books in the world." This may be putting it rather too strongly, but not even Dr. Johnson could call it an "enormous and disgusting hyperbole." What makes the book so interesting is largely Pliny's outlook. He seems to have lived in a permanent state of astonishment. He was convinced that the world around him was a most extraordinary place, chock-full of fantastic things. The result was that he instinctively accumulated all the most sensational "facts", theories, and anecdotes in circulation, not because he meant to be a sensational writer, but because such material tallied with his romantic preconceptions of the nature of reality. Thus the *Natural History* became a vast repository of statements which nearly always appeal to the imagination, however much they revolt common sense.

Moral sermons are not usually very entertaining, and Pliny's habit of inserting them at regular intervals might be expected to reduce his readability. Oddly enough, it has the opposite effect. For one thing, his comments often contain a good deal of wisdom; for another, they are expressed in a very effective form of rhetoric. But the chief value of these moralizing digressions is that they relate the most heterogeneous aspects of the physical universe to a single centre—man. This not only unifies what would otherwise be chaotic; it also keeps the subject-matter, however apparently remote, close to the reader's experience.

The lists of medical prescriptions, though monotonous in themselves, have a somewhat similar effect. They reveal first-century

* L. Thorndike, *History of Magic and Experimental Science*.

man as a strangely familiar figure, suffering from all our own minor ailments, and putting unlimited faith in patent medicines. He was evidently a martyr to insomnia, indigestion, and asthma; he worried ceaselessly about the lack of hair on his head, or the excess of it elsewhere; and he was uneasily obsessed by sex—or why the constant search for aphrodisiacs and antaphrodisiacs? Pliny's world may be a thing of the past, but its human inhabitants are curiously up to date.

III

As Pliny himself realized, his subject-matter does not lend itself easily to literary treatment, and except in the rhetorical passages his style is bare and graceless. His syntax, too, is often slovenly, which makes him rather tiresome to read in the original. He is, in fact, one of the few great authors who actually improve in translation—that is, when translated by a man like Philemon Holland.

"The translator-general in his age," as Thomas Fuller called him, was born in the same year as Spenser and Sir Walter Raleigh, 1552. After taking his M.A. at Trinity College, Cambridge, he went on to study medicine, and settled down at Coventry, where he had a small practice. He married in 1579, and produced ten children. In order to support them, he supplemented his income, first by translating, and then by teaching at the Coventry Free School, where he eventually became headmaster. In 1612 he was honoured with the freedom of Coventry, and five years later was chosen to deliver "a learned, elegant, and religious speech" of welcome to James I on his journey through Warwickshire. Finally, Fuller tells us, "this eminent *translator* was *translated* to a better life, anno Domini 1637."

His major translations include Livy's *Romane Historie,* Plutarch's *Morals,* Xenophon's *Cyrupaedia,* and *The Historie of Twelve Caesars* by Suetonius Tranquillus. A contemporary comment on his tremendous output has been preserved by Fuller, who had, as we have seen, a weakness for puns :

> Holland with his translations doth so fill us,
> He will not let *Suetonius* be *Tranquillus.*

But his most popular work was Pliny's *Historie of the World*, first published in 1601. The imaginative rendering of the dull words *Naturalis Historia* immediately suggests Holland's feeling for Pliny's grand project. It was just the title to appeal to the Elizabethan public. Raleigh must have thought so, anyway, for three years later he started writing his own *Historie of the World*.

As a doctor, Holland was well qualified to deal with the medical parts of the *Natural History*, and he felt sure that his contemporaries would benefit from Pliny's professional advice. The whole work, he thought, was

> not appropriate to the learned only, but accommodate to the rude peasant of the country; fitted for the painful artisan in town and city; pertinent to the bodily health of man, woman, and child; and in one word, suiting with all sorts of people living in a society and commonweal.

His only problem was a religious scruple : was it right to popularize a work which rejected the idea of Providence as "a toy and vanity worthy to be laughed at"? Fortunately, like Tennyson's friend, "he fought his doubts and gathered strength" to produce the best version of Pliny that has yet appeared. In Holland's English Pliny's most shapeless sentences take on rhythm and dignity, and his rhetorical passages become even more impressive. The sense of monotony almost inevitable in so exhaustive a work is somehow reduced to a minimum, and Holland's "mean and popular style", as he called it, seems so spontaneous and natural that one quite forgets one is reading a translation.

But Holland does not, like Chapman, completely rewrite his author. He always sticks fairly close to the Latin, and his insertions expand and clarify, rather than change the original. For instance, on page 289 he fills out a bare sentence in which Pliny had merely listed some remedies for sprains. Holland assigns certain remedies to certain types of sprain, explains the method of application in each case, and suggests how the injuries might have been incurred. By modern standards this is very free translation; but all Holland has really done is to move some useful footnotes up into the text.

In general, what he adds is vitality, grace, and wit : he is particularly good at giving epigrammatic form to conceits barely suggested, or clumsily expressed in the Latin. "I doubt not," he makes Pliny say rather charmingly, "but there be some who will . . . think us very simple for writing thus as we do of simples". Or again, in an outburst of indignation against "our wanton gluttons and bellygods", who send all over the world for rare delicacies :

> [They] have purveyors another way in Numidia and Athyopia, for the rare birds there about the sepulchres; among those sepulchres (I say) where instead of meeting with game, they stumble otherwhiles upon their own graves and never come home again.

Undoubtedly, as Fuller says, "Our Holland had the true knack of translating". His version of Pliny has even been recommended by a modern expert in Silver Latin as an adequate substitute for the original :

> For anyone not too rigidly concerned with Pliny's Latin, an excellent way to enjoy him would be to prop Philemon Holland's folio translation on a table, and browse, as one lists, among the big pages that give a feeling of spacious leisureliness by their size no less than by their generously expanded allowance of quaint English.

The trouble is that these folios are extremely rare (the last printing was in 1634); and in an age when the only bookrests in the shops are rickety contraptions of wire and plastic, even the "propping" is not as simple as it sounds. Both problems should, however, be solved by this selection.

IV

Holland made Pliny, in effect, an Elizabethan author, and as such he has had a considerable influence on English literature. Though Shakespeare seems to have known the *Natural History* in Latin, he probably read Holland's version when it came out in 1601, and *Othello,* written three years later, contains several echoes of Pliny. An obvious example is Othello's reference to

> The Anthropophagi, and men whose heads
> Do grow beneath their shoulders.

Less obvious, and more surprising, is the climax of the same speech :

> This only is the witchcraft I have used.

The source of this line, and perhaps of the whole scene in which it occurs (since there is no equivalent in Cinthio's *Hecatommithi*) is surely the anecdote on page 166 about a farmer who is accused of practising black magic. The train of thought from agriculture to marriage was possibly suggested by the fact that Holland's word for farming is *husbandry*.

Donne's *Progress of the Soul* (1601) contains a curious episode in which a very Plinian elephant goes to sleep, and a mouse crawls up its trunk :

> In which as in a gallery this mouse
> Walk'd, and surveyed the rooms of this vast house,
> And to the brain, the soul's bedchamber, went,
> And gnaw'd the life cords there; Like a whole town
> Clean undermin'd, the slain beast tumbled down.

It might almost have been written to substantiate Pliny's remark about elephants : "Of all other living creatures, they cannot abide a mouse". When Marvell speaks in *The Garden* of

> The Mind, that Ocean where each kind
> Does straight its own resemblance find,

he is thinking of Pliny's statement that the sea contains marine versions of all land-creatures (including fleas and lice). Sir Thomas Browne devotes a whole chapter of his *Vulgar Errors* to disproving and then allegorizing the theory that the beaver, when cornered, bites off its testicles. As for those pet properties of seventeenth-century poetry, the Phoenix, the Great Year, and the Music of the Spheres, their ultimate source may be Plato and Herodotus, but their chief publicizer was Pliny.

In the Age of Reason, Addison mentions the Music of the Spheres only to deny its objective existence :

> What though in solemn silence all
> Move round the dark terrestrial ball;
> What though no real voice nor sound
> Amidst their radiant orbs be found?

Certainly Pliny was not quite reasonable enough to appeal to the Augustans, but the Romantics brought him back into favour. Wordsworth's *Loadamia* was inspired by a sentence in the *Natural History,* which he paraphrased as the climax of the poem :

> Upon the side
> Of Hellespont (such faith was entertained)
> A knot of spiry trees for ages grew
> From out the tomb of him for whom she died;
> And ever, when such stature they had gained
> That Ilium's walls were subject to their view,
> The trees' tall summits withered at the sight;
> A constant interchange of growth and blight.

Byron's *Giaour* probably owes to Pliny (see page 117) his conversion to monogamy :

> But this was taught me by the dove,
> To die—and know no second love.

Shelley translated half of the *Natural History* while at Eton, and often re-read the original in later years. His biographer, Medwin, held Pliny responsible for "the first germ of his ideas respecting the nature of God", and a recent German scholar has traced innumerable Plinian precedents for the main features of Shelley's *weltanschauung*. On the level of imagery, I suspect that *Ozymandias* derives its central symbol from Pliny's account of various *colossi*, including the one ordered by Nero (pp. 378–380), and its fine concluding lines from the description of the desert round the pyramids (p. 442) :

And yet of all these huge monuments, there remain no tokens

of any houses built, no appearance of frames and engines requisite for such monstrous buildings : a man shall find all about them, far and near, fair sand and small red gravel.

Keats did not own a copy of the *Natural History*, but two passages in his poems suggest that somewhere on his travels through the realms of gold he got a chance of "looking into" Holland's Pliny. The first comes from the address to the Moon in *Endymion* :

> Thou art a relief
> To the poor patient oyster, where it sleeps
> Within its pearly house.

Now who would have thought of connecting the moon with an oyster but for Pliny's remarks on page 35? The second passage is in *The Eve of St. Agnes*. Young Porphyro emerges from Madeline's closet,

> Noiseless as fear in a wide wilderness.

The same highly individual simile is used to describe the environs of Mount Atlas (p. 51): "All is still and silent, like the fearful horror in desert wilderness."

Who now reads Pliny? Very few, perhaps; but apparently his soul still goes marching on through the minds of English writers. In Christopher Fry's *The Boy with the Cart* it seems that Cuthman's church will never be completed, because the king-post has swung out of position, and he cannot get it back. Cuthman is in despair, until a Carpenter appears to him, and with a touch of His finger lifts the heavy timber into place. No doubt there are many similar incidents in the Lives of the Saints; but the prototype may well be the story on page 446 about Diana's temple at Ephesus.

Still, the further we advance from Pliny's time, the more conjectural his influence is bound to become. If we want indisputable evidence, we must return to the Middle Ages. The immense popularity of the *Natural History* throughout that period is proved by the fact that over two hundred manuscripts survive.

Perhaps the oddest result of Pliny's zoology is the medieval bestiary, an allegorical form which flourished from the fifth to the fifteenth century. From his anthropology the most shameless piece of borrowing occurs in Mandeville's *Travels*. Sir John, the supposed traveller, is giving an eye-witness account of the inhabitants of Ethiopia :

> In that contree ben folk that han but o foot; and thei gon so blyve that it is mervaylle; and the foot is so large that it schadeweth all the body agen the sonne, whan they wole lye and reste hem.

V

Holland's Pliny runs to well over a million words. This fact may increase our respect for the translator, who took only a year to write it; all the same, most people will find the book a trifle too long to read from cover to cover. Fortunately we have Pliny's permission to skip, for he tells the future Emperor Titus :

> I have . . . prefixed before these books, the summary or contents of every one : and very carefully have I endeavoured, that you should not need to read them throughout, whereby all others also after your example, may ease themselves of the like labour : and as any man is desirous to know this or that, he may seek and readily find in what place to meet with the same.

But the reader of this selection will be, as it were, skipping blind, so I must explain the principle on which the extracts have been chosen.

I confess I have not tried to cater for scientists or serious historians of science. Thus I have tended to omit statements of well-known facts, in favour of dubious but entertaining theories, and illustrative anecdotes. On the other hand, I have aimed to give a tolerably representative picture of Pliny's world-view, and to provide material for a reliable estimate of his general methods and attitudes. I have also included many passages of moral or philosophical reflection, of nature-worship, and of social satire, because they contain some of his finest writing.

Sainte-Beuve called the *Natural History* "une grande mer d'érudition où il fait bon pêcher". No doubt everyone would prefer to do his own fishing, and will think poorly of other people's catches. I can only hope that my haul is large enough to provide something for every type of reader—from "grave and sober wits" to earnest seekers after unintentional humour.

With a great deal of help from Mrs. Mary Knowler, for which I am most grateful, I have modernized the spelling of words still in common use, except where this would involve a significant change of sound or associations. Thus *Affrick* does not become *Africa,* which to my mind is a totally different country. Most proper names, in fact, have been left in their original spelling, and so have words which are obsolete. The meaning of the latter, and of any other terms likely to cause difficulty, will be found in the Glossary.

The titles and summaries of contents preceding individual books are taken from Holland, but the headings of the extracts are my own: I hope that those few which betray twentieth-century habits of thought will not clash too violently with the Elizabethan tone of the text.

P.D.L.T.

THE FIRST BOOK

containeth the Dedicatory Epistle or Preface of the whole work, addressed to Titus Vespasian the Emperor. Also the names of the Authors out of which he gathered the History, which he prosecuteth in thirty-six Books: together with the Summary of every Chapter.

THE DEDICATORY EPISTLE

THESE BOOKS containing the History of Nature, which a few days since I brought to light (a new work in Latin, and namely among the Romans, your citizens and countrymen) I purpose by this epistle of mine to present and consecrate unto you, most sweet and gentle Prince (for this title accordeth fittest unto you, seeing that the name of Most mighty sorteth well with the age of the Emperor your father :) which haply might seem boldness and presumption in me, but that I know how at other times you were wont to have some good opinion of my toys and fooleries.

* * * * *

For mine own part, challenged I may be more still for this my importune and inconsiderate boldness, in that I would seem to present these books unto you, compiled of so slender stuff and matter as they be : for therein can be couched no great wit (which otherwise in me was ever mean and simple) neither admit they any digressions, orations, speeches, and discourses, ne yet admirable cases and variable chances, nor any other occurrent, either pleasant to rehearse, or delectable to hear. The truth is this, the nature of all things in this world, that is to say, matters concerning our daily and ordinary life, are here deciphered and declared, and that in barren terms, without any goodly show of

19

gay and glorious phrases : and whatever I have put down, concern it doth the basest points thereof, insomuch as for the most part I am to deliver the thing in hand, either in rustical speech, or else in foreign, nay, in barbarous language, such also as may not well be uttered, but with reserving honour to the hearers, and reverence to the readers.

Moreover, the way that I have entered into, hath not been trodden beforetime by other writers, being indeed so strange and uncouth, as a man's mind would not willingly travel therein. No Latin author among us hath hitherto once ventured upon the same argument, no one Grecian whatsoever hath gone through it and handled all : and no marvel, for many of us love not to take any pains, but study rather to pen matters of delight and pleasure. True it is, I must needs say, that others have made profession hereof, but they have done it with such subtlety and deepness, that all their travails and writings by that means, lie as it were dead and buried in darkness. Now come I, and take upon me to speak of everything, and to gather as it were a complete body of arts and sciences (which the Greeks call ἐγκυκλαπάιδείος) that are either altogether unknown or become doubtful, through the overmuch curiosity of fine wits : again, other matters are deciphered in such long discourses, that they are tedious to the readers, insomuch as they loathe and abhor them. A difficult enterprise it is therefore to make old stuff new, to give authority and credit to novelties, to polish and smooth that which is worn and out of use, to let a gloss and lustre upon that which is dim and dark, to grace and countenance things disdained, to procure belief to matters doubtful, and in one word, to reduce nature to all, and all to their own nature. And verily to give the attempt only and show a desire to effect such a design as this, although the same be not brought about and compassed, were a brave and magnificent enterprise. Certes of this spirit am I, that those learned men and great students, who making no stay but breaking through all difficulties, have preferred the profit of posterity before the tickling and pleasure of itching ears in these days; which I may protest that I have aimed at, not in this work only, but also in other of my books already : and I profess, that I wonder much at *T. Livius,* otherwise a most renowned and famous writer, who in a preface to one of his

books of the Roman history which he compiled from the foundation of Rome, thus protested, That he had gotten glory enough
by his former writing, and might sit still now and take his ease,
but that his mind was so restless and so ill could abide repose,
that contrariwise it was fed and nourished with travail and
nothing else. But surely methinks, in finishing those Chronicles,
he should in duty have respected the glory of that people which
had conquered the world and advanced the honour of the
Roman name, rather than displayed his own praise and commendation : Ywis, his demerit had been the greater, to have
continued his story as he did, for love of the subject matter,
and not for his private pleasure; to have I say performed that
piece of work more to gratify the state of Rome, than to content
his own mind and affection. As touching myself (forasmuch as
Domitius Piso saith, that books ought to be treasuries and store-
houses indeed, and not bare and simple writings) I may be bold
to say and aver, that in thirty-six Books I have comprised 20,000
things, all worthy of regard and consideration, which I have
collected out of 2,000 volumes or thereabout, that I have diligently read (and yet very few of them there be that men
learned otherwise, and studious, dare meddle withal, for the
deep matter and hidden secrets therein contained) and those
written by 100 several elect and approved authors : besides a
world of other matters, which either were unknown to our forefathers and former writers, or else afterwards invented by their
posterity. And yet I nothing doubt but many things there be,
which either surpass our knowledge, or else our memory hath
overslipped : for me we are, and men employed in many affairs.
Moreover, considered it would be, that these studies we follow
at vacant times and stolen hours, that is to say, by night season
only; to the end that you may know, how we to accomplish
this, have neglected no time which was due unto your service.
The days are wholly employed and spent in attendance upon
your person, we sleep only to satisfy nature, even as much as
our health requireth, and no more; contenting ourselves with
this reward, that whilst we study and muse (*as Varro saith*) upon
these things in our closet, we gain so many hours to our life; for
surely we live then only, when we watch and be awake.

THE SECOND BOOK

treateth of the World, Elements, and Stars

THE WORLD

THE WORLD, and this, which by another name men have thought
good to call Heaven (under the pourprise and bending cope
whereof, all things are emmantled and covered) believe we ought
in all reason to be a God, eternal, immeasurable, without beginning, and likewise endless. What is without the compass hereof,
neither is it fit for men to search, nor within man's wit to reach
and conceive. Sacred it is, everlasting, infinite, all in all, or rather
itself all and absolute : finite and limited, yet seeming infinite : in
all motions, orderly and certain : howbeit in show and judgement of men, uncertain, comprehending and containing all whatsoever, both without and within : Nature's work, and yet very
Nature itself, producing all things. Great folly it is then, and
mere madness, that some have devised and thought in their mind
to measure it; yea, and durst in writing set down the dimensions
thereof : that others again, by occasion hereupon taken or given,
have delivered and taught, that worlds there were innumerable :
as if we were to believe so many natures as there were Heavens :
or if all were reduced to one, yet there should be so many suns
and moons nevertheless, with the rest also of those immeasurable
and innumerable stars in that one : as though in this plurality of
worlds we should not always meet with the same question still at
every turn of our cogitation, for want of the utmost and some
end to rest upon : or, if this infiniteness could possibly be assigned
to Nature, the work-mistress and mother of all; the same might
not be understood more easily in that one Heaven which we see;

so great a work especially and frame as it is. Now surely a fantastical folly it is of all other follies, to go forth of it, and so to keep seeking without, as if all things within were well and clearly known already : as who would say, a man could take the measure just of any third thing, who knoweth not his own : or the mind of man see those things, which the very world itself may not receive.

THE MUSIC OF THE SPHERES

That the world thus framed, in a continual and uncessant circuit, with unspeakable swiftness turneth round about in the space of four and twenty hours, the rising and setting ordinarily of the sun hath left clear and doubtless. Now, whether it being in height infinite, and therefore the sound of so huge a frame, whiles it is whirled about, and never resteth in that revolution, cannot be heard with our ears, I cannot so easily resolve and pronounce : no more I assure you, than I may avouch the ringing of the stars that are driven about herewith, and roll with all their own spheres : or determine, that as the heaven moveth, it doth represent indeed a pleasant and incredible sweet harmony both day and night : although to us within, it seemeth to pass in silence.

THE FOUR ELEMENTS

I neither see any doubt made as touching the elements, that they be four in number. The highest, Fire : from whence are those bright eyes of so many shining stars. The next, Spirit, which the Greeks and our countrymen by one name call Air : Vital this element is, and as it giveth life to all things, so it soon passeth through all, and is intermedled in the whole : by the power whereof, the Earth hangeth poised and balanced just in the midst, together with the fourth element, of the Waters. Thus by a mutual intertainment one of another, divers natures are linked and knit together : so as the light elements are kept in and restrained by certain weights of the heavier, that they fly not out : and contrariwise, the massier be held up, that they fall not down, by means of the lighter, which covet to be aloft. So, through an equal endeavour to the contrary, each of them hold their own, bound as it were by the restless circuit of the very world : which, by reason that it runneth evermore upon itself, the earth falleth to be lowest, and the middle of the whole : and the same hanging steadily by the poles of the Heaven poiseth those elements by which it hangeth in a counterbalance. Thus it alone resteth unmovable, whilst the whole frame of the world turneth about it : and as it is knit and united by all, so all rest and bear upon the same.

THE PLANETS

Between the earth and heaven, there hang in the same spirit or element of air abovenamed, seven stars, severed one from another, and distant asunder certain spaces, which of their variable motion we call wandering planets, whereas indeed none stray and wander less than they. In the midst of them the sun taketh his course, as being the greatest and most puissant of all the rest : the very ruler, not of times and seasons only, and of the earth, but also of the stars and heaven itself. Believe we ought, this sun to be the very life, and (to speak more plainly) the soul of the whole world, yea, and the principal governance of nature : and no less than a God or divine power, considering his works and operations. He it is that giveth light to all things, and riddeth them from darkness, he hideth the other stars, and sheweth them again : he ordereth the seasons in their alternative course : he tempereth the year arising ever fresh and new again, for the benefit and good of the world. The lowering dimness of the sky he dispatcheth, yea, and cleareth the dark mists and cloudiness of man's mind : to other stars likewise he lendeth out his own light. Most excellent, right singular he is, as seeing all, and hearing all. For this, I see, is the opinion of *Homer* (the prince of learning) as touching him alone.

GOD

I suppose therefore that to seek after any shape of God, and to assign a form and image to him, bewrayeth man's weakness. For God, whosoever he be (if haply there be any other, but the very world) and in what part soever resiant, all sense he is, all sight, all hearing : he is all life, all soul, all of himself. And verily to believe that there be gods innumerable, and those according to men's virtues and vices, to wit, Chastity, Concord, Understanding, Hope, Honour, Clemency, Faith; or (as *Democritus* was of opinion) that there are two gods only, and no more, namely Punishment and Benefit: these conceits I say, make men's idleness and negligence the greater. But all cometh of this, that frail and crafty mortal men, remembering well their own infirmity, have digested these things apart, to the end that each one might from thence choose to worship and honour that whereof he stood in need most. And hereupon it is, that in sundry nations we find the same gods named diversely, according to men's devotion: and in one region ye shall have innumerable gods. The infernal powers beneath likewise, yea, and many plagues have been ranged by themselves, and reckoned for gods in their kind, whiles with trembling fear we desire that they were pacified. Which superstition, hath caused a chapel to be dedicated to the Fever, in the mount Palatium, even by public order from the state: likewise an altar to *Orbona*, near the temple of *Lares*: besides another erected to Bad fortune in Esquiliæ. And thereby we may conceive that there are a greater number of gods in heaven above, than of men upon earth: since that every one of their own accord make so many gods as they list, fitting themselves with *Iunoes* and *Genii* for their patrons. Now, certain nations there be that account beasts, yes, and some filthy things, for gods; yea, and many other matters more shameful to be spoken; swearing by stinking meats, by garlic, and such like. But surely, to believe that gods have contracted marriage, and that in so long continuance of time no children should be born between them: also that some are aged, and ever hoary and grey: others again young and always children: that they be black of colour and complexion, winged, lame, hatched of eggs, living and dying each other day; are mere fooleries, little better than childish toys. But it passeth and exceedeth all shameless impudence, to imagine adulteries among them: eftsoons also chiding, scolding, hatred, and malice: and more than that; how there be gods, patrons of theft and wickedness. Whereas in very deed, a god unto a man is he, that helpeth a man: and this is the true and direct pathway to everlasting glory.

*   *   *   *   *

Now, that the sovereign power and deity, whatsoever it is, should have regard of mankind, is a toy and vanity worthy to be laughed at. For can we choose but believe, can we make any doubt, but needs that divinity and Godhead must be polluted with so base and manifold a ministry. And hardly in manner may it be judged, whether of the twain be better and more expedient for mankind to believe, that the gods have regard of us; or to be persuaded that they have none at all : considering, that some men have no respect and reverence at all of the gods, others again so much, as it is a very shame to see their superstition. Addicted these are and devoted to serve them by foreign magic ceremonies : they wear their god upon their fingers in rings, yea, they worship and adore monsters : they condemn and forbid some meats; yet they devise others for them. Impose they do upon them hard and vengible charges to execute, not suffering them to rest and sleep in quiet. They choose neither marriages, nor children, nor yet any one thing else, but by the approbation and allowance of sacred rites and mysteries. Contrariwise, others there are so godless, that in the very Capitol they use deceit, and forswear themselves ever by *Iupiter* for all that he is ready to shoot his thunderbolts. And as some speed well enough with their wicked deeds and irreligion : so others again feel the smart and are punished by the saints whom they adore, and the holy ceremonies which they observe.

Howbeit, between both these opinions, men have found out to themselves a middle godhead and divine power, to the end that we should give still a more uncertain conjecture as touching God indeed. For, throughout the whole world, in every place, at all times and in all men's mouths, Fortune alone is sought unto and called upon : she only is named and in request; she alone is blamed, accused, and indicted. None but she is thought upon; she only is praised, she only is reproved and rebuked : yea, and worshipped is she, with railing and reproachful terms : and namely when she is taken to be wavering and mutable : and of the most sort supposed also blind : roving at random, inconstant, uncertain, variable, and favouring the unworthy : whatsover is laid forth, spent and lost, whatsoever is received, won and gotten : all that comes in, all that goes out, is imputed to Fortune : and in all men's reckoning and accounts, she makes up the book and sets all straight. So abject we are, so servile also and enthralled to Lots, that even the very chance of Lots is taken for a god, than which nothing maketh us more doubtful and ignorant of God.

Now there are another sort, that reject Fortune and Chance both, and will not abide them : but attribute the events and issues of things, to their own several stars, and go by the fatal horoscope or ascendent of their nativity : affirming that the same shall ever befall, which once hath been set down and decreed by God : so as he for ever after may sit still and rest himself. And this opinion beginneth now to settle and take deep root, insomuch as both the learned, and also the rude and ignorant multitude, run that way on end. For hence (behold) proceed the warnings and admonitions of lightnings, the fore-knowledge by oracles, the predictions of soothsayers, yea, and other contemptible things not worthy to be once spoken of; as sneezing, and stumbling with the foot, are counted matters of presage. *Augustus Caesar* of famous memory hath made report and left in writing, that his left foot shoe was untowardly put on before the right, on that very day, when he had like to have miscarried in a mutiny among his soldiers.

Thus these things every one do enwrap and entangle silly mortal men, void of all forecast and true understanding : so as this only point among the rest remaineth sure and certain, namely, that nothing is certain : neither is there ought more wretched and more proud withal, than man. For all lively creatures else take care only for their food : wherein Nature's goodness and bounty of itself is sufficient : which one point verily is to be preferred before all good things whatsoever, for that they never think of glory, of riches, of seeking for dignities and promotions, nor over and above, of death. Howbeit the belief that in these matters the gods have care of men's estate, is good, expedient, and profitable in the course of this life : as also that the vengeance and punishment of malefactors may well come late (while God is busily occupied otherwise in so huge a frame of the world) but never misseth in the end : and that man was not made next in degree unto God, for this, that he should be well near as vile and base as the brute beasts. Moreover, the chief comfort than man hath, for his imperfections in nature, is this, that even God himself is not omnipotent, and cannot do all things. For neither is he able to work his own death, would he never so fain, as man can do when he is weary of his life; the best gift which he hath bestowed upon him, amid so great miseries of his life : nor endow mortal men with everlasting life : nor yet recall, raise and revive those that once are departed and dead : nor bring to pass, that one who lived, did not live : or he that bear honourable offices, was not in place of rule and dignity. Nay, he hath no power over things done and past, save only oblivion : no more than he is able to effect (to come with pleasant reasons and arguments to prove our fellowship therein with God) that twice ten should not make twenty : and many such things of like sort. Whereby (no doubt) is evidently proved, the power of Nature, and how it is she, and nothing else, which we call God. I thought it not impertinent thus to divert and digress to these points, so commonly divulged, by reason of the usual and ordinary questions as touching the essence of God.

FALLING STARS

Let us return now to the rest of Nature's works. The stars which we said were fixed in the heaven, are not (as the common sort thinketh) assigned to every one of us; and appointed to men respectively : namely, the bright and fair for the rich; the less for the poor, the dim for the weak, the aged and feeble : neither shine they out more or less, according to the lot and fortune of everyone, nor arise they each one together with that person unto whom they are appropriate; and die likewise with the same : none yet as they set and fall, do they signify that anybody is dead. There is not ywis so great society between heaven and us, as that together with the fatal necessity of our death, the shining light of the stars should in token of sorrow go out and become mortal. As for them, the truth is this; when they are thought to fall, they do but shoot from a deal of fire, even of that abundance and overmuch nutriment which they have gotten by the attraction of humidity and moisture unto them : like as we also observe daily in the wicks and matches of lamps or candles burning, with the liquor of oil. Moreover, the celestial bodies, which make and frame the world, and in that frame are compact and knit together, have an immortal nature: and their power and influence extendeth much to the earth: which by their effects and operations, by their light and greatness might be known, notwithstanding they are so high and subtle withal, as we shall in due place make demonstration.

THE MOVEMENTS OF THE PLANETS

Certain it is, that the planet which they call *Saturne*, is the highest; and therefore seemeth least: also that he keepeth his course, and performeth his revolution in the greatest circle of all: and in thirty years' space at the soonest, returneth again to the point of his first place. Moreover, that the moving of all the planets, and withal of sun and moon, go a contrary course unto the starry heaven, namely, to the left hand (i.e. eastward:), whereas the said heaven always hasteneth to the right (westward). And albeit in that continual turning with exceeding celerity, those planets be lifted up aloft, and carried by it forcible into the West, and there set: yet by a contrary motion of their own, they pass everyone through their several ways eastward; and all for this, that the air rolling ever one way, and to the same part, by the continual turning of the heaven, should not stand still, grow dull, and as it were, congealed, while the globe thereof resteth idle; but dissolve and cleave, parted thus and divided, by the reverberation of the contrary beams, and violent cross influence of the said planets.

THE MOON

But the planet of the moon, being the last of all, most familiar with the earth, and devised by Nature for the remedy of darkness, outgoeth the admiration of all the rest. She with her winding and turning in many and sundry shapes, hath troubled much the wits of the beholders, fretting and fuming, that of this star, being the nearest of all, they should be most ignorant; growing as it doth, or else waning, evermore. One while bended pointwise into tips of horns: another whiles divided just in the half, and anon again in compass round, spotted sometimes and dark, and soon after on a sudden exceeding bright: one while big and full, and another while all at once nothing to be seen. Sometimes shining all night long, and otherwhiles late it is ere she riseth: she also helpeth the sun's light some part of the day: eclipsed, and yet in that eclipse to be seen. The same at the month's end lieth hidden, as what time (it is supposed) she laboureth and travaileth not. At one time ye shall see her below, and anon aloft: and that not after one manner, but one while reaching up close to the highest heaven, and anotherwhile ready to touch the mountains: sometimes mounted on high into the north, and sometime cast down below into the south. Which several constitutions and motions in her, the first man that observed, was *Endymeon*: and thereupon the voice went, that he was enamoured upon the moon.

ECLIPSES

Moreover, the eclipse of the moon and sun (a thing throughout the universal contemplation of Nature most marvellous, and like a strange and prodigious wonder) doth show the bigness and shadow of these two planets. For evident it is, that the sun is hidden by the coming between of the moon: and the moon again by the opposition of the earth: also that the one doth quit the other, in that the moon by her interposition bereaveth the earth of the sun's rays, and the earth again doth semblable by the moon. Neither is the night anything else but the shade of the earth. Now the figure of this shadow resembleth a pyramis, pointed forward, or a top turned upside down, namely, when as it falleth upon it with the sharp end thereof, nor goeth beyond the heights of the moon; for that no other star is in that manner darkened: and such a figure as it, always endeth point-wise. And verily, that shadows grow to nothing in great space of distance, appeareth by the exceeding high flight of some fowls. So as the confines of these shadows, is the utmost bound of the air, and the beginning of the fire. Above the moon all is pure and lightsome continually. And we in the night do see the stars, as candles or any other lights from out of darkness.

THE SIZE OF THE SUN

The reason of this lifteth up men's minds into heaven: and as if they beheld and looked down from thence, discovers unto them, the magnitude of the three greatest parts of the whole world. For the sun's light could not wholly be taken away from the earth, by the moon coming between, in case the earth were bigger than the moon. But the huge greatness of the sun is more certainly known, both by the shadow of the earth, and the body of the moon : so as it is needless to search and inquire into the largeness thereof, either by proof of eyesight, or by conjecture of the mind. How immeasurable it is, appeareth evidently by this, that trees which are planted on limits from east to west, casteth shadows equal in proportion; albeit they be never so many miles asunder in length : as if the sun were in the midst of them all. This appeareth also about the time of the equinoctial in all regions meridional, when the sun shineth directly plumb over men's heads, and causeth no shadow. In like manner, the shadows of them that dwell northerly under the solstitial circle in summer, falling all at noon-tide, northward, but at sun rising, westward, doing the same demonstration. Which possibly could not be, unless the sun were far greater than the earth.

THE COLOURS OF THE PLANETS

The reason of the planets' altitudes is it that tempereth their colours, according as they be nearer or farther off from the earth. For they take the likeness of the air, into the coasts whereof they enter, in their ascent : and the circle or circumference of another planet's motion, coloureth them as they approach either way, ascending or descending. The colder setteth a pale colour, the hotter a red, and the windy a fearful and rough hue. Only the points and conjunctions of the *Absides*, and the utmost circumferences, shew a dark black. Each planet hath a several colour, *Saturne* is white, *Iupiter* clear and bright, *Mars* fiery and red, *Venus* Oriental (or *Lucifer*) fair, Occidental (or *Vesper*) shining, *Mercury* sparkling his rays, the moon pleasant, the sun when he riseth burning, afterwards glittering with his beams.

THE ORIGIN OF LIGHTNING

Most men are ignorant of that secret, which by great attendance upon the heavens, deep clerks and principal men of learning have found out; namely, that they be the fires of the three uppermost planets, which falling to the earth, carry the name of lightnings, but those especially which are seated in the midst, to wit, about *Iupiter*, haply, because participating the excessive cold and moisture from the upper circle of *Saturne*, and the immoderate heat from *Mars* that is next under, by this means he dischargeth the superfluity: and hereupon it is commonly said, that *Iupiter* shooteth and darteth lightnings. Therefore, like as out of a burning piece of wood a coal of fire flieth forth with a crack, even so from a star is spit out as it were and voided forth this celestial fire, carrying with it presages of future things: so as the heaven sheweth divine operations, even in these parcels and portions which are rejected and cast away as superfluous. And this most commonly happeneth when the air is troubled, either because the moisture that is gathered, moveth and stirreth forward that abundance to fall; or else for that it is disquieted with the birth (as it were) proceeding from a great-bellied star, and therefore would be discharged of such excrements.

CELESTIAL HARMONY

But *Pythagoras* otherwhiles using the terms of music, calleth the space between the earth and the moon a tonus, saying, that from her to *Mercury* is half a tone: and from him to *Venus* in manner the same space. But from her to the sun as much and half again; but from the sun to *Mars* a tonus, that is to say, as much as from the earth to the moon. From him to *Iupiter* half a tonus: likewise from him to *Saturne* half a tonus: and so from thence to the Signifer Sphere or Zodiac so much, and half again. Thus are composed seven tunes, which harmony they call Diapason, that is to say, the generality or whole state of concent and accord, which is perfect music. In which, *Saturne* moveth by the doric tune: *Mercury* by Phtongus, *Iupiter* by the Phrygian, and the rest likewise: a subtlety more pleasant ywis than needful.

COMETS

A fearful star for the most part this comet is, and not easily

c

expiated : as it appeareth by the late civil troubles when *Octavius* was Consul : as also a second time by the intestine war of *Pompey* and *Caesar*. And in our days about the time that *Claudius Caesar* was poisoned, and left the Empire to *Domitius Nero*, in the time of whose reign and government, there was another in manner continually seen, and ever terrible. Men hold opinion, that it is material for presage to observe into what quarters it shooteth, or what stars' power and influence it receiveth : also what similitudes it resembleth, and in what parts it shineth out and first ariseth. For if it be like unto flutes or hautboys, it portendeth somewhat to musicians : if it appear in the privy parts of any signs, let ruffians, whoremasters, and such filthy persons take heed. It is respective to fine wits and learned men, if it put forth a triangular or foursquare figure with even angles, to any situations of the perpetual fixed stars. And it is thought to presage, yea, and to sprinkle and put forth poison, if it be seen in the head of the dragon, either north or south.

ST. ELMO'S FIRE

I have seen myself in the camp, from the soldiers' sentinels in the nightwatch, the semblance of lightning to stick fast upon the spears and spikes set before the rampiar. They settle also upon the cross sail-yards, and other parts of the ship, as men do sail in the sea : making a kind of vocal sound, leaping to and fro, and shifting their places as birds do which fly from bough to bough. Dangerous they be and unlucky, when they come one by one without a companion : and they drown those ships on which they light, and threaten shipwreck, yea, and they set them on fire if haply they fall upon the bottom of the keel. But if they appear two and two together, they bring comfort with them, and foretell a prosperous course in the voyage, as by whose coming, they say, that dreadful, cursed, and threatening meteor called Helena, is chased and driven away. And thereupon it is, that men assign this mighty power to *Castor* and *Pollux*, and invoke them at sea, no less than gods. Men's heads also in the even-tide are seen many times to shine round about, and to be of a light fire, which presageth some great matter. Of all these things there is no certain reason to be given, but secret these be, hidden with the majesty of Nature, and reserved within her cabinet.

THE DOG STAR

Who knoweth not, that when the dog star ariseth, the heat of the sun is fiery and burning? the effects of which star are felt exceeding much upon the earth. The seas at his rising do rage and take on, the wines in cellars are troubled, pools also and standing waters do stir and move. A wild beast there is in Aegypt, called *Orix*, which the Aegyptians say, doth stand full against the dog star when it riseth, looking wistly upon it, and testifieth after a sort by sneezing, a kind of worship. As for dogs, no man doubteth verily, but all the time of the canicular days they are most ready to run mad.

THE POWER OF THE MOON

Now certain it is, that the bodies of oysters, mussels, cockles, and all shell-fishes, grow by the power of the moon, and thereby again diminish : yea, and some have found out by diligent search into Nature's secrets, that the fibres or filaments in the livers of rats and mice, answer in number to the days of the moon's age : also that the least creature of all others, the pismire, feeleth the power of this planet, and always in the change of the moon ceaseth from work.

THUNDER AND LIGHTNING

Deny I would not therefore, but that the fiery impressions from stars above, may fall upon these clouds, such as we often-times see to shoot in clear and fair weather : by the forcible stroke whereof, good reason it is, that the air should be mightily shaken, seeing that arrows and darts when they are discharged, sing and keep a noise as they fly. But when they encounter a cloud, there ariseth a vapour with a dissonant sound (like as when a red hot iron maketh an hissing being thrust into water) and a smoky fume walmeth up with many turnings like waves. Hereupon storms do breed. And if this flatuosity or vapour do struggle and wrestle within the cloud, from thence it cometh that thunderclaps be heard; but if it break through still burning, then flieth out the thunderbolt : if it be longer time a-struggling, and cannot pierce through, then leames and flashes are seen. With these, the cloud is cloven; with the other, burst in sunder. Moreover, thunders are nothing else but the blows and thumps given by the fires beating hard upon the clouds : and therefore presently the fiery chinks and rifts of those clouds do glitter and shine. Possibly it is also, that the breath and wind elevated from the earth, being repelled back, and kept down by the stars, and so held in and restrained within a cloud, may thunder, whilst Nature choketh the rumbling sound, all the while it striveth and quarreleth; but sendeth forth a crack when it breaketh out, as we see in a bladder puffed up with wind. Likewise it may be, that the same wind or spirit whatsoever, is set on fire by fretting and rubbing, as it violently passeth headlong down. It may also be stricken by the conflict of two clouds, as if two stones hit against one another; and so the leames and flashes sparkle forth. So as all these accidents happen by chance medley, and be irregular. And hereupon come those brutish and vain lightnings, such as have no natural reason, but are occasioned by these impressions above-said. With these are mountains and seas smitten : and of this kind be all other blasts and bolts that do no hurt to living creatures. As for those that come from above, and of ordinary causes, yea, and from their proper stars, they always presage and foretell future events.

*   *   *   *   *

Of all those things which grow out of the earth, lightning blasteth not the laurel tree; nor entereth at any time above five foot deep into the ground : and therefore, men fearful of lightning, suppose the deeper caves to be the surest and most safe : or else booths made of skins of sea-beasts, which they call seals, or sea-calves; for of all creatures in the sea, this alone is not subject to the stroke of lightning : like as of all flying fowls the eagle (which for this cause is imagined to be the armour-bearer of *Iupiter*, for this kind of weapon).

UNUSUAL FORMS OF RAIN

Besides these things above, in this lower region under **Heaven**, we find recorded in monuments, that it rained milk and blood, when *M. Acilius* and *C. Porcius* were Consuls. And many times else besides it rained flesh, as namely, whilst *L. Volumnius* and *Serv. Sulpitius* were Consuls : and look what of it the fowls of the air caught not up nor carried away, it never putrified. In like manner, it rained iron in the Lucanes country, the year before that *M. Crassus* was slain by the Parthians, and together with him all the Lucanes his soldiers, of whom there were many in his army. That which came down in this rain, resembled in some sort sponges : and the wizards and soothsayers being sought unto, gave warning to take heed of wounds from above. But in the year that *L. Paulus* and *C. Marcellus* were Consuls, it rained wool about the castle Carissa, near to which a year after, *T. Annius Milo* was slain. At the time that the same *Milo* pleaded his own cause at the bar, there fell a rain of tiles and bricks, as it is to be seen in the records of that year.

THE SHAPE OF THE EARTH

The first and principal thing that offereth itself to be considered, is her figure, in which by a general consent we do all agree. For surely we speak and say nothing more commonly, than the round ball of the earth; and confess that it is a globe enclosed within two poles. But yet the form is not of a perfect and absolute round, considering so great height of hills, & such plains of downs : howbeit, if the compass thereof might be taken by lines, the ends of those lines would meet just in circuit, and prove the figure of a just circle. And this the very consideration of natural reason doth force and convince, although there were not those causes which we alleged about the heaven. For in it the hollow bending convexity boweth and beareth upon itself, and every way resteth upon the centre thereof, which is that of the earth. But this, being solid and close compact, ariseth still like as if it swelled, stretching and growing without-forth. The heaven bendeth and inclineth toward the centre, but the earth goeth from the centre, while the world with continual volubility and turning about it, driveth the huge and excessive globe thereof into the form of a round ball.

THE ANTIPODES

Much ado there is here, and great debate between learned men; and contrariwise those of the lewd and ignorant multiude : for they hold, that men are overspread on all parts upon the earth, and stand one against another, foot to foot : also that the Zenith or point of the Heaven is even and alike unto all : and in what part soever men be, they go still and tread after the same manner in the middes. But the common sort, ask the question and demand, how it happeneth that they opposite just against us, fall not into Heaven? as if there were not a reason also ready, that the Antipodes again should marvel why we fell not down? Now there is reason that cometh between, carrying a probability with it even to the multitude, were it never so blockish and unapt to learn; that in an uneven and unequal globe of the earth, with many ascents and degrees, as if the figure thereof resembled a pine apple, yet nevertheless it may be well enough inhabited all over in every place. But what good doth all this, when another wonder as great as it ariseth? namely, that itself hangeth, and yet falleth not together with us : as if the power of that spirit especially which is enclosed in the world, were doubted : or that anything could fall, especially when Nature is repugnant thereto, and affordeth no place whither to fall : for like as there is no seat of Fire, but in fire; of Water, but in water; of Air and spirit, but in air; even so, there is no room for Earth but in earth, seeing all the elements besides, are ready to put it back from them. Howbeit, wonderful it remaineth still, how it should become a globe, considering so great flatness of plains and seas? Of which doubtful opinion *Dicearchus* (a right learned man as any other) is a favourer; who, to satisfy the curious endeavours of kings and princes, had a charge and commission to level and take measure of mountains : of which he said, that Pelion the highest, was a mile and a half high by the plumb rule; and collected thereby, that it was nothing at all to speak of, in comparison of the universal rotundity of the whole. But surely in my conceit, this was but an uncertain guess of his, since that I am not ignorant, that certain tops of the Alps, for a long tract together, arise not under fifty miles in height.

RACIAL CHARACTERISTICS

Hereunto we must annex and join such things as are linked to celestial causes. For doubtless it is, that the Aethyopians by reason of the sun's vicinity, are scorched and tanned with the heat thereof, like to them that be adust and burnt, having their beards and bush of hair curled. Also, that in the contrary clime of the world to it, in the frozen and icy regions, the people have white skins, hair growing long downward, & yellow; but they be fierce and cruel by reason of the rigorous cold air : howbeit, the one as well as the other in this change and mutability, are dull and gross : and the very legs do argue the temperature. For in the Aethyopians the juice or blood is drawn upward again by the nature of heat : but among the nations septentrional, the same is driven to the inferior part, by reason of moisture apt to fall downward. Here there breed noisome and hurtful wild beasts : but there, be engendered creatures of sundry and divers shapes, especially fowls and birds of many form and figures. Tall they are of bodily stature, as well in one part as the other : in the hot regions, by occasion of the natural motion of fire; in the other, for the nourishment of moisture. But in the midst of the earth, there is an wholesome mixture from both sides : the whole tract is fertile and fruitful for all things, the habit of men's bodies of a mean and indifferent constitution. In the colour also there sheweth a great temperature. The fashions and manners of the people are civil and gentle, their senses clear and lightsome, their wits pregnant and capable of all things within the compass of Nature. They also bear sovereign rule, and sway empires and monarchies, which those uttermost nations never had : yet true it is, that even they who are out of the temperate zones, may not abide to be subject nor accommodate themselves unto these : for such is their savage and brutish nature that it urgeth them to living solitary by themselves.

FLOATING ISLANDS

Certain islands are always waving and never stand still, as in the country about Caecubum, Mutina, and Statonia. Also in the lake Vadimonis, and near the waters Cutyliae, there is a shadowy dark grove, which is never seen in one place a day and night together. Moreover, in Lydia, the isles Calanucae, are not only driven to and fro by winds, but also many be shoved and thrust with long poles, which way a man will : a thing that saved many a man's life in the war against *Mithridates*. There be other little ones also in the river Nymphaeus called Saltuares (or dancers) because in any consort of musicians singing, they stir and move at the stroke of the feet, keeping time and measure.

MAGNETIC MOUNTAINS

Two hills there be near the river Indus : the nature of the one is to hold fast all manner of iron, and of the other, not to abide it : and therefore if a man's shoe sole be clouted with hob nails, in the one of them a man cannot pluck away his foot, and in the other he can take no footing at all.

WHY THE SEA IS SALT

Thus by the fervent heat of the sun, all moisture is dried up : for we have been taught, that this planet is masculine, frying and sucking up the humidity of all things. Thus the broad and spacious sea hath the taste of salt sodden into it : or else it is, because when the sweet and thin substance thereof is sucked out from it, which the fiery power of the sun most easily draweth up, all the tarter and more gross parts thereof remaineth behind : and hereupon it is, that the deep water toward the bottom, is sweeter and less brackish than that above in the top. And surely, this is a better and truer reason of that unpleasant smack and taste that it hath, than that the sea should be a sweat issuing out of the earth continually.

UNDERGROUND GEOMETRY

Dionysidorus in another kind would be believed : (for I will not beguile you of the greatest example of Grecian vanity). This man was a Melian, famous for his skill in geometry : he died very aged in his own country: his near kinswomen (who by right were his heirs in remainder) solemnized his funerals, and accompanied him to his grave. These women (as they came some few days after to his sepulchre for to perform some solemn obsequies thereto belonging) by report, found in his monument an epistle of this *Dionysidorus*, written in his own name To them above, that is to say, To the living: and to this effect, namely, that he had made a step from his sepulchre to the bottom and centre of the earth, and that it was thither 42,000 stadia. Neither wanted there geometricians, who made this interpretation, that he signified that this epistle was sent from the middle centre of the earth, to which place downward from the uppermost aloft, the way was longest; and the same was just half the diameter of the round globe: whereupon followed this computation, that they pronounced the circuit to be 255,000 stadia.

THE THIRD BOOK

*describeth the first and second gulf, which the
Mediterranean Sea maketh in Europe*

PREFACE

HITHERTO HAVE we written of the position and wonders of the
earth, waters and stars, also we have treated in general terms, of
the proportion and measure of the whole world. Now it followeth,
to discourse of the parts thereof : albeit this also be judged an
infinite piece of work, nor lightly can be handled without some
reprehension : and yet in no kind of enterprise pardon is more
due; since it is no marvel at all, if he who is born a mortal man,
knoweth not all things belonging to man. And therefore, I will
not follow one author more than another, but every one as I
shall think him most true in the descriptions of each part.
Forasmuch as this hath been a thing common in manner to them
all, namely, to learn or describe the situations of those places
most exactly, where themselves were either born, or which they
had discovered and seen : and therefore, neither will I blame nor
reprove any man. The bare names of places shall be simply set
down in this my geography; and that with as great brevity as I
can : the excellency, as also the causes and occasions thereof,
shall be deferred to their several and particular treatises : for
now the question is as touching the whole earth in generality,
which mine intent is to represent unto your eyes : and therefore
I would have things thus to be taken, as if the names of
countries were put down naked, and void of renown and fame,
and such only as they were in the beginning, before any acts
there done; and as if they had indeed an endument of names,

but respective only to the world and universal nature of all.

Now the whole globe of the earth is divided into three parts, Europe, Asia, and Africa. The beginning we take from the West and the Firth of Gades, even whereas the Atlantic Ocean breaking in, is spread into the Inland and Mediterranean seas. Make your entrance there, I mean at the Straits of Gibraltar, and then Africke is on the right hand, Europe on the left, and Asia before you just between. The bounds confining these, are the rivers Tanais and Nilus. The mouth of the ocean at Gades (whereof I spake before) lieth out in length fifteen miles, and stretcheth forth in breadth but five, from a village in Spain called Mellaria, to the promontory of Africa, called the *White*, as *Turannius Graccula* born thereby, doth write. *T. Livius* and *Nepos Cornelius* have reported, that the breadth thereof where it is narrowest, is seven miles over, but ten miles where it is broadest. From so small a mouth (a wonder to consider) spreadeth the sea so huge and so vast as we see; and withal, so exceeding deep, as the marvel is no less in that regard. For why? in the very mouth thereof, are to be seen many bars and shallow shelves of white sands (so ebb is the water) to the great terror of ships and sailors passing that way. And therefore many have called those straits of Gibraltar, the entry of the Mediterranean sea. On both sides of this gullet, near unto it, are two mountains set as frontiers and rampiers to keep all in : namely, Abila for Africke, Calpe for Europe, the utmost end of *Hercules'* Labours. For which cause, the inhabitants of those parts call them, the two pillars of that god; and do verily believe, that by certain drains and ditches dug within the continent, the main ocean, before excluded, made way and was let in, to make the Mediterranean seas, where before was firm land : and so by that means the very face of the whole earth is clean altered.

ITALY

Neither am I ignorant, that it might be thought and that justly, a point of an unthankful mind and idle withal, if briefly in this sort, and as it were by the way, that land should be spoken of which is the nource of all lands. She also is the mother, chosen by the powerful grace of the gods, to make even heaven itself more glorious; to gather into one the scattered empires, to soften and make civil the rude fashions of other countries, and whereas the language of so many nations were repugnant, wild and savage, to draw them together by commerce of speech, conference and parley; to endue man with humanities; and briefly, that of all nations in the world, there should be one only country. But here, what should I do? So noble are all the places that a man shall come unto, so excellent is everything, and each State so famous and renowned, that I am fully possessed with them all, and to seek what to say. Rome city, the only fair face therein, worthy to stand upon so stately a neck and pair of shoulders, what work would it ask think you, to be set out as it ought? The very tract of Campaine by itself, so pleasant and goodly, so rich and happy, in what sort should it be described? So as it is plain and evident, that in this one place there is the workmanship of Nature wherein she joyeth and taketh delight. Now besides all this, the whole temperature of the air, is evermore so vital, healthy and wholesome, the fields so fertile, the hills so open to the sun, the forest so harmless, the groves so cool and shady, the woods of all sorts so bounteous and fruitful, the mountains yielding so many breathing blasts of wind; the corn, the vines, the olives so plentiful, the sheep so enriched with fleeces of the best wool, the bulls and oxen so fat and well fed in the neck; so many lakes and pools, such store of rivers and springs watering it throughout; so many seas and havens, that it is the very bosom lying open and ready to receive the commerce of all lands from all parts: and yet itself full willingly desireth to lie far into the sea to help all mankind. Neither do I speak now of the natures, wits and fashions of the men; nor yet of the nations abroad subdued with their eloquent tongue, and strong hand. Even the Greeks (a nation of all other most given to praise themselves beyond all measure) have given their judgement of her, in that they called some small part thereof, Great Greece. But in good faith, that which we did in the mention of the heaven, namely, to touch some known planets and a few stars, the same must we likewise do in this one part: only I would pray the readers to remember and carry this away, that I hasten to rehearse every particular thing through the whole round globe of the earth.

THE FOURTH BOOK

comprising the third gulf of Europe

THE HYPERBOREI

BEHIND THOSE hills and beyond the north pole, there is a blessed and happy people (if we may believe it) whom they call Hyperborei, who live exceedingly long, and many fabulous and strange wonders are reported of them. In this tract are supposed to be the two points or poles about which the world turneth about, and the very ends of the heavens' revolution. For six months together they have one entire day; and night as long, when the sun is clean turned from them : but their day beginneth not at the spring Aequinoctial (as the lewd and ignorant common people do imagine) and so continueth to the autumn : for once in the year, and namely at our mid-summer when the sun entereth into Cancer, the sun riseth with them : and once likewise it setteth, even in mid-winter with us, when the sun entereth Capricorn. The country is open upon the sun, of a blissful and pleasant temperature, void of all noisome wind and hurtful air. Their habitations be in woods and groves, where they worship the gods both by themselves, and in companies and congregations : no discord know they; no sickness are they acquainted with. They never die, but when they have lived long enough : for when the aged men have made good cheer, and anointed their bodies with sweet ointments, they leap from off a certain rock into the sea. This kind of sepulture, of all others is most happy.

NORTH SEA ISLANDERS

There be also named the isles Oonæ, wherein the inhabitants live of birds' eggs and oats. Others also, wherein men are born with horse feet, called thereupon Hippopades. Others again of the Panoti, who being otherwise naked, have mighty great ears that cover their whole bodies.

BRITAIN

Over against this tract, lieth Britannia, between the north and the west: an island renowned, both in Greek and Roman records. Opposite it is unto Germany, Gaul, and Spain, the greatest parts by far of all Europe, and no small sea between. Albion it was some time named, when all the islands were called Britanniae, of which anon we will speak. This island is from Gessoriacum, a coast town of the Morini, fifty miles, and take the next and shortest cut. In circuit, as *M. Pitheas* and *Isidorus* report, it containeth 3,825 miles. And now for these 30 years well near, the Roman captains grow into farther knowledge thereof, and yet not beyond the forest Caledonia, as near as it is. *Agrippa* supposeth, that it is in length 800 miles, and in breadth 300. Also that Ireland is as broad, but not so long by 200 miles. This island is seated above it, and but a very short cut or passage distant from it, to wit, 30 miles from the people Silures. Of other islands in this ocean, there is none by report, in compass more than 125 miles. Now there be Orcades 40, divided asunder by small spaces between: Acmodæ 7, and 30 Hæbudes. Also between Britain and Hibernia, Mona, Monapia, Ricnea, Vectis, Silimnus, and Andros: but beneath them, Siambis and Axantos: and on the contrary side toward the German sea, there lie scattered the Glessariæ, which the later Greek writers have named Electrides, for that Amber there, was engendered and bred. The farthest of all, which are known and spoken of, is Thule; in which there be no nights at all, as we have declared, about mid-summer, namely when the sun passeth through the sign Cancer; and contrariwise no days in mid-winter: and each of these times they suppose, do last six months, all day or all night. *Timaeus* the historiographer saith, that farther within-forth, and six days sailing from Britain, there lieth the island Mictis, in which white lead groweth : and, that the Britains do sail thither in winter vessels covered with leather round about and well sewed. There be that make mention of others beside, to wit, Scandia, Dumna, and Bergos, and the biggest of all the rest Nerigos, from which men sail to Thule. Within one day's sailing from Thule, is the frozen sea, named of some Cronium.

THE FIFTH BOOK

containeth the description of Affrick

MOUNT ATLAS

But in the coast and borders thereof, 50 miles from Lixus, there
runneth Subur a goodly plenteous river, and navigable, near to
the colony Banasa. As many miles from it is the town Sala,
standing upon a river of the same name, near now unto the
wilderness, much infested and annoyed with whole herds of
elephants, but much more with the nation of the Autololes,
through which lieth the way to Atlas the most fabulous mountain of all Affricke. For writers have given out, that this hill
arising out of the very midst of the sea sands, mounteth up to
the sky, all rough, ill-favoured, and overgrown on that side that
lieth to the shore of the ocean, unto which it gave the name :
and yet the same is shadowy, full of woods, and watered with
veins of spouting springs that way which looketh to Affricke,
with fruitful trees of all sorts, springing of the own accord, and
bearing one under another, in such sort, that at no time a man
can want his pleasure and delight to his full contentment. Moreover, that none of the inhabitants there are seen all day long :
all is still and silent, like the fearful horror in desert wilderness :
and as men come nearer and nearer unto it, a secret devotion
ariseth in their hearts, and besides this fear and horror, they are
lifted up above the clouds, and even close to the circle of the
moon. Over and besides that the same hill shineth oftentimes
with many flashes of fire, and is haunted with the wanton
lascivious Aegipanes and Satyres, whereof it is full, that is re-
soundeth with noise of haut-boys, pipes and fifes, and ringeth

again with the sound of tabors, timbrels, and cymbals. These be the reports of great and famous writers, to say nothing of the labours and works both of *Hercules* and *Perses* there: and to conclude, that the way unto it is exceeding great, and not certainly known.

THE INHABITANTS OF AETHYOPIA

Those Atlantes, if we will believe it, degenerate from the rites and manners of all other men: for neither call they one another by any name: and they look wistly upon the sun, rising and setting, with most dreadful curses, as being pernicious to them and their fields: neither dream they in their sleep, as other men. The Troglodites dig hollow caves, and these serve them for dwelling houses: they feed upon the flesh of serpents. They make a gnashing noise, rather than utter any voice, so little use have they of speech one to another. The Garamants live out of wedlock, and converse with their women in common. The Augylæ do no worship to any but to the devils beneath. The Gamphasantes be all naked, and know no wars, but sort themselves with no foreigner. The Blemmyi, by report, have no heads, but mouth and eyes both in their breast. The Satyres besides their shape only, have no properties nor fashions of men. The Aegipanes are shaped, as you see them commonly painted. The Himantopodes be some of them limber-legged and tender, who naturally go creeping by the ground.

THE SOURCE OF THE NILE

The river Nilus arising from unknown springs, passeth through deserts and hot burning countries: and going thus a mighty way in length, is known by fame only, without arms, without wars which have discovered and found out all other lands. It hath his beginning, so far forth as *Iaba* was able to search and find out, in a hill of the lower Mauritania, not far from the ocean, where a lake presently is seen to stand with water, which they call Nilides. In it are found these fishes, called Alabetæ, Coracini, Siluri, and the Crocodile. Upon this argument and presumption Nilus is thought to spring from hence, for that the portrait of this source is consecrated by the said prince at Caesarea, in Iseum, and is there at this day seen. Moreover, observed it is, that as the snow or rain do satisfy the country in Mauritania, so Nilus doth increase. When it is run out of this lake, is scorneth to run through the sandy and overgrown places, and hideth himself for certain days' journey. And then soon after out of a greater lake, it breaketh forth in the country of the Massaesyli, with Mauritania Caesariensis, and looketh about viewing men's company, carrying the same arguments still of living creatures bred within it. Then, once again being received within the sands, it is hidden a second time for twenty days' journey, in the deserts as far as to the next Aethyopes : and so soon as he hath once again espied a man, forth he starteth (as it should seem) out of that spring, which they called Nigris. And then dividing Affrick from Aethyopia, being acquainted, if not presently with people, yet with the frequent company of wild and savage beasts, and making shade of woods as he goeth, he cutteth through the midst of the Aethiopians : there surnamed Astapus, which in the language of those nations signifieth a water flowing out of darkness. Thus dasheth he upon such an infinite number of islands, and some of them so mighty great, that albeit he bear a swift stream, yet he is not able to pass beyond them in less space than five days. About the goodliest and fairest of them Meroe, the channel going on the left hand is called Astabores, that is to say, the branch of a water coming forth of darkness : but that on the right hand Astusapes, which is as much as, lying hid, to the former signification. And never taketh the name of Nilus, before his waters meet again and accord all whole together. And even so was he aforetime named Siris, for many miles space : and of *Homer* altogether Aegyptis : and of others, Triton : here and there, and ever and anon hitting upon islands, and stirred as it were with so many provocations : and at the last enclosed and shut within mountains, and in no place carrieth he a rougher and swifter stream, whilst the water that he beareth, hasteneth to a place of the Aethypians called Catadupi, where in the last fall amongst the rocks that stand in his way, he is supposed not to run, but to rush down with a mighty noise. But afterwards he becometh more mild and gentle, as the course of his stream is broken, and his violence tamed and abated, yea, and partly wearied with his long way: and so though with many mouths of his, he dischargeth himself into the Aegyptian sea.

ALEXANDRIA

But right worthy of praise is Alexandria, standing upon the coast of the Aegyptian sea, built by *Alexander* the Great on Africke side, 12 miles from the mouth of Canopus, near to the lake Marcotis: which was before-time called Arapotes. *Dinochares* the Architect (a man renowned for his singular wit many ways) laid the model and platform thereof by a subtle and witty device: for having taken up a circuit of 15 miles for the city, he made it round like to a Macedonian cloak, full in the skirts, bearing out into angles and corners, as well on the left hand as the right, so as it seemed to lie in folds and plaits; and yet even then he set out one-fifth part of all this plot for the king's palace.

THE JORDAN

The river Jordan springeth from the fountain Paneades, which gave the surname to the city Caesarea, whereof we will speak more. A pleasant river it is, and as the site of the country will permit and give leave, winding and turning in and out, seeking as it were for love and favour, and applying itself to please the neighbour inhabitants. Full against his will, as it were, he passeth to the lake of Sodom, Asphaltites, that ill-favoured and cursed lake: and in the end falleth into it, and is swallowed up of it, where amongst those pestilent and deadly waters, he loseth his own that are so good and wholesome. And therefore to keep himself out of it as long as he possibly could, upon the first opportunity of any valleys, he maketh a lake, which many call Genesara, which is 16 miles long, and six broad.

THE ESSENI

Along the west coast, inhabit the Esseni. A nation this is, living alone and solitary, and of all others throughout the world most admirable and wonderful. Women they see none: carnal lust they know not: they handle no money: they lead their life by themselves, and keep company only with date trees. Yet nevertheless, the country is evermore well peopled, for that daily numbers of strangers resort thither in great frequency from other parts : and namely, such as be weary of this miserable life, are by the surging waves of frowning fortune driven hither, to sort with them in their manner of living. Thus for many thousand years (a thing incredible, and yet most true) a people hath continued without any supply of new breed and generation. So mightily increase they evermore, by the wearisome estate and repentance of other men.

THE SIXTH BOOK

handleth the Cosmography of Asia

THE BLACK SEA

THE SEA called Pontus Euxinus, and named by the Greeks in old times Axenos, for the hard usage that passengers found at the hands of those savage nations upon the coasts thereof, is spread also between Europe and Asia, upon a very spite and special envy of Nature, as it should seem, unto the earth, and a wilful desire to maintain still the sea in his greatness, and to fulfil his greedy and endless appetite. For contented she was not to have environed the whole earth with the main ocean, yea, and taken from it a great part thereof, with exceeding rage overflowing the same, and laying all empty and naked : it sufficed not, I say, to have broken through the mountains, and so to rush in, and after the sea had dismembered Caspe from Affricke, to have swallowed up much more by far than is left behind to be seen : no nor to have let Propontis gush through Hellespont, and so to encroach again upon the earth and gain more ground : unless from the straits of Bosphorus also he enlarge himself into another huge and vast sea, and yet is never content, until the lake Moeotis also with his strait, meet with him as he thus spreadeth abroad and floweth at liberty, and so join together and part as it were, their stolen good between them. And verily that all this is happened maugre the earth, and that it made all resistance that it could, appeareth evidently by so many straits and narrow passages lying between these two elements or so contrary nature (considering that in Hellespont, the space is not above 875 paces from land to land : and at the two Bosphori the sea is so pass-

57

able, that oxen or kine may swim at ease from the one side to the other : and hereupon they both took their name :) the which vicinity serveth very well to entertain and nourish amity among nations, separated by nature one from another : and in this disunion as it were, appeareth yet a brotherly fellowship and unity. For the cocks may be heard to crow, and the dogs to bark, from the one side to the other : yea, and men out of these two worlds may parley one to another with audible voice, and have commerce of speech together, if the weather be calm, and that the winds do not carry away the sound thereof.

SPECIAL SOURCES OF INFORMATION

Hitherto have we treated and gone through the nations and the inhabitants of the coasts upon the Mediterranean sea. Now are we to speak of the people inhabiting the very midland parts of the main within : wherein I protest, and deny not, but that I will deliver many things otherwise than the ancient geographers have set down : forasmuch as I have made diligent search into the state of those regions, as well by inquiry of *Domitius Corbulo* (who lately went with an army through those quarters) as of divers kings and princes, who made repair to Rome with suits and supplications, but especially of those kings' sons that were left as hostages in Rome.

THE ARNUPHEÆ

At the fall and descent of which mountains, I have heard say, that certain people named Arnupheæ inhabited : a nation not much unlike in their manner of life to the Hyperboreans. They have their habitations in forests; their feeding is upon berries of trees : shorn they be all and shaven, for both women and men count it a shame to have hair on their heads : otherwise they are civil enough in their conversation and behaviour : and therefore, by report, they are held for a sacred people and inviolable, in so much as those cruel nations and inhuman that border upon them, will offer them no abuse; neither do they respect them only, but also in regard and honour of them, they forbear those also that fly unto them as a place of franchise and privilege.

THE SERES

The first people of any knowledge and acquaintance, be the Seres, famous for the fine silk that their woods do yield. They kembe from the leaves of their trees the hoary down thereof, and when it is steeped in water, they card and spin it, yea, and after their manner make thereof a sey or web, whereupon the dames here with us have a double labour both of undoing, and also of weaving again this kind of yarn. See what ado there is about it, what labour and toil it costeth, and how far set it is : and all for this, that our ladies and wives when they go abroad in the street may cast a lustre from them, and shine again in their silks and velvets. As for the Seres, a mild and gentle kind of people they are by nature : howbeit, in this one point they resemble the brute and wild beasts, for that they cannot away in the commerce with other nations, with the fellowship and society of men, but shun and avoid their company, notwithstanding they desire to traffic* with them.

INDIA

When ye are over Ganges, the first region upon the coast that you set foot into, is that of the Gandaridae and the Calingae, called Parthalis. The king of this country hath in ordinance for his wars 80,000 foot, 1,000 horse, and 700 elephants, ready upon on hour's warning to march. As for the other nations of the Indians that live in the champion plain countries, there be diverse states of them, of more civility than the mountainers. Some apply themselves to tillage and husbandry : others set their minds upon martial feats : one sort of them practise merchants' trade, transporting their own commodities into other countries, and bringing in foreign merchandise in to their own. As for the nobility and gentry, those also that are the richest and mightiest among them, they manage the affairs of state and commonweal, and sit in place of justice, or else follow the court, and sit in counsel with the king. A fifth estate there is besides in great

* Even at this day they set abroad their wares with the prices, upon the shore, and go their ways : then the foreign merchants come and lay down the money, and have away the merchandise : and so depart without any communications at all

request, & namely of philosophers and religions, given wholly to the study of wisdom and learning; and these make profession of voluntary death : and verily, when they are disposed to die at any time, they make a great funeral fire, cast themselves into it, and so end their days. Besides all these, one thing there is amongst them half brutish, and of exceeding toil and travail (and yet it is that which partly maintaineth all the other estates above-said) namely, the practice of hunting, chasing and taming elephants. And in very truth, with them they plough their ground, upon them they ride up and down : with these beasts are they best acquainted : they serve in the wars for the maintenance of their liberty, and defence of their frontiers against invasion of enemies.

CEYLON

It hath been of long time thought by men in ancient days, that Taprobane was a second world, in such sort as many have taken it to be the place of the Antipodes, and called it, the Antichthones' world. But after the time of *Alexander* the Great, and the voyage of his army into those parts, it was discovered and known for a truth, both that it was an island, and what compass it bare. *Onesicratus* the Admiral of his fleet, hath written, that the elephants bred in this island be bigger, more fierce and furious for war-service, than those of India. *Megasthenes* saith, that there is a great river which parteth it in twain, and that the people thereof dwelling along the river, be called Palæogoni : adding moreover, that it affordeth more gold, and bigger pearls by far, than India doth. *Eratosthenes* also took the measure thereof, and saith, that in length it beareth 7,000 stadia, and in breadth 5,000 : that in it there be no cities and great towns, but villages to the number of 700. It beginneth at the Levant sea of Oriental Indians, from which it stretcheth and extendeth between the east and west of India : and was taken in times past to lie out into the sea from the Prasian country twenty days' sailing. But afterwards, for that the boats and vessels used upon this sea in the passage thither, were made and wound of papyr reeds like those of the river Nilus, and furnished with the same kind of tackling, the voyage thither from the foresaid country was gauged within a less time : and well known it was, that according to the sail of our ships and galleys, a man might arrive there in seven days. All the sea lying between, is very ebb, full of shallows and shelves, no more than five fathom deep. Howbeit in certain channels that it hath, it is so deep that it cannot be sounded, neither will any anchors reach the bottom and there rest : and withal, so strait and narrow these channels are, that a ship cannot turn within them : and therefore to avoid that necessity of turning about in these seas, the ships have prows at both ends, and are pointed each way. In sailing, they observe no star at all. As for the North pole, they never see it : but they carry ever with them certain birds in their ships, which they send out oftentimes when they seek for land, observing ever their flight; for knowing well that they will fly to land, they accompany them, and bend their course accordingly; neither use they to sail more than one quarter in the year : and for one hundred days after the sun is entered to Cancer, they take most heed and never make sail; for during that time it is winter season with them. And thus much we come to knowledge of, by relation of ancient writers. But we came to far better intelligence, and more notable information, by certain ambassadors coming out of that island, in the time of *Claudius Caesar* the Emperor : which happened upon this occasion and after this manner. It fortuned, that a freed slave of Annius Plocamus, who had farmed of the exchequer the customs of impost of the Red Sea, as he made sail about the coasts of Arabia, was in such wise driven with the north winds besides the realm of Carmania, and that for the space of fifteen days, that in the end he fell with an harbour thereof called Hippuros, and there arrived. When he was set on land, he found the king of that country so courteous, that he gave him entertainment for six months, and entreated him with all kindness that could be devised. And as he used to discourse and question with him about the Romans and their Emperor, he recounted unto him at large of all things. But among them other reports that he heard, he wondered most of all at their justice in all their dealings, and was in love therewith, and namely, that their deniers of the money which was taken were always of like weight, notwithstanding that the sundry stamps and images upon the pieces shewed plainly that they were made

by divers persons. And hereupon especially was he moved and
solicited to seek for the alliance and amity of the people of
Rome : and so dispatched four ambassadors of purpose, of whom
one *Rachias* was the chief and principal personage. By these
ambassadors we were informed of the state of that island, namely,
that it contained five hundred great towns in it : and that there
was a haven therein regarding the south coast, lying hard under
Palesimundum the principal city of all that realm, and the king's
seat and palace : that there were by just account 200,000 of
commoners and citizens : moreover, that within this island there
was a lake 270 miles in circuit, containing in it certain islands
good for nothing else but pasturage, wherein they were fruitful;
out of which lake issued two rivers, the one, Palesimundas, passing near to the city abovesaid of that name, and running into
the haven with three streams, whereof the narrowest was five
stadia broad, and the largest fifteen; the other northward on
India side, named Cydara : also that the next cape of this
country to India, is called Colaicum, from which to the nearest
port of India is counted four days sailing : in the midst of which
passage, there lieth in the way, the Island of the Sun. They said
moreover, that the water of this sea was all of a deep green
colour; and more than that, full of trees growing within it :
insomuch as the pilots with their helms many times brake off
the heads and tops of those trees. The stars about the North
pole, Septentriones, the Wains or Bears, they wondered to see
here among us in our hemisphere : as also the brood-hen, called
Virgiliæ in Latin, as if it had been another heaven. They confessed also they never saw with them, the moon above the ground
before it was eight days old, nor after the sixteenth day. That the
Canopus, a goodly great and bright star about the pole Antarc-
tic, used to shine all night with them. But the thing that they
marvelled and were most astonished at was this, that they
observed the shadow of their own bodies fell to our hemisphere,
and not to theirs; and that the sun arose on their left hand and
set on their right, rather than contrariwise. Furthermore they
related, that the front of that island of theirs which looked towards India, contained 10,000 stadia, and reached from the
south-east beyond the mountains Enodi. Also, that the Seres were
within their kenning, whom they might easily discover from out

of this their island; with whom they had acquaintance by their means of traffic and merchandise: and that *Rachias* his father used many times to travel thither, affirming moreover, that if any strangers came thither, they were encountered and assailed by wild and savage beasts: and that the inhabitants themselves were giants of stature, exceeding the ordinary proportion of men, having red hair, eyes of colour bluish, their voices for sound horrible, for speech not distinct nor intelligible for any use of traffic and commerce. In all things else their practice is the same that our merchants and occupier do use: for on the farther side of the river, when wares and commodities are laid down, if they list to make exchange they have them away, and leave other merchandise in lieu thereof to content the foreign merchant. And verily no greater cause have we otherwise to hate and abhor this excessive superfluity, than to cast our eye so far and consider with ourselves, what it is that we seek for, from what remote parts we fetch it, and to what end we so much desire all this vanity. But even this island Taprobane, as far off as it is, seeming as it were cast out of the way by Nature, and divided from all this world wherein we live, is not without these vices and imperfections wherewith we are tainted and infected. For even gold and silver also is there, in great request and highly esteemed: and marble, especially if it be fashioned like a tortoise shell. Gems and precious stones; pearls also, such as be orient and of the better sort, are highly priced with them: and herein consisteth the very height of our superfluous delights. Moreover, these ambassadors would say, that they had more riches in their island, than we at Rome, but we more use thereof than they. They affirmed also, that no man with them had any slaves to command: neither slept they in the morning after daylight, nor yet at all in the daytime. That the manner of building their houses was low, somewhat raised above the ground and no more ado: that their markets were never dear, nor price of victuals raised. As for courts, pleading of causes, and going to law, they knew not what it meant. *Hercules* was the only god whom they worshipped. Their king was always chosen by the voices of the people: wherein they had these regards; that he were aged, mild and childless: but in the case he should beget children afterward, then he was deposed from his regal dignity, to the end that the kingdom should not in process of time be hereditary and held by succession, but by election only. This king being thus chosen and invested, hath thirty other governors assigned unto him by the people: neither can any person be condemned to death, unless he be cast by the more part of them, and plurality of voices: and thus condemned as he is, yet may he appeal unto the people. Then are there seventy judges deputed to sit upon his cause: and if it happen that they assoile and quit this party condemned: then those thirty who condemned him, are displaced from the state and dignity, with a most grievous and bitter rebuke, and for ever after, as disgraced persons live in shame and infamy. As for the king, arrayed he is in apparel as prince *Bacchus* went in old time: but the subjects and common people are clad in the habit of Arabians. If it fortune that the king offend, death is his punishment: howbeit, no man taketh in hand to do execution. All men turn away their faces from him, and deign him not a look or a word. But to do him to death in the end, they appoint a solemn day of hunting, right pleasant and agreeable unto tigers and elephants, before which beasts they expose their king, and so he is presently by them devoured. Moreover, in that island good husbands they are for their ground, and till the same most diligently. Vines have they no use of at all: for all sorts of fruits otherwise they have abundance. They take also a great pleasure and delight in fishing, and especially in taking of tortoises: and so great they are found there, that one of their shells will serve to cover an house: and so the inhabitants do employ them instead of roofs. They count an hundred years no long life there: that is the ordinary time of their age. Thus much we have learned and known as touching Taprobane.

THE ISLAND OF THE SUN

They make relation likewise of the Island of the Sun, named also the couch or bed of the nymphs: This island is red all over, and no living creature will live therein, but is consumed and perisheth no man knoweth how or upon what cause.

BABYTACE

Upon that branch of the river Tigris that taketh his course northward, standeth the town Babytace : and from Sufa it is 135 miles. The people of this country are the only men in the world that hate gold : and in very truth get it they do, and when they have it they bury it sure enough within the ground, that it might serve for no use.

THE ARABIANS

The Arabians wear mitres or turbans ordinarily upon their heads, or else go with their hair long and never cut it : as for their beards, them they shave, save only on their upper lip, which they let grow still : and yet some there be of them that suffer their beards to grow long and never cut them. But this one thing I marvel much at, that being such an infinite number of nations as they be, the one half of them live by robbery and thieving, howsoever the other live by traffic and merchandise.

THE SUEZ CANAL

Beyond which, you enter into the land of Tyra : and there is the port Daneon to be seen, from which *Sesostris* a king of Egypt, was the first that imagined and devised to draw one arm of it with a channel navigable, into Nilus, in that part where it runneth to the place called Delta, and that for sixty-two miles space, which is between the said river and the Red Sea. This enterprise of his was followed by *Darius* king of the Persians : yea and by *Ptolomaus* king of Egypt, second of that name, who made a channel 100 foot over, and thirty deep, for thirty-seven miles in length and an half, even to the bitter fountains. But this design was interrupted and the ditch went no farther, for fear of a general deluge and inundation : for found it was, that the Red Sea lay above the land of Egypt three cubits. Some allege not that to be the cause, but this, namely, that if the sea were let into Nilus, the sweet water thereof (whereof they drink only and of none else) should be corrupted thereby and marred.

E

PIRATES

Over and besides, the Arabians named Assitæ, do much harm
and annoyance from out of the islands which they hold, unto
merchants that traffic that way : for these Arabians, according
as their name doth import, couple bottles made of good ox
leather, two by two together, and going upon them with ease as
if it were a bridge under them, scour the seas, and shooting their
poisoned arrows, practise piracy, to the great loss and mischief
of merchants and sailors.

MORE INHABITANTS OF AETHYOPIA

All Aethyopia in general was in old time called Aetheria :
afterwards Atlantia : and finally of *Vulvan's* son Aethiops, it
took the name Aethyopia. No wonder it is, that about the coasts
thereof there be found both men and beasts of strange and
monstrous shapes, considering the agility of the sun's fierce heat,
so strong and powerful in those countries, which is able to frame
bodies artificially of sundry proportions, and to imprint and
grave in them divers forms. Certes, reported it is, that far within
the country eastward there are a kind of people without any
nose at all on their face, having their visage all plain and flat.
Others again without any upper lip, and some tongueless. Moreover, there is a kind of them that want a mouth, framed apart
their nostrils : and at one and the same hole, and no more, taketh
in breath, receiveth drink by drawing it in with an oaten straw,
yea, and after the same manner feed themselves with the grains
of oats, growing of their own accord without man's labour and
tillage for their only food. And others there be, who instead of
speech and words, make signs, as well with nodding their heads,
as moving their other members. There are also among them,
that before the time of *Ptolomeus Lathyrus* king of Egypt, knew
no use at all of fire. Furthermore, writers there be, who have
reported, that in the country near unto the moors and marshes
from whence Nilus issueth, there inhabit those little dwarfs called
Pygmei.

A DOG KING

Upon the coast of Affricke inhabit the Ptoeambati and Ptoemphanæ : who have a dog for their king, and him they obey, according to the signs which he maketh by moving the parts of his body, which they take to be his commandments, and religiously they do observe them.

SOME INCREDIBLE TALES

The region above Sirbithim, where the mountains do end, is reported to have upon the sea coast certain Aethyopians called Nisicastes and Nisites, that is to say, men with three or four eyes apiece : not for that they are so eyed indeed, but because they are excellent archers, & have a special good eye in aiming at their mark, which lightly they will not miss. *Bion* affirmeth moreover, that from that clime of the heaven which beareth above the greater Syrtes, & bendeth toward the South Ocean sea, they be called Dalion, to wit, the Cisorians and Longopores, who drink and use rain water only. And beyond Oecalices for five days journey, the Usibalks, Isuelians, Pharuseans, Valians and Cispians. All the rest are nothing but deserts not inhabited. But then he telleth fabulous and incredible tales of those countries. Namely, that westward there are people called Nigroe, whose king hath but one eye, and that in the middle of his forehead. Also he talketh of the Agriophagi, who live most of panthers' and lion's flesh. Likewise of the Pomphagi, who eat all things whatsoever. Moreover, of the Anthropophagi, that feed of man's flesh. Furthermore, of the Cynamolgi, who have heads like dogs. Over and besides, the Artabatites who wander and go up and down in the forests like four-footed savage beasts.

GORGONS

Just over against this cape, as *Xenophon Lampsacenus* reporteth, lie the islands called Gorgates, where sometimes the Gorgons kept their habitation, and two days sailing they are thought to be from the firm land. *Hanno,* a great commander and general of the Carthaginians, landed there with an army :

who made this report from hence : that the women were all over their bodies hairy : as for the men, he could not catch one of them, so swift they were of foot that they escaped out of all sight : but he flayed two of these Gorgon women and brought away their skins, which for a testimonial of his being there, and for a wonder to posterity, he hung up in *Juno's* temple, where they were seen, until Carthage was won and sacked.

THE SEVENTH BOOK

treateth of man, and his inventions

PREFACE

THUS AS you see, we have in the former books sufficiently
treated of the universal world, of the lands, regions, nations, seas,
islands, and renowned cities therein contained. It remaineth now
to discourse of the living creatures comprised within the same,
and their natures : a point doubtless that would require as deep
a speculation, as any part else thereof whatsoever, if so be the
spirit and mind of man were able to comprehend and compass
all things in the world. And to make a good entrance into this
treatise and history, methinks of right we ought to begin at man,
for whose sake it should seem that Nature made and produced
all other creatures besides : though this great favour of hers, so
bountiful and beneficial in that respect, hath cost them full
dear. Insomuch, as it is hard to judge, whether in so doing she
hath done the part of a kind mother, or a hard and cruel step-
dame. For first and foremost, of all other living creatures, man
she hath brought forth all naked, and clothed him with the good
and riches of others. To all the rest, given she hath sufficient to
clad them everyone according to their kind : as namely, shells,
cods, hard hides, pricks, shag, bristles, hair, down feathers, quills,
scales, and fleeces of wool. The very trunks and stems of trees
and plants, she hath defended with bark and rind, yea and the
same sometimes double, against the injuries both of heat and
cold : man alone, poor wretch, she hath laid all naked upon the
bare earth, even on his birthday, to cry and wraule presently
from the very first hour that he is born into the world : in such

sort, as among so many living creatures, there is none subject to
shed tears and weep like him. And verily to no babe or infant is
it given once to laugh before he is forty days old, and that is
counted very early and with the soonest. Moreover, so soon as he
is entered in this manner to enjoy the light of the sun, see how
he is immediately tied and bound fast, and hath no member at
liberty, a thing that is not practised upon the young whelps of
any beast among us, be he never so wild. The child of man
thus untowardly born, and who another day is to rule and command all other, lo how he lyeth bound hand and foot, weeping
and crying, and beginning his life with misery, as if he were to
make amends and satisfaction by his punishment unto Nature,
for this only fault and treaspass, that he is born alive. O folly of
all follies, ever to think (considering this simple beginning of
ours) that we were sent into this world to live in pride and carry
our head aloft. The first hope that we conceive of our strength,
the first gift that time affordeth us, maketh us no better yet than
four-footed beasts. How long is it ere we can go alone? how long
before we can prattle and speak, feed ourselves, and shew our
meat strongly? what a while continueth the mould and crown of
our heads to beat and pant, before our brain is well settled; the
undoubted mark and token that bewrayeth our exceeding great
weakness above all other creatures? What should I say of the
infirmities and sicknesses that soon seize upon our feeble bodies?
what need I speak of so many medicines and remedies devised
against these maladies: besides the new diseases that come every
day, able to check and frustrate all our provision of physic whatsoever? As for all other living creatures, there is not one, but by a
secret instinct of nature knoweth his own good, and whereto he is
made able: some make use of their swift feet, others of their flight
wings: some are strong of limb; other are apt to swim, and
practise the same: man only knoweth nothing unless he is taught;
he can neither speak, nor go, nor eat, otherwise than he is trained
to it: and to be short, apt and good at nothing he is naturally,
but to pule and cry. And hereupon it is, that some have been of
this opinion, that better it had been, and simply best for a man,
never to have been born, or else speedily to die. None but we do
sorrow and wail, none but we are given to excess and superfluity infinitely in everything, and shew the same in every mem-

ber that we have. Who but we again are ambitious and vain-glorious? who but we are covetous and greedy of gathering good? We and none but we desire to live long and never to die, are superstitious, careful of our sepulture and burial, yea, and what shall betide us when we are gone. Man's life is most frail of all others, and in least security he liveth: no creature lusteth more after everything than he: none feareth like unto him, and he is more troubled and amazed in his fright: and if he be set once upon anger, none more raging and wood than he. To conclude, all other living creatures live orderly and well, after their own kind: we see them flock and gather together, and ready to make head and stand against all others of a contrary kind: the lions as fell and savage as they be, fight not one with another: serpents sting not serpents, nor bite one another with their venomous teeth: nay the very monsters and huge fishes of the sea, war not amongst themselves in their own kind: but believe me, man at man's hand receiveth most harm and mischief.

THE WONDERS OF NATURE

In our cosmography and reports of nations and countries, we have spoken in general of all mankind, spread over the face of the whole earth: neither is it our purpose at this present to decipher particularly all their customs and manners of life, which were a difficult enterprise, considering how infinite they be, and as many in manner as there be societies and assemblies of men. Howbeit I think it good, not to overpass all, but to make relation of some things concerning those people especially, who live farthest remote from our seas; among whom, I doubt not but I shall find such matter, as to most men will seem both prodigious and incredible. And verily, who ever believed that the Aethyo-pians had been so black, before he saw them with his eye: nay what is it, I pray you, that seemeth not a wonder at the first sight? How many things are judged impossible before they are seen done and effected? And certes, to speak a truth, the power and majesty of Nature, in every particular action of hers and small things, seemeth incredible, if a man consider the same severally, and enter not into a general conceit of her wholly as she is. For to say nothing of the painted peacocks' feathers, of the sundry spots of tigers, *luzurnes*, and panthers, of the various colours and marks of so many creatures besides : let us come to one only point, which to speak of seemeth but small, but being deeply weighed and considered, is a matter of exceeding great regard, and that is, the varieties of men's speech; so many tongues and divers languages are amongst them in the world, that one stranger to another seemeth well near to be no man at all. But come to view and mark the variety that appeareth in our face and visage, albeit there be not past ten parts or little more therein, see how among so many thousands as we are, you shall not find any two persons, who are not distinct in countenance and different one from another : a thing that no artificer nor painter (be he never so cunning and his craftsmaster every way) can perform, but in a few pictures, and take what need he can with all his curious affectation. And yet thus much must I advertise the readers of this mine history by the way, that I will not pawn my credit for many things that herein I shall deliver, nor bind them to believe all I write as touching strange and foreign nations : refer them rather I will to mine authors, whom in all points (more doubtful than the rest) I will cite and allege, whom they may believe if they list : only let them not think much to follow the Greek writers, who from time to time in this behalf have been more diligent in penning, and more curious in searching after antiquities.

MORE HUMAN ODDITIES

That there be Scythians, yea, and many kinds of them that feed ordinarily of man's flesh, we have shewed already in our former discourses. A report haply that would be thought incredible, if we did not consider and think withal, how in the very middle and heart of the world, even in Sicily and Italy, here hard by, there have been such monsters of men, namely the Cyclopes and Lystrigones : nay, if we were not credibly informed, that even of late days, and go no farther than to the other side of the Alps, there be those that kill men for sacrifice after the manner of those Scythian people; and that wants not much of chewing and eating their flesh. Moreover, near unto those Scythians that inhabit toward the pole Arctic, and not

far from that climate which is under the very rising of the north-
east wind, and about that famous cave or hole out of which that
wind is said to issue, which place they call Ges-clithron, (the
cloisture or key of the earth) the Arimaspians by report do dwell,
who as we have said before, are known by this mark, for having
one eye only in the midst of their forehead : and these maintain
war ordinarily about the metal mines of gold, especially with
griffons, a kind of wild beasts that fly, and use to search gold
out of the veins of those mines (as commonly it is received :)
which savage beasts (as many authors have recorded, and namely
Herodotus and *Aristeas* the Proconnesian, two writers of greatest
name) strive as eagerly to keep and hold those golden mines, as
the Arimaspians to disseize them thereof, and get away the gold
from them. Above those, are other Scythians called Anthropophagi, where is a country named Abarimon, within a certain
vale of the mountain Imaus, wherein are found savage and wild
men, living and conversing usually among the brute beasts, who
have their feet growing backward, and turned behind the calves
of their legs, howbeit they run most swiftly. These kind of men
can endure to live in no other air nor in any other clime else
than their own, which is the reason that they cannot be drawn
to come unto other kings that border upon them, nor could be
brought unto *Alexander* the great : as *Beton* hath reported, the
marshal of that prince's camp, and who also put down his geasts
and journeys in writing. The former Anthropophagi or eaters of
man's flesh whom we have placed about the North pole, ten days
journey by land above the river Borysthenes, use to drink out
of the skulls of men's heads, and to wear the scalps, hair and all,
instead of mandellions or stomachers before their breasts, according as *Isogonus* the Nicean witnesseth. The same writer affirmeth
moreover, that in Albanie there be a sort of people born with
eyes like owls, whereof the sight is fire red : who from their childhood are grey headed, and can see better by night than day. He
reporteth also, that ten days' journey beyond Borysthenes, the
Sauromates never eat but one meal of meat in three days. *Crates*
of Pergamus saith, that in Hellespont about Parium, there was a
kind of men (whom he nameth Ophiogenes) that if one were
stung with a serpent, with touching only, will ease the pain : and
if they do but lay their hands upon the wound, are wont to

draw forth all the venom out of the body. And *Varro* testifieth, that even at this day there be some there who warish and cure the stinging of serpents with their spittle, but there are but few such as he saith. *Agatharcides* writeth, that in Africa the Psyllians (so called of King Psyllus) from whose race they were descended, and whose sepulchre or tomb is at this day present to be seen in a part of the greater Syrtes, could do the like. These men had naturally that in their own bodies, which like a deadly bane and poison would kill all stark dead. And by this means they used to try the chastity and honesty of their wives. For so soon as they were delivered of children, their manner was to expose and present the silly babes newborn, unto the most fell and cruel serpents they could find : for if they were not right but gotten in adultery, the said serpents would not avoid & fly from them. This nation verily in general hath been defeated, & killed up in manner all, by the Nasamones, who now inhabit those parts wherein they dwelt : howbeit, a kind remaineth still of them, descended from those that made shift away and fled, or else were not present at the said bloody battle, but there are very few of them at this day left. The Marsians in Italy at this present continue with the like natural virtue against serpents : whom being reputed for to have descended from Lady *Circe's* son, the people in this regard do highly esteem, and are verily persuaded, that they have in them the same faculty by kind. And what great wonder is this, considering that all men carry about them that which is poison to serpents : for if it be true that is reported, they will no better abide the touching with man's spittle, than scalding water cast upon them : but if it happen to light within their jaws, or get into their mouth, especially if it come from a man that is fasting, it is present death. Beyond those Nasamones, and their neighbours, confining upon them (the Machlyes) there be found ordinarily Hermaphrodites, called Androgyni, of a double nature, and resembling both sexes, male and female, who have carnal knowledge one of another interchangeably by turns, as *Calliphanes* doth report. *Aristotle* saith moreover, that on the right side of their breast they have a little teat or nipple like a man, but on the left side they have a full pap or dug like a woman. In the same Africa, both *Isogonus* and *Nymphodorus* do avouch, there be certain houses and families of sorcerers: who, if they chance to bless, praise, and speak good words, bewitch presently withal; insomuch as sheep therewith die, trees wither, and infants pine and winder away. *Isogonus* added furthermore, that such like there are among the Triballians and Illyrians, who with their very eyesight can witch, yea, and kill those whom they look wistly upon any long time, especially if they be angered, and that their eyes bewray their anger: and more subject to this danger be men grown, than children under fourteen years of age. This also is in them more notable and to be observed, that in either eye they have two sights or apples. Of this kind and property, as *Apollonides* mine author saith, there be certain women in Scythia named Bithyæ. *Philarchus* witnesseth, that in Pontus also the whole race of the Thibians, and many others besides, have the same quality, & can do the like: & known they are (saith he) by these marks, in one of their eyes they have two sights, in the other the print or resemblance of an horse. He reporteth besides of these kind of men, that they will never sink or drown in the water, be they charged never so much with weighty and heavy apparel. Not unlike to these there are a sort of people in Aethyopia called Pharnaces, whose sweat if it chance to touch a man's body, presently he falleth into a phthisic or consumption of the lungs. And *Cicero* a Roman writer here among us testifieth, that generally all women that have such double apples in their eyes, have a venomous sight, and do hurt therewith. See how Nature, having engraffed naturally in some men this unkind appetite (like wild beasts) to feed commonly upon the bowels and flesh of men, hath taken delight also & pleasure to give them inbred poisons in their whole body, yea, and venom in the very eyes of some; that there be no naughtiness in the whole world again, but the same might be found in man. Not far from Rome city, within the territory of the Falisci, there be some few houses and families called Hirpix, which at their solemn yearly sacrifice celebrated by them in the honour of *Apollo* upon the mount Soracte, walk upon the pile of wood as it is on fire, in great jollity, and never a whit are burnt withal. For which cause ordained it is by an express arrest or act of the Senate, that they should be privileged, and have immunity of warfare and all other services whatsoever.

Some men there be that have certain members and parts of their bodies naturally working strange and miraculous effects, and in some cases medicinable. As for example, king *Pyrrhus*, whose great toe of his right foot was good for them that had big, swelled, or indurate spleens, if he did but touch the parties diseased, with that toe. And they say moreover, that when all the rest of his body was burned (after the manner) in the funeral fire, that great toe the fire had no power to consume : so, that it was bestowed in a little case for the nonce, and hung up in the temple for an holy relic. But principally above all other countries, India and the whole tract of Aethyopia is full of these strange and miraculous things. And first and foremost, the beasts bred in India be exceeding big, as it may appear by their dogs, which for proportion are much greater than those in other parts. And trees be growing there to that tallness, that a man cannot shoot a shaft over them. The reason hereof is the goodness and fatness of the ground, the temperate constitution of the air, and the abundance of water : which is the cause also that under one fig tree (believe it that list) there may certain troops and squadrons of horsemen stand in convert, shaded with the boughs. And as for reeds, they be of such a length, that between every joint they will yield sufficient to make boats able to receive three men apiece, for to row therein at ease. There are to be seen many men above five cubits tall : never are they known once to spit : troubled they are not with pain in the head, toothache, or grief of the eyes; and seldom or never complain they of any sorance in other parts of the body, so hardy are they, and of so strong a constitution through the moderate heat of the sun. Over and besides, among the Indians be certain philosophers, whom they call Gymnosophists, who from sun rising to the setting thereof are able to endure all the day long, looking full against the sun, without winking or once moving their eyes, & from morning to night can abide to stand sometimes upon one leg, and sometimes upon the other in the sand, as scalding hot as it is. Upon a certain mountain named Milus, there be men whose feet grow the other way backward, and of either foot they have eight toes, as *Megasthenes* doth report. And in many other hills of that country, there is a kind of men with heads like dogs, clad all over with the skins of wild beasts, who in lieu of speech

used to bark: armed they are and well appointed with sharp
and trenchant nails; they live upon the prey which they get by
chasing wild beasts, and fowling. *Ctesias* writeth that there were
discovered and known of them above 120,000 in number. By
whose report also, in a certain country of India the women bear
but once in their life, and their infants presently wax grey so
soon as they are born into the world. Likewise, that there is a
kind of people named Monoscelli that have but one leg apiece,
but they are most nimble, and hop wondrous swiftly. The same
men are also called Sciopodes, for that in hottest season of the
Summer, they lie along on their back, and defend themselves
against the sun's heat with their feet: and these people as he
saith are not far from the Troglodites. Again, beyond these westward, some there be without heads standing upon their necks,
who carry eyes in their shoulders. Among the western mountains
of India the Satyres haunt (the country wherein they are is
called the region of the Cartaduli), creatures of all other most
swift in footmanship: which one whiles run with all four; otherwhiles upon two feet only like men: but so light-footed they
are, that unless they be very old or sick, they can never be taken.
Tauron writeth, that the Choromandæ are a savage and wild
people: distinct voice and speech they have none, but instead
thereof, they keep an horrible gnashing and hideous noise: rough
they are and hairy all over their bodies, eyes they have red like
the houlets, and toothed they be like dogs. *Eudoxus* saith, that
in the southern parts of India, the menkind have feet a cubit
long, but the women so short & small, that thereupon they
be called Struthopodes, i.e. sparrow footed. *Megasthenes* is mine
author, that among the Indian Nomades there is a kind of
people, that instead of noses they have two small holes, and
after the manner of snakes have their legs and feet limmer,
wherewith they crawl and creep, and named they are Syrictæ.
In the utmost marches of India, eastward, about the source and
head of the river Ganges, there is a nation called the Astomes,
for that they have no mouths: all hairy over the whole body,
yet clothed with the soft cotton and down that come from the
leaves of trees: they live only by the air, and smelling to sweet
odours, which they draw in at their nostrils: no meat nor drink
they take, only pleasant savours from divers and sundry roots,

flowers, and wild fruits growing in the woods they entertain : and those they use to carry about with them when they take any far journey, because they would not miss their smelling. And yet if the scent be anything strong and stinking, they are soon therewith overcome, and die withal. Higher in the country, and above these, even in the edge and skirts of the mountains, the Pygmaei Spythamei are reported to be : called they are so, for that they are but a cubit or three shaftments (or spans) high, that is to say, three times nine inches. The clime wherein they dwell is very wholesome, the air healthy, and ever like to the temperature of the Spring : by reason that the mountains are on the north side of them, and bear off all cold blasts. And these pretty people *Homer* also hath reported to be much troubled and annoyed by cranes. The speech goeth, that in the springtime they set out all of them in battle array, mounted upon the back of rams and goats, armed with bows and arrows, and so down to the seaside they march, where they make foul work among the eggs and young cranelings newly hatched, which they destroy without all pity. Thus for the three months that their journey and expedition continueth, and then they make an end of their valiant service : for otherwise if they should continue any longer, they were never able to withstand the new flights of this fowl, grown to some strength and bigness. As for their houses and cottages, made they are of clay or mud, fowls' feathers, and birds' egg shells. Howbeit, *Aristotle* writeth, that these Pygmæans live in hollow caves & holes under the ground. For all other matters he reporteth the same that all the rest. *Isogonus* saith, that certain Indians named Cyrni, live a hundred and forty years. The like he thinketh of the Aethyopian Macrobii, and the Seres : as also of them that dwell upon the mount Athos : and of these last rehearsed, the reason verily is rendered to be thus, because they feed of vipers' flesh, and therefore is it that neither lice breed in their heads, not other vermin in their cloths, for to hurt and annoy their bodies. *Onesicritus* affirmeth, that in those parts of India where there are no shadows to be seen, the men are five cubits of stature, and two hand breadths over : that they live 130 years : and never age for all that and seem old, but die then, as if they were in their middle and settled age. *Crates* of Pergamus nameth those Indians who live about an hundred year, Gymetes: but others there be, and those not a few, that call them Macrobii. *Ctesias* saith there is a race or kindred of the Indians named Pandore, inhabiting certain valleys, who live two hundred years: in their youthful time the hair of their head is white, but as they grow to age, waxeth black. Contrariwise, others there be near neighbours to the Macrobii, who exceed not forty years, and their women bear but once in their lifetime. And this also is avouched by *Agatharcides*, who affirmeth moreover, that all their feeding is upon locusts, and that they are very quick and swift of foot. *Clitarchus* and *Megasthenes* both nameth them Mandri, and make account that they have three hundred villages in their country. Over and besides, that the women bring forth children when they are but seven years old, and wax aged at forty. *Artemidorus* affirmeth, that in the island Taprobana the people live exceeding long without any malady or infirmity of the body. *Duris* maketh report, that certain Indians engender with beasts, of which generation are bred certain monstrous mongrels, half beasts and half men. Also, that the Calingian women of India conceive with child at five years of age, & live not above eight. In another tract of that country, there be certain men with long shagged tails most swift and light of foot: and some again that with their ears cover their whole body. The Orites are neighbours to the Indians, divided from them only by the river Arbis, who are acquainted with no other meat but fish: which they split and slice into pieces with their nails, and roast them against the sun, and then make bread thereof as *Clitarchus* makes report. *Crates* of Pergamus saith likewise, that the Troglodites above Aethyopia be swifter than horses: and that some Aethyopians are above eight cubits high. And these are a kind of the Aethyopian Nomades, called Syrobatæ, as he saith, dwelling along the river Astapus, toward the North pole. As for the nation called Menismini, they dwell from the ocean sea twenty days' journey, who live of the milk of certain beasts that we call Cynocephales, having heads and snouts like dogs. And whole herds and flocks of the females they keep and feed, killing the male of them all, save only to serve for maintenance of the breed. In the deserts of Africa ye shall meet oftentimes with fairies, appearing in the shape of men and women, but they vanish soon away like fantastical illusions. See how Nature is disposed for the nonce to devise full wittily in this and such like pastimes to play with mankind, thereby not only to make herself merry, but to set us a wondering at such strange miracles. And I assure you, thus daily and hourly in a manner playeth she her part, that to recount every one of her sports by themselves, no man is able with all his wit and memory. Let it suffice therefore, to testify and declare her power, that we have set down these prodigious and strange works of hers, shewed in whole nations. And then go forward to discourse of some particulars, approved and known in man.

PRODIGIOUS BIRTHS

Of late years, and no longer since than in the latter end of the reign of *Augustus Caesar*, at Ostia there was a woman (a Commoner's wife) delivered at one birth of two boys and as many girls, but this was a prodigious token and portended no doubt the famine that ensued soon after. In Peloponnesus there is found one woman that brought forth at four births twenty children, five at once, and the greater part of them all did well, and lived. *Trogus* is mine author, that in Aegypt it is an ordinary thing for a woman to have seven at a burden.

*   *   *   *   *

As for *Alcippe*, she was delivered of an elephant, marry that was a monstrous and prodigious token, and foreshewed some heavy fortune that followed after. As also in the beginning of the Marsians' war, there was a bondwoman brought forth a serpent. In sum, there be many mishapen monsters come that way into the world, of divers and sundry forms. *Claudius Caesar* writeth, that in Thessalie there was born a monster called an Hippocentaur, i.e. half a man and half a horse : but it died the very same day. And verily, after he was come to wear the diadem, we ourselves saw the like monster, sent unto him out of Aegypt, embalmed and preserved in honey. Among many strange examples appearing upon record in chronicles, we read of a child in Sagunt, that very year that it was forced and razed by *Anniball*, which, so soon as it was come forth of the mother's womb, presently returned into it again.

CHANGES OF SEX

It is no lie nor fable, that females may turn to be males. For we have found it recorded in the yearly chronicles called Annales, that in the year when *Pub. Licinius Crassus*, and *C. Cassius Longinus* were Consuls of Rome, there was in Cassinum a maid child, under the very hand and tuition of her parents, without suspicion of being a changeling, become a boy: and by an ordinance of the soothsayers called Aruspices, was confined to a certain desert island, and thither conveyed. *Licinius Mutianus* reporteth, that himself saw at Argos one named *Arescon*, who beforetime had to name *Arescusa*, and a married wife: but afterwards in process of time, came to have a beard, and the genital parts testifying a man, and thereupon wedded a wife. After the same sort he saw (as he saith) at Smyrna, a boy changed into a girl. I myself am an eye-witness, that in Africa one L. Cossicius, a citizen of Tisdrita, turned from a woman to be a man, upon the very marriage day: and lived at the time that I wrote this book.

A LONG GESTATION

Massurius writeth, that *L. Papyrius* the Praetor or lord chief justice, when a second heir in remainder made claim, and put in plea for his inheritance of the goods, made an award, and gave judgement against him, in the behalf of an infant the right heir, born after the decease of his father; upon this, that the mother came in and testified how she was delivered of that child, within thirteen months after the death of the testator: the reason was, because there is no definite time known nor set down for women to go with child.

THE FRAILTY OF MAN

I am abashed much, and very sorry to think and consider what a poor and ticklish beginning man hath, the proudest creature of all others: when the smell only of the snuff of a candle put out, is the cause oftentimes that a woman falleth into untimely travail. And yet see, these great tyrants, and such as delight only in carnage and bloodshed, have no better original.

F

Thou then that presumest upon thy bodily strength, thou that standest so much upon fortune's favours and hast thine hands full of her bountiful gifts, taking thyself not to be a foster child and nurseling of hers, but her natural son born of her own body: thou, I say, that busiest thy head evermore, and settest thy mind upon conquests and victories: thou that art upon every good success and pleasant gale of prosperity puffed up with pride, and takest thyself for a god, never thinkest that thy life, when it was hung upon so single a thread, with so small a matter might have miscarried. Nay, more than that, even at this day in more danger art thou than so, if thou chance to be but stung or bitten with the little tooth of a serpent: as if no more but the very kernel of a raisin goes down thy throat wrong, as it did with the poet *Anacreon*, which cost him his life. Oh, as *Fabius* a Senator of Rome, and lord chief justice besides, who in a draught of milk fortuned to swallow a small hair, and was strangled withal. Well then, think better of this point. For he verily that will evermore set before his eyes and remember the frailty of man's estate, shall live in this world uprightly and in even balance, without inclining more to one side, than unto another.

FAMILY LIKENESSES

In the race and family of the *Lepidi*, it is said there were three of them (not successively one after another, but out of order after some intermission) who had every one of them when they were born, a little pannicle or thin skin growing over the eye. Some have been known to resemble their grandsires: and of two twins, one hath been like the father, the other the mother: but he that was born a year after, hath been so like his elder brother, as if he had been one of the twins. Some women there be that bring all their children like to themselves: and others again, as like to their husbands: and some like neither the one nor the other. Ye shall have women bring all their daughters like to their fathers, and contrariwise, their sons like the mothers. The example is notable, and yet undoubtedly true, of one *Nicaus*, a famous wrestler of Constantinople, who having to his mother a woman begotten in adultery by an Aethyopian, and yet with white skin, nothing different from other women of that country, was himself black, and resembled his grandsire, the Aethyopian abovesaid. Certes, the cogitations and discourses of the mind make much for these similitudes and resemblances whereof we speak : and so likewise many other accidents and occurrent objects, are thought to be very strong and effectual therein, whether they come by sight, hearing, and calling to remembrance; or imaginations only conceived, and deeply apprehended in the very act of generation, or the instant of conception. The wandering cogitation also and quick spirit either of father or mother, flying to and fro all on a sudden, from one thing to another, at the same time, is supposed to be one cause of this impression, that maketh either the foresaid uniform likeness, or confusion and variety. And hereupon it cometh, and no marvel it is, that men are more unlike one another, than other creatures : for the nimble motions of the spirit, the quick thoughts, the agility of the mind, the variety of discourse in our wits, imprinteth diverse forms, and many marks of sundry cogitations. Whereas the imaginative faculty of other living creatures is unmovable, and always continueth in one : in all it is alike, and the same still in every one, which causeth them always to engender like to themselves, each one in their several kind.

MENSTRUATION

But to come again to women, hardly can there be found a thing more monstrous than is that flux and course of theirs. For if during the time of this their sickness, they happen to approach or go over a vessel of wine, be it never so new, it will presently sour : if they touch any standing corn in the field, it will wither and come to no good. Also, let them in this estate handle any grasses, they will die upon it : the herbs and young buds in a garden if they do but pass by, will catch a blast, and burn away to nothing. Sit they upon or under trees while they are in this case, the fruit which hangeth upon them will fall. Do they but see themselves in a looking-glass, the clear brightness thereof turneth into dimness, upon their very sight. Look they upon a sword, knife, or any edged tool, be it never so bright, it waxeth duskish, so doth also the lively hue of ivory. The very bees in the hive die. Iron and steel presently take rust, yea, and brass likewise, with a filthy, strong, and poisoned stink, if they lay but hand thereupon. If dogs chance to taste of women's fleures, they run mad therewith : and if they bite anything afterwards, they leave behind them such a venom, that the wounds are incurable : nay the very clammy slime bitumen, which at certain times of the year floateth and swimmeth upon the lake of Sodom, called Asphaltites in Iurie, which otherwise of the own nature is pliable enough, soft and gentle, and ready to follow what way a man would have it, cannot be parted and divided asunder (for by reason of the viscosity, it cleaveth and sticketh like glue, and hangeth all together, pluck as much as a man will at it), but only by a thread that is stained with this venomous blood. Even the silly pismires (the least creature of all others) hath a perceivance & sense of this poison, as they say : for they cast aside and will no more come to that corn, which they have once found by taste to be infected with this poison.

ZOROASTER

Zoroastres was the only man that ever we could hear of, who laughed the same day that he was born : his brain did so evidently pant and beat, that it would bear up their hands that laid them upon his head : a most certain presage and fore-token of that great learning that afterwards he attained unto.

NATURAL DELICACY

Finally, observed it is, that the dead corpse of a man floateth upon the water with the face upward, but contrariwise women swim grovelling, as if Nature had provided to save their honesty and cover their shame, even when they are dead.

FEATS OF STRENGTH

Varro in his treatise of prodigious and extraordinary strength, maketh report of one *Tritanus*, a man that of body was but little and lean withal, howbeit of incomparable strength, much renowned in the fence school, and namely, in handling the

Samnites' weapons, wearing their manner of armour, and performing their feats and masteries of great name. He maketh mention also of a son of his, a soldier, that served under *Pompeius* the Great, who had all over his body, yea, and throughout his arms and hands, some sinews running straight out in length, others crossing over-thwart lattice-wise : and he saith moreover of him, that when an enemy out of the camp gave him defiance and challenged him to a combat, he would neither put on defensive harness, nor yet arm his right hand with offensive weapon; but with naked hand made means to foil and overcome him, and in the end when he had caught hold of him, brought him away perforce into his own camp with one finger. *Iunius Valens* a captain, pensioner, or centurion of the guard soldiers about *Augustus Caesar,* was wont alone to bear up a chariot laden with certain hogs heads or a butt of wine, until it was discharged thereof, and the wine drawn out : also his manner was with one hand to stay a coach against all the force of the horses striving and straining to the contrary : and to perforce other wonderful masteries, which are to be seen engraven upon his tomb : and therefore (qd. *Varro*) being called *Hercules Rusticellus,* he took up his mule upon his back and carried him away. *Fusius Salvius* having two hundred pound weights at his feet, and as many in his hands, and twice as much upon his shoulders, went withal up a pair of stairs or a ladder. Myself have seen one named *Athanatus,* do wonderful strange matters in the open shew and face of the world, namely, to walk his stations upon the stage with a cuirass of lead weighing 500 pounds, booted besides with a pair of buskins or greaves about his legs that came to as much in weight. As for *Milo* the great wrestler of Crotone, when he stood firm upon his feet, there was not a man could make him stir one foot : if he held a pomegranate fast within his hand, no man was able to stretch a finger of his and force it out at length. It was counted a great matter, that *Philippides* ran 1,140 stadia, to wit, from Athens to Lacedaemon in two days, until *Lanisis* a courier of Lacedaemon, and *Philonides* footman to *Alexander* the great, ran between Sicyone and Olis in one day. 1,200 stadia. But now verily at this day we see some in the grand cirque, able to endure in one day the running of 160 miles. And but a while ago we are not ignorant, that when

Fonteius and *Vipsanus* were Consuls, a young boy but nine years old, between noon and evening ran seventy-five miles. And verily a man may wonder the more at this matter, and come to the full conceit thereof, if he does but consider, that it was counted an exceeding great journey that *Tiberius Nero* made with three chariots (shifting from one to the other fresh) in a day and a night, riding post-haste unto his brother *Drusus* then lying sick in Germany, and all that, was but 200 miles.

GOOD EYESIGHT

We find in histories as incredible examples as any be, as touching quickness of eyesight. *Cicero* hath recorded, that the whole Poem of *Homer* called Ilias, was written in a piece of parchment, which was able to be couched within a nut shell. The same writer maketh mention of one that could see and discern outright 135 miles. And *M. Varro* nameth the man, and saith he was called *Strabo* : who affirmeth thus much moreover of him, that during the Carthaginian war he was wont to stand and watch upon Lilybæm, a cape in Sicily, to discover the enemy's fleet loosing out of the haven of Carthage, and was able to tell the very just number of the ships. *Callicrates* used to make pismires and other such like little creatures, out of ivory so artifically, that other men could not discern the parts of their body one from another. There was one *Myrmecides,* excellent in that kind of workmanship : who of the same matter wrought a chariot with four wheels and as many steeds in so little room, that a silly fly might cover all with her wings. Also he made a ship with all the tackling to it, no bigger than a little bee might hide with her wings.

MEMORY

As touching memory, the greatest gift of Nature, and most necessary of all others for this life; hard it is to judge and say who of all others deserved the chief honour therein : considering how many men have excelled, and won much glory in that behalf. King *Cyrus* was able to call every soldier that he had through his whole army, by his own name. *L. Scipio* could do the like by all the citizens of Rome. Semblably, *Cineas* Ambassador of king *Pyrrhus,* the very next day that he came to Rome, both knew and also saluted by name all the Senate, and the whole degrees of gentlemen and cavallierie in the city. *Mithridates* the king, reigned over two and twenty nations of diverse languages, and in so many tongues gave laws and ministered justice unto them, without truchman : and when he was to make speech unto them in public assembly respectively to every nation, he did perform it in their own tongue, without interpreter. One *Charmides* or *Carmadas,* a Grecian, was of so singular a memory, that he was able to deliver by heart the contents word for word of all the books that a man could call for out of any library, as if he read the same presently within book. At length the practice hereof was reduced into an art of memory : devised and invented first by *Simonides Melicus,* and afterwards brought to perfection and consummate by *Metrodorus Scepsius* : by which a man might learn to rehearse again the same words of any discourse whatsoever, after once hearing. And yet there is not a thing in man so frail and brittle again as it, whether it be occasioned by disease, by casual injuries and occurrents, or by fear, through which it faileth sometime in part, and otherwhiles decayeth generally, and is clean lost. One with the stroke of a stone, fell presently to forget his letters only, and could read no more : otherwise his memory served him well enough. Another, with a fall from the roof of a very high house, lost the remembrance of his own mother, his next kinsfolk, friends and neighbours. Another, in a sickness of his forgot his own servants about him : and *Messala Corvinus* the great orator, upon the like occasion, forgot his own proper name. So fickle and slippery is man's memory : that oftentimes it assayeth and goeth about to leese itself, even whilst a man's body is otherwise quiet and in health. But let sleep creep at any time upon us, it seemeth to be vanquished, so as our poor spirit wandereth up and down to seek where it is, and to recover it again.

JULIUS CAESAR

For vigour and quickness of spirit, I take it, that *C. Caesar* dictator, went beyond all men besides. I speak not now of his virtue and constancy, neither of his high reach and deep wit, whereby he apprehended the knowledge of all things under the cope of heaven; but of that agility of mind, that prompt and ready conceit of his, as nimble and active as the very fire. I have heard it reported of him, that he was wont to write, to read, to indite letters, and withal to give audience unto suitors and hear their causes, all at one instant. And being employed, as you know he was, in so great and important affairs, he ordinarily indited letters to four secretaries or clerks at once : and when he was free from other great business, he would otherwise find seven of them work at one time. The same man in his days fought fifty set battles with banners displayed against his enemies : in which point, he alone outwent *M. Marcellus,* who was seen forty times save one in the field. Besides this carnage of citizens that he made in the civil wars when he obtained victory, he put to the sword 1,192,000 of his enemies, in one battle or other. And certes for mine own part, I hold this for no special glory and commendation of his, considering so great injury done to mankind by this effusion of blood : which in some part he hath confessed himself, in that he hath forborne to set down the overthrows and bloodshed of his adversaries (fellow-citizens) during the civil wars.

THE DOCTOR WHO WAS NEVER ILL

But *Asclepiades* the Prusian, surpassed all others in this kind, who was the first author of that new sect which bare his name, rejected the ambassador, the large promises and favours offered by king *Mithridates* : found out the way and means to make wine wholesome and medicinable for sick folk : and recovered a man to his former state of health, who was carried forth upon his bier to be buried : and lastly he attained to the greatest name, for laying a wager against fortune, and pawning his credit so far, as he should not be reputed a physician, in case he ever were known to be sick, or any way diseased. And in truth the wager he won. For his hap was to live in health until he was very aged, and then to fall down from a pair of stairs and so to die suddenly.

A PREMATURE FUNERAL

Aviola, one that had been Consul, came again to himself when he was cast or put into the funeral fire to be burnt : but because the flame was so strong that no man could come near to recover him, burnt he was quick.

A SAD HOMECOMING

We read in chronicles, that the ghost of *Hermotimus Clazomenius* was wont usually to abandon his body for a time, and wandering up and down into far countries, used to bring him news from remote places, of such things as could not possibly be known, unless it had been present there : and all the while his body lay, as it were, half dead in a trance. This manner it continued so long, until the Cantharidæ, who were his mortal enemies, took his body upon a time in that ecstasy, and burnt it to ashes : and by that means disappointed his poor soul when it came back again, of that sheath, as it were, or case, where she meant to bestow herself.

A HAPPY DEATH

But of all others, *M. Ofilius Hilarus* an actor and player in comedies, as it is reported by ancient writers, died most secure of death, and with the greatest circumstances about it. For after he had done much pleasure to the people, and made them sport to their contentment upon his birthday, he kept a feast at home in his house : and when the supper was set forth upon the table, he called for a mess of hot broth in a porringer to drink of : and withal, casting his eye upon the mask or visor that he put on that day, fitted it again to his visage, and took off the chaplet or garland from his bare head, and set it thereupon : in this habit, disguised as he sat, he was stark dead and key cold before any man perceived it : until he that leaned next unto him at the board, put him in mind of his pottage that had cooled, and when he made no answer again, they found in what case he was. These examples all be of happy deaths.

THE EIGHTH BOOK

sheweth unto us, land creatures, and their kinds

PERFORMING ELEPHANTS

IN THE late solemnity of tourneys and sword-fight at the sharp, which *Germanicus Caesar* exhibited to gratify the people, the elephants were seen to show pastime with leaping and keeping astir, as if they danced, after a rude and disorderly manner. A common thing it was amongst them to fling weapons and darts in the air so strongly, that the winds had no power against them; to flourish also beforehand, yea, and to encounter and meet together in fight like sword-fencers, and to make good sport in a kind of Morris dance: and afterwards to go on ropes and cords: to carry (four together) one of them laid at ease in a litter, resembling the manner of women newly brought a-bed: last of all, some of them were so nimble and well practised, that they would enter into an hall or dining place where the tables were set full of guests, and pass among them so gently and daintily, weighing as it were their feet in their going, so as they would not hurt or touch any of the company as they were drinking.

*   *   *   *   *

This is known for certain, that upon a time there was one elephant among the rest, not so good of capacity, to take out his lessons, and learn that which was taught him : and being beaten and beaten again for that blockish and dull head of his, was found studying and conning those feats in the night, which he had been learning in the day time. But one of the greatest wonders of them was this, that they could mount up and climb against a rope; but more wonderful, that they should slide down again with their heads forward. *Mutianus,* a man who had in his time been thrice Consul, reporteth thus much of one of them, that he had learned to make the Greek characters, and was wont to write in that language thus much, *this have I written and made on offering of the Celtic spoilts.* Likewise he saith, that himself saw at Puteoli, a certain ship discharged of elephants embarked therein; and when they should be set ashore, and forced to go forth of the vessel, to which purpose there was a bridge made for them to pass over, they were affrighted at the length thereof, bearing out so far from the land into the water : and therefore to deceive themselves, that the way might not seem so long, went backward with their tails to the bank, and their heads toward the sea.

THE ELEPHANT WHO FELL IN LOVE

After they have taken one to another once, they never change : neither fall they out and fight about their females, as other creatures do most deadly and mortally. And this is not for want of love and hot affection that way. For reported it is of one elephant, that he cast a fancy and was enamoured upon a wench in Egypt that sold nosegays and garlands of flowers. And lest any man should think that he had no reason thereto, it was no ordinary maiden, but so amiable, as that *Aristophanes* the excellent Grammarian, was wonderfully in love with her.

THE BONASUS

There is (they say) a wild beast of Paeonia, which is called Bonasus, with a mane like an horse, otherwise resembling a bull : marry, his horns bend so inward with their tips toward his head, that they serve him in no stead at all for fight, either to offend or defend himself; and therefore, all the help that he hath, is in his good footmanship; and otherwhiles in his flight by dunging, which he will squirt out from behind him three acres in length. This ordure of his is so strong and hot, that it burneth them that follow after him in chase, like fire, if haply they touch it.

WHY LIONS ARE FIERCE

These lionesses are very lecherous, and this is the very cause that the lions are so fell and cruel . . . The lion knoweth by scent and smell of the pard, when the lioness his mate hath played false, and suffered herself to be covered by him : and presently with all his might and main runneth upon her for to chastise and punish her. And therefore when a lioness hath done a fault that way, she either goeth to a river, and washeth away the strong and rank savour of the pard, or else keepth aloof, and followeth the lion far off, that he may not catch the said smell.

THE CHIVALRY OF LIONS

The lion alone of all wild beasts is gentle to those that humble themselves unto him, and will not touch any such upon their submission, but spareth what creature soever lieth prostrate before him. As fell and furious as he is otherwhiles, yet he dischargeth his rage upon men, before that he setteth upon a woman, and never preyeth upon babies unless it be for extreme hunger. They are verily persuaded in Libya, that they have a certain understanding, when any man doth pray or entreat them for anything. I have heard it reported for a truth, by a captive woman of Getulia, (which being fled was brought home again to her master) that she had pacified the violent fury of many lions within the woods and forests, by fair language and gentle speech; and namely, that for to escape their rage, she hath been so hardy as to say, she was a silly woman, a banished fugitive, a sickly, feeble, and weak creature, an humble suitor and lowly suppliant unto him the noblest of all other living creatures, the sovereign and commander of all the rest, and that she was too base and not worthy that his glorious majesty should prey upon her.

HOW TO CURE AN UPSET STOMACH

The lion is never sick but of the peevishness of his stomach, loathing all meat : and then the way to cure him, is to tie unto him certain she apes, which with their wanton mocking and making mows at him, may move his patience and drive him for the very indignity of their malapert sauciness, into a fit of madness; and then, as soon as he hath tasted their blood, he is perfectly well again : and this is the only remedy.

ELPIS AND THE LION

Semblably, *Elpis* a Samian being arrived and landed in Affricke, chanced to espy near the shore, a lion, gaping wide and seeming afar off to whet his teeth at him in menacing wise : he fled apace to take a tree, and called upon god *Bacchus* to help him (for then commonly we fall to our prayers when we see little or no hope of other help), but the lion stopped him not in his flight, albeit he could have crossed the way well enough; but laying himself down at the tree root with that open mouth of his wherewith he had scared the man, made signs to move pity and compassion. Now so it was, that the beast having lately fed greedily, had gotten a sharp bone within his teeth which put him to exceeding pain; besides that, he was almost famished and he looked pitifully up to the man, showing how he was punished himself among those very weapons wherewith he was to annoy others, and after a sort with dumb and mute prayers besought his help. *Elpis* advised him well a pretty while, and besides that he was not very forward to venture upon the wild beast, he stayed the longer and made the less haste, whilst he considered rather this strange and miraculous accident, than otherwise greatly feared. At the last he cometh down from the tree, and plucketh out the bone, whilst the lion held his mouth handsomely to him, and composed himself to receive his helpful hand as fitly as possibly he could. In recompense of which good turn, it is said, that so long as this ship of his lay there at anchor, the lion furnished him and his company with good store of venison ready killed to his hand.

THE MANTICHORA

Ctesias writeth, that in Aethyopia likewise there is a beast which he calleth Mantichora, having three ranks of teeth, which when they meet together are let in one within another like the teeth of combs: with the face and ears of a man, with red eyes, of colour sanguine, bodied like a lion, and having a tail armed with a sting like a scorpion: His voice resembleth the noise of a flute and trumpet sounded together: very swift he is, and man's flesh of all others he most desireth.

WOLVES AND WEREWOLVES

It it commonly thought likewise in Italy, that the eyesight of wolves is hurtful; in so much, as if they see a man before he espy them they cause him to lose his voice for the time. They that be bred in Affricke and Aegypt, are but little, and withal nothing lively but without spirit. In the colder clime, they be more eager and cruel. That men may be transformed into wolves, and restored again to their former shapes, we must confidently believe to be a loud lie, or else give credit to all those tales which we have for so many ages found to be mere fabulous untruths. But how this opinion grew first, and is come to be so firmly settled, that when we would give men the most opprobrious words of defiance we can, we term them *Versipelles*, I think it is not much amiss in a word to show. *Euanthes* a writer among the Greeks, (of good account and authority) reporteth, that he found among the records of the Arcadians, that in Arcadia there was a certain house and race of the *Antaei,* out of which one evermore must of necessity be transformed into a wolf: and when they of that family have cast lots who it shall be, they use to accompany the party upon whom the lot is fallen, to a certain mere or pool in that country: when he is thither come, they turn him naked out of all his clothes, which they hang upon an oak thereby: then he swimmeth over the said lake to the other side, and being entered into the wilderness, is presently transfigured and turned into a wolf, and so keepeth company with his like of that kind for nine years' space: during which time, (if he forbear all the while to eat man's flesh) he returneth again to the same pool or pond, and being swum over it, receiveth his former shape again of a man, save only that he shall look nine years elder than before. *Fabius* added one thing more and saith, that he findeth again the same apparel that was hung up in the oak aforesaid. A wonder it is to see, to what pass these Greeks are come in their credulity : there is not so shameless a lie, but it findeth one or other of them to uphold and maintain it.

THE HIPPOPOTAMUS

The same river Nilus bringeth forth another beast called Hippopotamus, i.e. a riverhorse. Taller he is from the ground than the crocodile : he hath a cloven foot like a boeufe : the back, mane, and hair of a horse : and he hath his neighing also. His muzzle or snout turneth up : his tail twineth like the boar's, and his teeth likewise are crooked and bending downwards as the boar's tusks, but not so hurtful : the skin or hide of his back unpenetrable (whereof are made targets and head-pieces of doughty proof, that no weapon will pierce) unless it be soaked in water, or some liquor. He eateth down the standing corn in the field : and folk say, that he setteth down beforehand where he will pasture and feed day by day : and when he setteth forward to any field for his relish, he goeth always backward, and his tracks are seen leading from thence, to the end, that against his return he should not be forelaid, nor followed by his footing.

RATS

The rats of Pontus, which be only white, come not abroad all winter : they have a most fine and exquisite taste in their feeding; but I wonder how the authors that have written this, should come to the knowledge of so much. Those of the Alps likewise i.e. Marmotanes, which are as big as Brocks or badgers, keep in, during winter : but they are provided of victuals before-hand which they gather together and carry into their holes. And some say, when the male or female is laden with grass and herbs, as much as it can comprehend within all the four legs, it lieth upon the back with the said provision upon their bellies, and then cometh the other, and taketh hold by the tail with the mouth, and draweth the fellow into the earth : thus do they one by the other in turns : and hereupon it is, that all that time their backs are bare, and the hair worn off.

A FAITHFUL DOG

But this passeth all, which happened in our time, and standeth upon record in the public registers, namely, in the year that *Appius Iunius* and *P. Silus* were Consuls, at what time as *T. Sabinus* and his servants were executed for an outrage committed upon the person of *Nero,* son of *Germanicus* : one of them that died had a dog which could not be kept from the prison door, and when his master was thrown down the stairs (called Scalæ Gemoniæ) would not depart from his dead corpse, but kept a most piteous howling and lamentation about it, in the sight of a great multitude of Romans that stood round about to see the execution and the manner of it : and when one of the company threw the dog a piece of meat, he straightways carried it to the mouth of his master lying dead. Moreover, when the carcass was thrown into the river Tiberis, the same dog swam after, & made all the means he could to bear it up afloat that it should not sink : and to the sight of this spectacle, and fidelity of the poor dog to his master, a number of people ran forth by heaps out of the city to the waterside.

OEDIPUS

There was another great horse hoodwinked because he should cover a mare : but perceiving after that he was unhooded that he served as a stallion to his own dam that foaled him, ran up to a steep rock with a downfall, and there for grief cast himself down and died.

WIND-FOALS

In Portugal, along the river Tagus, and about Lisbon, certain it is, that when the west wind bloweth, the mares set up their tails, and turn them full against it, and so conceive that genital air instead of natural seed : in such sort, as they became great withal, and quicken in their time, and bring forth foals as swift as the wind, but they live not above three years.

TWO INTELLIGENT GOATS

Mutianus reporteth, that he had occasion upon a time to mark the wit of this creature : It happened, that upon a narrow thin plank that lay for a bridge, one goat met another coming both from divers parts : now by reason that the place was so narrow that they could not pass by, nor turn about, nor yet retire backwards blindly, considering how long the plank was, and so slender withal; moreover, the water that ran underneath ran with a swift stream, and threatened present death if they failed and went besides : *Mutianus* (I say) affirmeth, that he saw one of them to lie flat down, and the other to go over his back.

THE NINTH BOOK

layeth before us all fishes, and creatures of the water

MERMAIDS AND MERMEN

As FOR the mermaids called Nereides, it is no fabulous tale that goeth of them : for look how painters draw them, so they are indeed : only their body is rough and scaled all over, even in those parts where they resemble a woman. For such a mermaid was seen and beheld plainly upon the same coast near to the shore : and the inhabitants dwelling near, heard it afar off when it was dying, to make piteous moan, crying and chattering very heavily. Moreover, a lieutenant or governor under *Augustus Caesar* in Gaul, advertised him by his letters, that many of these Nereides or Mermaids were seen cast upon the sands, and lying dead. I am able to bring forth for mine authors divers knights of Rome, right worshipful persons and of good credit, who testify that in the coast of the Spanish ocean near unto Gades, they have seen a merman, in every respect resembling a man as perfectly in all parts of the body as might be. And they report moreover, that in the night season he would come out of the sea aboard their ships : but look upon what part soever he settled, he weighed the same down, and if he rested and continued there any long time, he would sink it clean.

THE DOLPHIN AND THE SCHOOLBOY

In the days of *Augustus Caesar* the Emperor, there was a dolphin entered the gulf or pool Lucrinus, which loved wondrous well a certain boy, a poor man's son : who using to go every day to school from Baianum to Puteoli, was wont also about noon-tide to stay at the waterside, and to call unto the dolphin, *Simo, Simo,* and many times would give him fragments of bread, which of purpose he ever brought with him, and by this mean allured the dolphin to come ordinarily unto him at his call. (I would make scruple and bash to insert this tale in my story and tell it out, but that *Mecanas Fabianus, Flavius Alfius,* and many others have set it down for a truth in their chronicles). Well in process of time, at what hour soever of the day, this boy lured for him and called *Simo,* were the dolphin never so closen hidden in any secret and blind corner, out he would and come abroad, yea and scud amain to this lad : and taking bread and other victuals at his hand, would gently offer him his back to mount upon, and then down went the sharp pointed prickles of his fins, which he would put up as it were within a sheath for fear of hurting the boy. Thus when he had him once on his back, he would carry him over the broad arm of the sea as far as Puteoli to school; and in like manner convey him back again home : and thus he continued for many years together, so long as the child lived. But when the boy was fallen sick and dead, yet the dolphin gave not over his haunt, but usually came to the wonted place, & missing the lad, seemed to be heavy and mourn again, until for very grief and sorrow (as it is doubtless to be presumed) he also was found dead upon the shore.

A PLEASANT SIGHT

In the north parts of France all the Lampreys have in their right jaw seven spots, resembling the seven stars about the north pole, called *Charlemaine's* waine. They be a yellow colour, and glitter like gold, so long as the Lampreys be alive : but with their life they vanish away and be no more seen, after they be dead. *Vedius Pollio,* a gentleman of Rome by calling, and one of the great favourites and followers of *Augustus Caesar,* devised experiments of cruelty by the means of this creature. For he caused certain slaves condemned to die, to be put into the stews where these Lampreys or Muraenes were kept, to be eaten and devoured of them : not for that there were not wild beasts enough upon the land for this feat, but because he took pleasure to behold a man, torn and plucked in pieces all at once : which pleasant sight he could not see by any other beasts upon the land.

INEQUALITY OF THE SEXES

The male of the cuttle's kind, are spotted with sundry colours more dark and blackish, yea and more firm and steady, than the female. If the female be smitten with a trout-spear, or such like three-forked weapon, they will come to aid and succour her, but she again is not so kind to them : for if the male be strucken, she will not stand to it, but runneth away.

THE NAUTILOS

But among the greatest wonders of nature, is that fish, which of some is called Nautilos, of others Pompilos. This fish, for to come aloft above the water, turneth upon his back, and raiseth or heaveth himself up by little and little : and to the end he might swim with more ease, as disburdened of a sink, he dischargeth all the water within him at a pipe. After this, turning up his two foremost claws or arms, he displayeth and stretched out between them, a membrane or skin or a wonderful thinness; this serveth him instead of a sail in the air above water : with the rest of his arms or claws, he roweth and laboureth under water; and with his tail in the mids, he directeth his course, and steereth as it were with an helm. Thus holdeth he on and maketh way in the sea, with a fair show of a foist or galley under sail. Now if he be afraid of anything in the way, he makes no more ado but draweth in water to ballaise his body, and so plungeth himself down and sinketh to the bottom.

THE OCTOPUS

Moreover, the said *Trebius Niger* affirmeth, that there is not any other beast nor fish in the sea more dangerous to do a man a mischief within the water, than is this pourcuttle or many-feet polypus : for if he chance to light upon any of these divers under the water, or any that have suffered shipwreck and are cast away, he assails them in this manner : He catcheth fast hold of them with his claws or arms, as if he would wrestle with them, and with the hollow concavities and nooks between, keepeth a sucking of them; and so long he sucketh and soaketh their blood (as it were cupping-glasses to their bodies in divers places) that in the end he draweth them dry. But the only remedy is this; to turn them upon their back, and then they are soon done and their strength gone : for let them lie so, they stretch out themselves abroad and have not the power to clasp or comprehend anything.

THE POACHER

The rest which mine author hath related as touching this fish, may seem rather monstrous lies and incredible, than otherwise : for he affirmeth, that at Carteia there was one of the polypi, which used commonly to go forth of the sea, and enter into some of their open cisterns and vauts among their ponds and stews, wherein they kept great sea-fishes, and otherwhiles would rob them of their salt-fish, and so go his ways again which he practised so long, that in the end he gave himself the anger and displeasure of the masters and keepers of the said ponds and cisterns, with his continual and immeasurable filching: whereupon they staked up the place and impaled it round about, to stop all passage thither. But this thief gave not over his accustomed haunt for all that, but made means by a certain tree to clamber over and get to the foresaid salt fish; and never could he be taken in the manner nor discovered, but that the dogs by their quick scent found him out and bayed at him : for as he returned one night toward the sea, they assailed and set upon him on all sides, and therewith raised the foresaid keepers, who were affrighted at this so sudden an alarm, but more at the same sight which they saw. For first and foremost this polypi fish was of an immeasurable and incredible bigness : and besides, he was besmeared and berayed all over with the brine and pickle of the foresaid salt-fish, which made him both hideous to see to, and also to stink withal most strongly. Who would ever have looked for a polyp there, or taken knowledge of him by such marks as these? Surely they thought no other, but that they had to deal and encounter with some monster : for with his terrible blowing and breathing that he kept, he drove away the dogs, and otherwhiles with the ends of his long stringed winding feet, he would lash and whip them; sometimes with his stronger claws like arms he rapped and knocked them well and surely, as it were with clubs. In sum, he made such good shift for himself, that hardly and with much ado they could kill him, albeit he received many a wound by trout-spears which they lanced at him. Well, in the end his head was brought and shewed to *Lucullus* for a wonder, and as big it was as a good round hogshead or barrel that would take and contain fifteen amphores: and his beards (for so *Trebius* termed his claws and long-stringed feet) carried such a thickness and bulk with them, thaat hardly a man could fathom one of them about with both his arms, such knockers they were, knobbed and knotted like clubs, and withal thirty foot long. The concavities within them, and hollow vessels like great basins, would hold four or five gallons apiece: and his teeth were answerable in proportion to the bigness of his body. The rest was saved for a wonder to be seen, and weighed 700 pound weight.

MOTHER OF PEARL

As touching the shell that is the mother of pearl, as soon as it perceiveth and feeleth a man's hand within it, by and by she shutteth, and by that means hideth and covereth her riches within; for well noteth she that she is sought for. But let the fisher look well to his fingers, for if he catch his hand between, off it goeth: so trenchant and sharp an edge she carrieth, that is able to cut it quite a-two. And verily this is a just punishment for the thief, and none more: albeit she be furnished and armed with other means of revenge. For they keep for the most part about craggy rocks, and are there found: and if they be in the deep, accompanied lightly they are with cursed sea-dogs. And yet all this will not serve to scare men away from fishing after them: for why? our dames and gentlewomen must have their ears behanged with them, there is no remedy.

PEARLS

Our dames take a great pride in a bravery, to have these not only hang dangling at their fingers, but also two or three of them together pendant at their ears. And names they have forsooth newly devised for them, when they serve their turn in this their wanton excess and superfluity of riot: for when they knock one against the other as they hang at their ears or fingers, they call them crotalia, i.e. cymbals: as if they took delight to hear the sound of their pearls rattling together. Nowadays also it is grown to this pass, that mean women and poor men's wives affect to wear them, because they would be thought rich: and a by-word it is among them, that a fair pearl at a woman's ear is as good in the street where she goeth as an usher to make way, for that everyone will give such the place. Nay, our gentlewomen are come now to wear them upon their feet, and not at their shoe latchets only, but also upon the startops and fine buskins, which they garnish all over with pearl. For it will not suffice nor serve their turn to carry pearls about them, but they must tread upon pearls, go among pearls, and walk as it were on a pavement of pearls.

THE PRICE OF HER JEWELLERY

I myself have seen *Lollia Paulina* (late wife, and after widow, to *Caius Caligula* the emperor) when she was dressed and set out, not in stately wise, nor of purpose for some great solemnity, but only when she was to go unto a wedding supper, or rather to a feast when the assurance was made, and great persons they were not that made the said feast: I have seen her, I say, so beset and bedecked all over with emeralds and pearls, disposed in rows, ranks, and courses one by another: round about the attire of her head, her cawle, her borders, her peruke of hair, her bongrace and chaplet; at her ears pendant, about her neck in a carcanet, upon her wrist in bracelets, & on her fingers in rings; that she glittered and shone again like the sun as she went. The value of these ornaments, she esteemed and rated at 400 hundred thousand sestertii; and offered openly to prove it out of hand by her books and accounts and reckonings. Yet were not these jewels the gifts and presents of the prodigal prince her husband, but the goods and ornaments from her own house, fallen unto her by way of inheritance from her grandfather, which he had gotten together even by the robbing and spoiling of whole provinces. See what the issue and end was of those extortions and outrageous exactions of his: this was it, that *M. Lollius* slandered and defamed for receiving bribes and presents of the kings in the East; and being out of favour with *C. Caesar*, son of *Augustus*, and having lost his amity; drank a cup of poison, and prevented his judicial trial: that forsooth his nice *Lollia* all to-behanged with jewels of 400 hundred thousand sestertii, should be seen glittering, and looked at of every man by candlelight all a suppertime.

CLEOPATRA'S PEARLS

Two only pearls there were together, the fairest and richest that ever have been known in the world: and those possessed at one time by *Cleopatra* the last queen of Egypt; which came into her hands by means of the great kings of the East, and were left unto her by descent. This princess, when *M. Antonius* had strained himself to do her all the pleasure he possibly could, and had feasted her day by day most sumptuously, & spared for no cost: in the height of her pride and wanton bravery (as being a noble courtesan, and a queen withal) began to debase the expense and provision of *Antonie*, and made no reckoning of all his costly fare. When he thereat demanded again how it was possible to go beyond this magnificence of his: she answered again, that she would spend upon him in one supper 100 hundred thousand sestertii. *Antonie*, who would needs know how that might be (for he thought it was impossible) laid a great wager with her about it, and she bound it again, and made it good. The morrow after, when this was to be tried, and the wager either to be won or lost, *Cleopatra* made *Antonie* a supper (because she would not default, and let the day appointed to pass) which was sumptuous and royal enough: howbeit, there was no extraordinary service seen upon the board: whereat *Antonius* laughed her to scorn, and by way of mockery required to see a bill with the account of the particulars. She again said, that whatsoever had been served up already was but the overplus above the rate and proportion in question, affirming still, that she would yet in that supper make up the full sum that she was seazed at: yea, herself alone would eat above the reckoning, and her own supper should cost 600 hundred thousand sestertii : and with that commanded the second service to be brought in. The servitors that waited at her trencher (as they had in charge before) set before her one only cruet of sharp vinegar, the strength whereof is able to resolve pearls. Now she had at her ears hanging those two most precious pearls, the singular and only jewels of the world, and even Nature's wonder. As *Antonie* looked wistly upon her, and expected what she would do, she took one of them from her ear, steeped it in the vinegar, and so soon as it was liquified, drank it off. And as she was about to do like by the other, *L. Plancius* the judge of that wager, laid fast hold upon it with his hand, and pronounced withal, that *Antonie* had lost the wager. Whereas the man fell into a passion of anger. There was an end of one pearl : but the fame of the fellow thereof may go with it : for after that this brave queen the winner of so great a wager, was taken prisoner and deprived of her royal estate, that other pearl was cut in twain, that in memorial of that one half supper of theirs, it should remain unto posterity, hanging at both the ears of *Venus* at Rome, in the temple Pantheon. And yet as prodigal as these were, they shall not go away with the prize in this kind, but shall lose the name of the chief and principal, in superfluity of expense. For long before their time, *Clodius* the son of *Aesope* the Tragedian Poet, the only heir to his father, who died exceeding wealthy, practised the semblable in two pearls of great price : so that *Antonie* needeth not to be overproud of his triumvirate, seeing that he hath to match him in all his magnificence, one little better than a stage-player : who upon no wager at all laid (and that was more princely, and done like a king), but only in a bravery, and to know what taste pearls had, mortified them in vinegar, and drank them up. And finding them to content his palate wondrous well, because he would not have all the pleasure by himself, and know the goodness thereof alone, he gave to every guest at his table one pearl apiece to drink in like manner.

CO-OPERATION

The nacre also called pinnæ, is of the kind of shell fishes. It is always found and caught in muddy places, but never without a companion, which they call pinnoter or pinnophylax. And it is no other but a little shrimp, or in some places, the smallest crab; which beareth the nacre company, and waiteth upon him for to get some victuals. The nature of the nacre is to gape wide, and showeth unto the little fishes her seely body, without any eye at all. They came leaping by and by close unto her: and feeling they have good leave, grow so hardy and bold, as to skip into her shell and fill it full. The shrimp lying in spiall, seeing this good time and opportunity, giveth token thereof to the nacre secretly with a little pinch. She hath no sooner this signal, but she shuts her mouth, and whatsoever was within, crusheth and killeth it presently: and then she divides the booty with the little crab or shrimp, her sentinel and companion. I marvel therefore so much the more at them who are of opinion, that fishes and beasts in the water have no sense.

THE RAM-FISH

This fish is a very strong thief at sea, and makes foul work where he cometh: for one while he squatteth close under the shade of big ships that ride at anchor in the bay, where he lieth in ambush to wait when any man for his pleasure would swim and bath himself, that so he might surprise them: otherwhiles he putteth out his nose above the water, to spy any small fisher boats coming, & then he swimmeth close to them, overturneth and sinketh them.

A MENACE TO DIVERS

The divers that use to plunge down into the sea, are annoyed very much with a number of sea-hounds that come about them, and put them in great jeopardy. And they say, that these fishes have a certain dim cloud or thin web, growing and hanging over their heads, resembling broad, flat, and gristly fishes, which clingeth them hard, and hindereth them from retiring back and giving way. For which cause the said divers (as themselves say) carry down with them certain sharp pricks or goads fastened to long poles: for unless they be poked at and pricked with them, they will not turn their back; by reason (as I suppose) of a mist before their eyes, or rather of some fear and amazedness that they be in. For I never heard of any man that found the like cloud or mist (for this term they give unto that unhappy thing whatever it be) in the range of living creatures. But yet much ado they have and hard hold with these hound-fishes notwithstanding: for they lay at their bellies and groins, at their heels, and snap at every part of their bodies that they can perceive to be white. The only way and remedy is to make head directly affront them, and to begin with them first, and so to terrify them: for they are not so terrible to a man, but they are as afraid of him again. Thus within the deep they are indifferently even matched: but when the divers mount up and rise again above water, then there is some odds between, and the man hath the disadvantage, and is in more danger; by reason that whiles he laboureth to get out of the water, he faileth of means to encounter with the beast, against the streams and surges of the water. And therefore his only recourse is, to have help and aid from his fellows in the ship: for having a cord tied at one end about his shoulders, he shaketh it with his left hand, to give sign in what danger he is, whiles he maintaineth fight with the right, by taking into it the puncheon with the sharp point beforesaid; and so at the other end they draw him to them: and they need otherwise to pull and hale him but softly: marry when he is near once to the ship, unless they give him a sudden jerk and snatch him up quickly, they may be sure to see him worried and devoured before their face: yea and when they are at the point to be plucked up, and even now ready to go aboard, they are many times caught away out of their fellows' hands, if they bestir not themselves the better, and put their own good will to the help of them within the ship; namely, by plucking up their legs and gathering their bodies nimbly together round as it were in a ball. Well may some from shipboard poke at the dogs aforesaid with forks; others thrust at them with trout spears and such like weapons, and all never the nearer: so crafty and cautelous is this foul beast, to get under the very belly of the bark, and so maintain combat in safety. And therefore all the care that these fishers have, is to provide for this mischief, and to lie in wait for to entrap these fell, unhappy, and shrewd monsters.

SEA-VERMIN

In sum, what is there not bred within the sea? Even the very fleas that skip so merrily in summer time within victualling houses and inns, and bite so shrewdly: as also lice that love best to lie close under the hair of our heads, are there engendered and to be found: for many a time the fishers twitch up their hooks, and see a number of these skippers and creepers settled thick about their baits which they laid for fishes. And this vermin is thought to trouble the poor fishes in their sleep by night within the sea, as well as us on land.

LAMPREYS

In process of time folk grew to have a love and cast a fancy to some one several fish above the rest. For the excellent orator *Hortensius* had an house at Bauli, upon the side that lieth to Baiæ, and a fish-pond to it belonging: and he took such an affection to one lamprey in that pool, that when it was dead (by report) he could not hold but weep for love of it. Within the same pool belonging to the said house, *Antonia* the wife of *Drusus* (unto whom they fell by inheritance) had so great a liking to another lamprey, that she could find in her heart to deck it, and to hang a pair of golden earrings about the gills thereof. And surely for the novelty of this strange sight, and the name that went thereof, many folk had a desire to see Bauli, and for nothing else.

THE TENTH BOOK

speaks of flying fowls and birds

OSTRICHES

A WONDER this is in their nature, that whatsoever they eat (and great devourers they be of all things, without difference and choice) they concoct and digest it. But the veriest fools they be of all others. For as high as the rest of their body is, yet if they thrust their head and neck once into any shrub or bush, and get it hidden, they think then they are safe enough, and that no man seeth them.

THE PHOENIX

But the Phoenix of Arabia passeth all others. Howbeit, I cannot tell what to make of him: and first of all, whether it be a tale or no, that there is never but one of them in the whole world, and the same not commonly seen. By report he is as big as an eagle: for colour, as yellow & bright as gold (namely, all about the neck); the rest of the body a deeper purple: the tail azure blue, intermingled with feathers among, of rose carnation colour: and the head bravely adorned with a crest and pennache finely wrought; having a tuft and plume thereupon, right fair and goodly to be seen. *Manilius*, the noble Roman senator, right excellently well seen in the best kind of learning and literature, and yet never taught by any, was the first man of the long Robe, who wrote of this bird at large, & most exquisitely. He reporteth, that never man was known to see him feeding: that in Arabia he is held a sacred bird, dedicated unto the sun: that he liveth 660 years: and when he groweth old, and begins to decay, he builds himself a nest with the twigs and branches of the canell or cinnamon, and the frankincense trees: and when he hath filled it with all sort of sweet aromatic spices, yieldeth up his life thereupon. He saith moreover, that of his bones and marrow there breedeth at first as it were a little worm: which afterwards proveth to be a pretty bird. And the first thing that this young new phoenix doth, is to perform the obsequies of the former phoenix late deceased: to translate and carry away his whole nest into the city of the sun near Panchæa, and to bestow it full devoutly there upon the altar. The same *Manilius* affirmeth, that the revolution of the great year so much spoken of, agreeth just with the life of this bird: in which year the stars return again to their first points, and give signification of times and seasons, as at the beginning: and withal, that this year should begin at high noon, that very day when the sun entereth the sign *Aries*. And by his saying, the year of that revolution was by him shewed, when *P. Licinius* and *M. Cornelius* were Consuls. *Cornelius Valerianus* writeth, that whiles *Q. Plautius* and *Sex. Papinius* were Consuls, the phoenix flew into Egypt. Brought he was hither also to Rome in the time that *Claudius Caesar* was censor, to wit, in the eight hundredth year from the foundation of Rome: and shewed openly to be seen in a full hall and general assembly of the people, as appeareth upon the public records: howbeit, no man ever made any doubt, but he was a counterfeit phoenix, and no better.

THE EAGLE

Subtle she is and witty: for when she hath seized upon tortoises, and caught them up with her talons, she throweth them down from aloft to break their shells. And it was the fortune of the poet *Aeschylus* to die by such a means. For when he was foretold by wizards out of their learning, that it was his destiny to die upon such a day by something falling upon his head: he thinking to prevent that, got him forth that day into a great open plain, far from house or tree, presuming upon the security of the clear and open sky. Howbeit, an eagle let fall a tortoise, which lit upon his head, dashed out his brains, and laid him asleep for ever.

*   *   *   *   *

There happened a marvellous example about the city Sestos, of an eagle : for which in those parts there goeth a great name of an eagle, and highly is she honoured there. A young maiden had brought up a young eagle by hand : the eagle again to requite her kindness, would first when she was but little, fly abroad a-birding, and ever bring part of that she had gotten unto her said nurse. In process of time, being grown bigger and stronger, would set upon wild beasts also in the forest, and furnish her young mistress continually with store of venison. At length it fortuned that the damsel died : and when her funeral fire was set a burning, the eagle flew into the midst of it, and there was consumed into ashes with the corpse of the said virgin. For which cause, and in memorial hereof, the inhabitants of Sestos, and the parts there adjoining, erected in that very place a stately monument, such as they call Heröum, dedicated in the name of *Iupiter* and the virgin, for that the eagle is a bird consecrated unto that god.

RAVENS

Ravens for the most part lay five eggs : and the common sort are of opinion, that they conceive and engender at the bill, or lay their eggs by it : and therefore if women great with child chance to eat a raven's egg, they shall be delivered of their children at the mouth : and generally shall have hard labour, if such an egg be but brought into the house where such great-bellied women be. *Aristotle* denieth this and saith, that the ravens conceive by the mouth, no more than the Egyptian ibis : and he affirmeth, that it is nothing else but a wantonness which they have in billing and kissing one another, which we see them to do oftentimes; like as the daws and pigeons also.

A COCK THAT SPOKE

We find in record among our annals, that within the territory

H

of Ariminum, in that year when *Marcus Lepidus* and *Quintus Catulus* were Consuls, there was a dunghill cock did speak : and it was about a farmhouse in the country belonging unto one *Galerius*. But this happened never but once, for ought that I could ever hear or learn.

CRANES

The nation of the pretty Pygmies enjoy a truce and cessation from arms, every year (as we have said before) when the Cranes, who use to wage war with them, be once departed and come into our countries. And verily, if a man consider well how far it is from hence to the Levant sea, it is a mighty great journey that they take, and their flight exceeding long. They put not themselves in their journey, nor set forward without a council called before, and a general consent. Then fly aloft, because they would have a better prospect to see before them : and for this purpose a captain they choose to conduct them, whom the rest follow. In the rearward behind there be certain of them set and disposed to give signal by their manner of cry, for to range orderly in ranks, and keep close together in array : and this they do by turns each one in his course. They maintain a set watch all the night long, and have their sentinels. These stand upon one foot, and hold a little stone within the other, which by falling from it, if they should chance to sleep, might awaken them, and reprove them for their negligence. Whilst these watch, all the rest sleep, couching their heads under their wings : and one while they rest upon the one foot, and otherwhiles they shift to the other. The captain beareth up his head aloft into the air, and giveth signal to the rest what is to be done. These cranes if they be made tame and gentle, are very playful and wanton birds : and they will one by one dance (as it were) and run the round with their long shanks stalking full untowardly. This is for certain known, that when they mind to take a flight over the sea Pontus, they will fly directly at the first to the narrow straits of the said sea, lying between the two capes Criu-Metophon and Carambis, and then presently they ballaise themselves with stones in their feet, and sand in their throats, that they fly more steady and endure the wind. When they be half way over, down they fling those stones: but when they are come to the continent, the sand also they disgorge out of their craw.

SWANS

Some say that the swans sing lamentably a little before their death, but untruly, I suppose: for experience in many hath shewed the contrary. Howbeit, these fowls use to eat and devour one another.

QUAILS

Whensoever at any time they are upon their remove and departure out of these parts, they persuade the other birds to bear them company: and by their inducements, there go in their train the glottis, atis, and the cychramus. As for the glottis, he putteth forth a long tongue, whereupon he hath that name. This bird is very forward at the first setting out (as being desirous to be a traveller, to see far countries, and to change the air): and the first day's journey he undertaketh with pleasure: but soon finding the tediousness and pains in flying he repents that ever he enterprised the voyage. To go back again without a company, he is ashamed: and to come lag behind he is loth: howbeit, for that day he holdeth out so so, and never goeth farther: for at the next resting place that they come unto, he fair leaveth the company and stayeth there; where lightly he meeteth with such another as himself, who the year before was left behind. And thus they do from time to time, year by year.

THE NIGHTINGALE

The nightingale for fifteen days and nights together, never giveth over but chanteth continually, namely, at that time as the trees begin to put out their leaves thick. And surely this bird is not to be set in the last place of those that deserve admiration: for is it not a wonder that so loud and clear a voice should come from so little a body? Is it not as strange that she should hold her wind so long, and continue with it as she doth? Moreover, she alone in her song keepeth time and measure truly; she riseth and falleth in her note just with the rules of music and perfect harmony : for one while, in one entire breath she draweth out her tune at length treatable; another while she quavereth, and goeth away as fast in her running points : sometime she maketh stops and short cuts in her notes, another time she gathereth in her wind and singeth descant between the plain song : she stretcheth her breath again, and then you shall have her in her catches and divisions : anon all of a sudden, before a man would think it, she drowneth her voice, that one can scarce hear her : now and then she seemeth to record to herself; and then she breaketh out to sing voluntary. In sum, she varieth and altereth her voice to all keys : one while, full of her largs, longs, breves, semibreves, and minims; another while in her crotchets, quavers, semiquavers, and double semiquavers : for at one time you shall hear her voice full and loud, another time as low; and anon shrill and on high : thick and short when she list; drawn out at leisure again when she is disposed : and then (if she be so pleased) she riseth & mounteth up aloft, as it were with a wind-organ. Thus she altereth from one to another, and singeth all parts, the treble, the mean, and the bass. To conclude, there is not a pipe or instrument again in the world (devised with all the art and cunning of man so exquisitely as possibly might be) that can afford more music that this pretty bird doth out of that little throat of hers.

*   *   *   *   *

And that no man should make a doubt that there is great art and cunning herein, do but mark, how there is not one nightingale but hath many notes and tunes. Again, all of them have not the same, but every one a special kind of music by herself : nay, they strive who can do best, and one laboureth to excel another in variety of song and long continuance : yea and evident it is, that they contend in good earnest with all their will and power : for oftentimes she that hath the worse and is not able to hold out with another, dieth for it, and sooner giveth she up her vital breath, than giveth over her song. Ye shall have the young nightingales study and meditate how to sing, by themselves : ye shall have them listen attentively to the old birds when they sing, and to take out lessons as it were from them, whom they would seem to imitate stave by stave. The scholar, when she hath given good ear unto her mistress, presently rehearseth what she hath heard; and both of them keep silence for a time in their turns. A man shall evidently perceive when the young bird hath learned well, and when again it must be taught how to correct and amend wherein it did amiss: yea and how the teachers will seem to reprove and find a fault. No marvel therefore if one of these nightingales carry the price (in the market) of a bondslave; yea and a higher too, than a man might in old time have bought a good page and harness-bearer.

DOVES

Next after partridges, the nature of doves would be considered, since that they have in a manner the same qualities in that respect: howbeit, they be passing chaste, and neither male nor female change their mate, but keep together one true unto the other. They live (I say) as coupled by the bond of marriage: never play they false one by the other, but keep homes still, and never visit the holes of others. They abandon not their own nests, unless they be in state of single life or widowhood by the death of their fellow. The females are very meek and patient: they will endure and abide their emperious males, notwithstanding otherwhiles they be very churlish unto them, offering them wrong and hard measure; so jealous be they of the hens, and suspicious, though without any cause and occasion given: for passing chaste and continent by nature they are. Then shall ye hear the cocks grumble in the throat, quarrel and complain, and all to-rate the hens: then shall ye see them peck and job at them cruelly with their beaks; and yet soon after, by way of satisfaction and to make amends again for their curst usage, they will fall to billing and kissing them lovingly, they will make court unto them and woo them kindly, they will turn round about many times together by way of flattery, and as it were by prayers seek unto them for their love.

CAPRIMULGI

The Caprimulgi (so called of milking goats) are like the bigger kind of ouzels. They be night-thieves; for all the day long they

see not. Their manner is to come into the sheep-herds' cotes
and goat-pens, and to the goats' udders presently they go, and
suck the milk at their teats. And look what udder is so milked,
it giveth no more milk, but misliketh and falleth away afterwards, and the goats become blind withal.

THE CHURCHING OF HENS

The hens of country houses have a certain ceremonious
religion. When they have laid an egg, they fall a trembling and
quaking, and all to-shake themselves. They turn about also, as
in procession, to be purified, and with some festue or such like
thing, they keep a ceremony of hallowing, as well themselves
as their eggs.

THE RAVEN AND THE SHOEMAKER

Let us not defraud the ravens also of their due praise in this
behalf, considering, that the whole people of Rome hath testified
the same not only by taking knowledge, but also by a public
revenge and exemplary punishment. And thus stood the case. In
the days of *Tiberius* the Emperor, there was a young raven
hatched in a nest upon the church of *Castor* and *Pollux*, which,
to make a trial how he could fly, took his first flight into a
shoemaker's shop just over against the said church. The master
of the shop was well enough content to receive this bird, as
commended to him from so sacred a place, and in that regard
set great store by it. This raven in short time being acquainted
to man's speech, began to speak, and every morning would fly
up to the top of the rostra or public pulpit for orations, where,
turning to the open Forum and market place, he would salute
and bid good morrow to *Tiberius Caesar*, and after him, to
Germanicus and *Drusus* the young princes, both *Caesars*, every
one by their names: and anon the people of Rome also that
passed by. And when he had done so, afterwards would fly
again to the shoemaker's shop aforesaid. This duty practised he
and continued for many years together, to the great wonder and
admiration of all men. Now it fell out so, that another shoemaker, who had taken the next corviners' shop unto him, either

upon a malicious envy that he occupied so near him, or some sudden spleen and passion of choler (as he would seem to plead for his excuse) for that the raven chanced to meute a little, and set some spot upon a pair of his shoes, killed the said raven. Whereat the people took such indignation, that they rising in an uproar, first drove him out of that street, and made that quarter of the city too hot for him : and not long after murdered him for it. But contrariwise, the carcass of the dead raven was solemnly interred, and the funeral performed with all ceremonial obsequies that could be devised. For the corpse of this bird was bestowed in a coffin, couch, or bed, and the same bedecked with chaplets and garlands of fresh flowers of all sorts, carried upon the shoulders of two black Moors, with minstrels before, sounding the haut-boy, and playing on the fife, as far as to the funeral fire, which was piled and made in the right hand of the causey Appia, two miles without the city, in a certain plain or open field, called Rediculi. So highly reputed the people of Rome that ready wit and apt disposition in a bird, as they thought it a sufficient cause to ordain a sumptuous burial therefore : yea, and to revenge the death thereof, by murdering a citizen of Rome in that city, wherein many a brave man and noble person died, and no man ever solemnized their funerals : in that city I say which affordeth not one man to revenge the unworthy death of that renowned *Scipio Aemylianus*, after he had won both Carthage and Numantia.

EGGS

All eggs have within them in the mids of the yolk, a certain drop as it were, of blood, which some think to be the heart of the chicken, imagining that, to be the first that in every body is formed & made : and certainly a man shall see it within the very egg to pant and leap. As for the chick, it taketh the corporal substance, and the body of it is made of the white, waterish liquor in the egg : the yellow yolk serveth for nourishment : whilst the chick is unhatched and within the egg, the head is bigger than all the body besides : and the eyes that be compact and thrust together, be more than the very head. As the chick within groweth bigger, the white turneth into the mids and is enclosed within the yolk. By the twentieth day (if the egg be stirred) ye shall hear the chick to peep within the very shell: from that time forward, it beginneth to plume and gather feathers: and in this manner lieth it within the shell, the head resting upon the right foot, and the same head under the right wing: and so the yolk by little and little decreaseth and faileth.

THE DRUNKARD OF SYRACUSA

There goeth a pretty jest of a notable drunkard of Syracusa, whose manner was when he went into the tavern to drink, for to lay certain eggs in the earth, and cover them with mould: and he would not rise nor give over bibbing, until they were hatched.

THE ANXIOUS MOTHER

But above all it is a sport alone, to see the manner of an hen that hath sitten upon ducks' eggs and hatched them, how at the first she will wonder to have a team of ducklings about her, and not acknowledge them for her own: but soon after, she will cluck and call this doubtful brood to her, very carefully and diligently: but at the last, when she perceiveth them (according to their kind) to take the water and swim, how she will mourn and lament about the fish-pool, that it would pity one's heart to see them what moan they will make.

THE MATING OF SNAKES

As then engender together, they clip and embrace, and so entangled they be and enwrapped one about the other, that a man who saw them, would think they were one serpent with two heads. In the very act of generation, the male thrusteth his head into the mouth of the female; which she (for the pleasure and delectation that she taketh) gnaweth and biteth off.

MESSALINA

Men and women both, and none but they, repent at first the loss of their maidenhead. A very presage (no doubt) of a life to ensue full of trouble and misery, that thus should begin with repentance. All other creatures have their set times and certain seasons in the year when they engender, as hath been shewed before: but all is one with us, and no hour of day or night comes amiss. Other creatures know when they have enough, and rest satisfied: we only are insatiable that way, and cannot see to make an end. The Empress *Messalina*, wife of *Claudius Caesar*, thinking it the only victory for a lady and queen to excel in this feat, chose the most gallant and commonest strumpet in all Rome, to try masteries and to contend with for the best game: and in very truth, she won the prize: for in the space of twenty-four hours she outwent her (a beastly thing to be written) no fewer than twenty-five times.

DOGS

Dogs commonly when they be half-year old, are thought to lift up their leg when they piss, and that is a sign they are come to their full strength and perfection: but bitches all that time piss sitting upon their buttocks.

MICE AND RATS

But above all, mice and rats for fruitfulness do pass. And therefore I cannot put off the discourse of them any longer: and yet therein I must follow *Aristotle* for mine author, and the report withal of the soldiers that served under *Alexander* the great. It is said that they engender by licking, without any other kind of copulation: and that one of them hath brought six score at a time: also that in Persia there have been young mice found with young, even in the belly of the old dam.

LEOPARDS AND CATS

In the same Africa the leopards lie in await among the thickets of trees, hidden within the branches; and to seize upon them that pass by, and make spoil even from the place where fowls use to perch. As for cats, mark I pray you how silent they be, how soft they tread when they steal upon the silly birds: how secret lie they in espial for the poor little mice to leap upon them. Their own dung and excrements they will rake up and hide in the earth, knowing full well, that the smell thereof will bewray where they are.

ETYMOLOGICAL PREJUDICE

The royal eagle hateth the wren, and why? because (if we may believe it) he is named Regulus (i.e. the petty-king).

THE SPIDER AND THE SERPENT

The spider espying a serpent lying along under the shade of a tree where she spinneth, slideth down upon a fine thread to the head of the serpent, and stingeth him so deep into the brain, that he falleth a-hissing and grinding his teeth : he keepeth a-winding and turning about, but hath not the power to break the thread that hangeth above, nor yet to fly from the spider; insomuch, as the serpent lieth there dead in the place.

SLEEP AND DREAMS

The question, whether living creatures sleep or no? is not very difficult, but soon decided. For plain it is, that of land creatures, all that wink and close their eyes do sleep. As for those in the water, that they also sleep (though but a little) even they are of opinion who otherwise make doubt of the rest. And this they do not collect and gather by their eyes (for lids they have none to shut) but because they are seen to lie so still and quiet, as fast and sound asleep, stirring no part, but a little wagging their tails, and seeming to start and be affright at any sudden noise made in the water. And for the tunnies, we may avouch more confidently of their repose : for they come of purpose to sleep under the banks or rocks. And flat broad fishes lie so still sleeping among the shelves, that oftentimes a man may take them up with his hand. The dolphins and whales be heard to rout and snort again, they sleep so soundly. Moreover, as touching insects, no man need to doubt that they sleep, so quietly do they lie & make no noise : nay, if you bring a candle or other light, and set it even before their eyes, you shall not have them to awake nor move. An infant after it is born, sleepeth for certain months at the first, and in manner doth nothing else. But the elder he waxeth, wakeful he is every day more than other. Babes at the very beginning do dream. For they will waken and start suddenly in a fright : and as they lie asleep, keep a-sucking of their lips, as if they were at the breast heads. Some never dream at all. And if such chance contrary to this custom, for to dream once, it hath been counted for a sign of death, as we have seen and proved by many examples and experiments. And here in this place there offereth itself a great question, and very disputable *pro* & *contra,* grounded upon many experiments of both sides : namely whether the soul of man while the body is at rest, forseeth things to come? and how it should do so? or whether this be a thing of mere chance and altogether conjectural, as many others be? And surely if we go by histories, we may find as many of the one side as the other. Howbeit all men in manner agree in this, that dreams either immediately upon drinking wine and full stomach, or else after the first sleep, are vain and of no effect. As for sleep, it is nothing else but a retreat and withdrawing of the soul into the mids of itself. Evident it is, that horses, dogs, kine, oxen, sheep, and goats do dream. Whereupon it is credibly also thought, that all creatures which bring forth their young quick and living, do the same. As for those that lay eggs, it is not so certain that they dream : but resolved it is, that they all do sleep.

THE ELEVENTH BOOK

telleth us of Insects

BEES

THE MANNER of their business is this. All the day time they have a standing watch and ward at their gates, much like to the *corps de guard* in a camp. In the night they rest until the morning : by which time, one of them awaketh and raiseth all the rest with two or three big hums or buzzes that it giveth, to warn them as it were with sound of trumpet. At which signal given, the whole troop prepareth to fly forth, if it be a fair and calm day toward : for they do both foresee and also foreshew when it will be either windy or rainy, and then will they keep within their strength and fort. Now when the weather is temperate (which they foreknow well enough) and that the whole army is on foot and marched abroad, some gather together the virtue of the flowers within their feet and legs : others fill their gorge with water, and charge the down of their whole body with drops of such liquor. The younger sort of them go forth to work, and carry such stuff as is before-named, whilst the elder labour and build within the hive. Such as carry the flowers above-said, stuff the inner parts of their legs behind (and those nature for that purpose hath made rough) with the help of their forefeet; and those again are charged full by the means of their muffle. Thus being full laden with their provision, they return home to the hive, drawn even together round as it were in a heap, with their burden : by which time, there be three or four ready to receive them, and those ease and discharge them of their load. For this you must think, that they have their several offices within. Some are busy in building, others in plastering and over-casting, to make all smooth and fine : some be at hand to serve the workmen with stuff that they need; others are occupied in getting ready meat and victuals out of that provision which is brought in : for they feed not by themselves, but take their repast together, because they should both labour and eat alike, and at the same hour. As touching the manner of their building, they begin first above to make arch-work embowed, in their combs, and draw the frame of their work downward; where they make two little alleys for every arch or vault, the one to enter in by, the other to go forth at. The combs that are fastened together in the upper part, yea and on the sides, are united a little, and hang all together. They touch not the hive at all, nor join to it. Sometime they are built round, otherwhiles winding bias, according to the proportion of the hive. A man shall find in one hive honeycombs sometimes of two sorts : namely, when two swarms of bees accord together : and yet each one have their rites and fashions by themselves. For fear least their combs of wax should be ready to fall, they uphold them with partition walls, arched hollow from the bottom upward, to the end that they might have passage every way to repair them. The foremost ranks of their combs in the forefront, commonly are built void and with nothing in them, because they should give no occasion for a thief to enter upon their labours. Those in the back part of the hive, are ever fullest of honey : and therefore when men would take out any combs, they turn up the hives behind. Bees that are employed in carrying on honey, choose always to have the wind with them, if they can. If haply there do arise a tempest or a storm whilst they be abroad, they catch up some little stony grit to balance and poise themselves against the wind. Some say, that they take it and lay it upon their shoulders. And withal, they fly low by the ground under the wind when it is against them, and keep along the bushes, to break the force thereof. A wonder it is to see and observe the manner of their work. They mark and note the slow-backs, they chastise them anon, yea, and after-wards punish them with death. No less wonderful also it is to consider how neat and clean they be. All filth and trumpery they remove out of the way : no foul thing, no odour lieth in the hive to hinder their business. As for the dung and excrements of such as are working within, they be laid all on a heap in some by-corner, because they should not go far from their work: and in foul weather (when otherwise they have nought to do), they turn it forth. Toward evening, their noise beginneth to slack and grow less and less: until such time as one of them flieth about with the same loud humming, wherewith she waketh them in the morning, and thereby giveth a signal (as it were) and command-ment for to go to rest: much after the order in a camp. And then of a sudden they are all hushed and silent.

*   *   *   *   *

And there verily, men use when they take the honey forth of the hives, to weigh the combs, and so by weight dispense & set out how much they will leave them for their food: having this opinion, that they are bound to deal in justice & equity even with the very bees: insomuch as it is commonly said, if they be defrauded of their due in this society, and part-taking, & find falsehood in fellowship, they will die for grief: and so both the old stock will be lost, and the hope also of a new increase. In the first place therefore this is a rule, that such folk only be set about this business to drive the hives, who are neat and clean. A thief, and a woman whilst she is in her monthly sickness, they abhor.

*   *   *   *   *

What should a man now dispute about *Hercules,* about whether there was but one of that name or many? Likewise as touching the Sepulchre of Prince *Bacchus,* where and which it is. As also trouble his head in many other suchlike antiquities, buried by long continuance of time. For behold, in one small matter that is daily seen in our country houses, in a thing annexed to our farms, and whereof there is such store, all authors who have written of agriculture are not yet resolved: namely, whether the king of bees alone hath no sting, and is armed only with majesty? or, whether nature hath bestowed a sting upon him, and denied him only the use thereof? For certain it is, that this great commander over the rest, doth nothing with his sting: & yet a wonder it is to see, how they all are ready to obey him. When he marcheth abroad, the whole army goeth forth likewise: then they assemble together, and environ him round about; they are his guard, and so close they keep united together, that they will not suffer him once to be seen. At other times, when all his people are busy in labour, himself (as a right good captain) overseeth their works, goeth about from one to another, encouraging them in well-doing, and exhorting them to ply their business: himself only exempt from all other travail and pain-staking. About his person he hath a certain guard ever atten-dant: he hath his lictors and officers always in readiness, in token of majesty and princely port. He never setteth forward, but when the whole swarm is prest likewise to go forth: and in truth, long time before, a man may perceive that they be about a voyage and expedition; for, many days together there is an extraordinary humming and noise within, whilst they prepare to dislodge, trussing up as it were their bag and baggage, and expecting only a fair day of remove. And suppose that the king have in some battle lost one of his wings, yet will not his host forsake him and fly. When they be in march each one desireth and striveth to be next the prince, as taking a joy and pride to be seen of him, how lustily they perform their devoir. If he begin to be weary, they support him with their shoulders: if he be tired indeed and faint outright, they carry him full and whole. If any one of their own company chance to fail for very weari-ness, and do drag behind, or stray aside and wander out of the way, it will yet endeavour to follow the army only by the smell and scent. When the king once settleth and taketh up his resting place, there they all pitch down their tents and encamp.

*   *   *   *   *

Over and besides, bees naturally are many times sick; and that do they shew most evidently: a man shall see it in them by their heavy looks, and by their unlustiness to their business: ye shall mark how some will bring forth others that be sick and diseased, into the warm sun, and be ready to minister unto them and give them meat. Nay, ye shall have them to carry forth their dead, and to accompany the corpse full decently, as in a solemn funeral. If it chance that the king be dead of some pestilent malady, the commons and subjects mourn, they take thought and grieve with heavy cheer and sad countenance: idle they be, &

take no joy to do anything : and gather in no provision. they
march not forth : only with a certain doleful humming they
gather round about his corpse, and will not away. Then requisite
it is and necessary, to sever and part the multitude, and so to
take away the body from them; otherwise they would keep a
looking at the breathless carcass, and never go from it, but still
moan and mourn without end. And even then also they had need
be cherished and comforted with good victuals, otherwise they
would pine away and die with hunger.

SPIDERS

But the third kind of spiders, be they which are so wonderful
for their fine spinning and skilful workmanship : these weave
the great and large cobwebs that we see; and yet their very
womb yieldeth all the matter and stuff whereof they are made.
Whether it be, that at some certain season naturally their belly
is so corrupt (as *Democritus* saith :) or that within it there is a
certain bed (as it were) which engendereth the substance of silk.
But surely whatever it is, so sure and steady nails the spider
hath; so fine, so round, and even a thread she spins, hanging
thereunto herself, and using the weight of her own body instead
of a wherve; that a wonder it is to see the manner thereof. She
beginneth to weave at the very mids of the web, and when she
hath laid the warp, bringeth over the woof in compass round.
The mashes and marks she dispenseth equally by even spaces;
yet so, as every course groweth wider than other : and albeit they
do increase still from narrow to be broader, yet are they held and
tied fast by knots that can not be undone. Mark, I pray you, how
artificially she hideth the snares in that net of hers, made into
squares, to catch the poor flies. A man would not think (who
seeth the long yarn in her web wrought serce-wise, smoothed
and polished so cunningly, and the very manner of the woof so
gluish and clammy as it is, of itself) that all were to any purpose,
and served for that which she intendeth. See withal, how slack
and hollow the net is made, to abide the wind, for fear of breaking; and thereby so much the better also to fold and enwrap
whatsoever cometh within her reach ! What a craft is this of hers
to leave the upper part thereof in the front undone, as if she

I

were weary (for so a man may guess, when he can hardly see the reason) and (as it is in hunters' net and toil) that so soon as those nets be stumbled upon, they should cast the flies headlong into the lap and concavity of the net? To come now unto her nest and hole: Is there any architecture comparable to the vault and arched frame? And for to keep out the cold, how is it wrought with a deeper and longer nap than the rest! What subtlety is this of hers, to retire into a corner so far from the mids, making semblance as though she meant nothing less than that she doth, and as if she went about some other business! Nay, how close lieth she, that it is impossible for one to see, whether any body be within or no! What should I speak of the strength that this web hath to resist the puffs and blasts of winds? of the toughness to hold and not break, notwithstanding a deal of dust doth weigh and bear it down? Many a time ye shall see a broad web reaching from one tree to another: and this is when she learneth to weave and beginneth to practise and try her skill. She stretcheth a thread, and warpeth in length from the top of the tree down to the very ground; and up again she whirls most nimbly by the same thread: so as at one time, she spinneth and windeth up her yarn. Now if it chance that anything light into her net, how watchful, how quick sighted, how ready is she to run? Be it never so little snared even in the very skirt and utmost edge thereof, she always scuds into the mids; for so by shaking the whole net, she entangleth the fly or whatsoever it be, so much the more. Look what is rent therein, she presently doth mend and repair, and that so even and small, that a man cannot see where the hole was darned and drawn up again.

SCORPIONS

Some are of opinion, that they likewise devour their young, save only one who is more sly and crafty than the rest, who gets upon the rump behind of the mother, and there sits, being assured that he is safe enough in that place, both from sting of tail and tooth in mouth. This scorpion revengeth the death of his own brethren and sisters: for in the end he skips upon the back of father and mother both, where he gnaweth and eateth them to death.

TICKS

There is a creature as foul and illfavoured as the rest, which hath evermore the head fast sticking within the skin of a beast, and so by sucking of blood liveth, and swelleth withal. The only living creature of all other that hath no way at all to rid excrements out of the bodie : by reason whereof, when it is too full, the skin doth crack and burst, and so his very food is cause of his own death.

BALDNESS

Seldom do women shed their hair clean, and become bald : but never was there any gelded man known to be bald : nor any others that be pure virgins, and have not sacrificed unto *Venus*. The hair growing beneath the ventricles of the brain, and under the crown of the head, like as also about the temples and ears, falleth not off quite. Man alone of all creatures, groweth to be bald : I speak not of those that are so by nature.

THE HUMAN BRAIN

But man, for his bigness and proportion hath the most brain of all other : and the same is the moistest and coldest part that he hath within his body. Enfolded it is within two tunicles or kels, above and beneath : whereof, if the one be pierced and wounded, (to wit, *Pia mater*) there is no way but present death. Also, men commonly have more brains than women.

THE EYES OF EMPERORS

It is reported of *Tiberius Caesar* the Emperor to have had this property by himself, that if he were awakened in the night, for a while he could see everything as well as in the clear daylight; but soon after, by little and little, the darkness would overcast and shadow all again : a gift that no man in the world was ever known to have but himself. *Augustus Caesar* of famous memory, had red eyes like to some horses : and indeed wall-eyed he was, for the white thereof was much bigger than in other men : which also was the cause, that if a man looked earnestly upon him, and beheld them wistly (and a man could not anger him worse) he would be displeased, & highly offended. *Claudius Caesar* had a fleshy substance about the corners of his eyes, that took up a good part of the white, and many times they were very red and bloodshot. *C. Caligula* the Emperor, his eyes were ever set in his head, and stiff again. *Nero* had a very short sight; for unless he winked (as it were) and looked narrow with his eyes, he could not well see aught, were it never so near.

THE VEINS OF THE EYES

Many right skilful masters in chirurgery, and the best learned anatomists, are of opinion, that the veins of the eyes reach to the brain. For mine own part, I would rather think, that they pass into the stomach. This is certain, I never knew a man's eye plucked out of his head, but he fell to vomiting upon it, & the stomach cast up all within it.

HOW CATS CAN DRIVE ONE MAD

Lions, libards, and all of that sort, yea and cats, have their tongues rough and uneven, made like a file with many small edges lapping one over another : in such sort, as that with licking it will wear the skin of a man so thin, that their spittle and moisture when it cometh near unto the blood and the quick, will drive oftentimes into rage and madness, those whom they so lick, yea although otherwise they be made tame and gentle to come to hand.

THE PRIEST WHO STAMMERED

Metellus the high priest and chief sacrificed at Rome, had such a stutting and stammering tongue (by report) that against he should dedicate the temple of the goddess *Opifera,* he laboured so with his tongue for utterance, for certain months together, and took such pains, as if he had been upon the rack.

THE HEART OF A HERO

It is reported of some men, that they have hearts all hairy: and those are held to be exceeding strong and valorous. Such was *Aristomenes* the Messenian, who slew with his own hands 300 Lacedaemonians. Himself being sore wounded and taken prisoner, saved his own life once, and made an escape out of the cave of a stone quarry, where he was kept as in a prison: for he gat forth by narrow fox-holes under the ground. Being caught a second time, whilst his keepers were fast asleep, he rolled himself to the fire, bound as he was, and so without regard of his own body, burnt in sunder the bonds wherewith he was tied. And at the third taking, the Lacedaemonians caused his breast to be cut and opened, because they would see what kind of heart he had: and there they found it all overgrown with hair.

THE MIDRIFF

To this part are we beholden for our quick wit, this membrane of the midriff we may thank for our ready conceit and understanding: to which effect, charged it is with no flesh, but composed of fine and subtle sinews. The same likewise is the very especial seat of mirth: as we may perceive evidently by tickling under our arm holes, unto which it reacheth: and as in no place of man's body the skin is more fine and tender, so it taketh as great pleasure to be tickled & lightly scratched there. And hereupon it is, that in solemn combats of swordfencers at utterance with the sharp, as also in field battles, we have many a time seen men wounded and thrust through the midriff, to die laughing.

FAT

Some creatures there be that will never be fat, as the hare and partridge. Generally, whatsoever is barren, be it male or female, will soon feed fat. Sooner grow they to be old which are overfat. No living creatures there are but have a certain fat in their eyes. And the tallow in anything whatsoever, is senseless: for neither hath it arteries nor veins. The fat also and grease in

most of them, is without sense : And hereupon it is, that some
affirm, how mice and rats have gnawn and eaten fat hogs whilst
they were alive, and made them nests in their backs : yea, and
Lucius Apronius sometimes consul had a son so fat that he could
not go, so heavy was he laden with grease; insomuch, as he was
fain to take some of his grease forth of the body, and so discharge himself and become lighter.

ASSES' MILK

It is thought also to be very good for to make women's skin
fair and white. Certes the Empress *Poppaea*, wife to *Domitius
Nero*, had always whereosever she went, five hundred she-asses
milch, in her train : and in their milk she bathed and washed her
whole body, as in an ordinary bain, supposing that thereby her
skin was not only whiter, but also more neat, smooth, and void
of rivels.

ACOUSTICS

Moreover, as touching the voice, there be strange and wonderful matters reported, and those worth the rehearsal in this place.
For first and foremost, we do see, that upon the scaffold or stage
in public theatres, if the floor be strewn over well and thick with
sawdust or sand, the voice of the actors will be drowned &
lost, yea, and remain still above the scaffold, as if it were there
buried : also where there be hollow & uneven walls round
about : or empty dry vats or tuns set, the voice will be taken up
in them, and pass no farther. But the same voice, between two
walls directly set one along by another, runneth apace, yea, and
through a vault it may be heard from the one end to the other,
be the sound never so low; provided, that all be smooth and
even between, and nothing to hinder the passage thereof.

DIET AND DIGESTION

To come now unto men's diet : their best and most wholesome
feeding is upon one dish and no more, and the same plain and
simple : for surely this huddling of so many meats one upon

another of diverse tastes, is pestiferous: but sundry sauces are more dangerous than that. As touching our concoction: all tart and sharp meats are of hard digestion: also fullness and surfeiting: hasty and greedy feeding likewise be enemies to digestion, and hurtful to the stomach. In sum, we digest our meat more hardly in summer than in winter, and in age worse than in youth. Now to help and remedy all this excess and enormity, vomit hath been devised: but use it whosoever will, he shall find the natural heat of his body thereby to decay: he shall sensibly perceive that it hurteth the teeth, and eyes especially. To go to bed upon a full stomach, and to digest in sleep, is better to make a man fat and corpulent, than strong and lusty. And therefore wrestlers and champions who are acquainted with full and liberal diet, use rather to walk after meat for to digest. And in one word, much watching maketh best digestion.

THE TWELFTH BOOK

treateth of drugs and odoriferous plants

PLANE-TREES

BUT AFTERWARDS they came to be so highly esteemed, that for to make them grow the better, men would be at the cost to water them with wine : for this was found by experience, that nothing was so good for them as to pour wine to their roots. Thus have we taught even our trees also to drink wine, and be drunk. The plane trees of any great name at first, were those that grew in the walking place of the Academia in Athens; where the root of one outwent the boughs, 36 cubits in length. Now in this age there groweth a famous one in Lycia, near unto the high way where men pass to and fro, & it hath a pleasant cold fountain adjoining to it : the same is hollow within like to an house, and yieldeth a cave of 81 foot in compass : but it carrieth such an head withal like a grove, so large, so broad, & so branched, that every arm resembleth one entire tree : insomuch, as the shade thereof taketh up and spreadeth a great way into the fields. And because in every respect, it might resemble a very cabin and cave indeed, there are stony banks and seats within, in form of an arbour round about, made as it were of pumice stone overgrown with moss. And in truth, this tree and the situation thereof, is so admirable, that *Licinius Mutianus* thrice Consul, and lately lieutenant general and governor of that province, thought this one thing worthy to be recorded as a memorial to posterity, that he and eighteen more persons of his company, used to dine and sup within the hollowness of that tree : where the very leaves yielded of the own sufficient bed and bench-room to rest and repose themselves: where they might sit secured from danger of wind to blow upon them : where whiles he sat at meat, he wished nothing more than the pleasure to hear the showers of rain to pat drop by drop, and rattle above his head upon the leaves: & finally, that he took much more delight to lie within the same cabin, than in a stately chamber built of fine marble, all glorious within with hangings of tapestry and needlework, of sundry colours, and the same seeled overhead with an embowed roof laid with beaten gold.

PEPPER

As for pepper, I wonder greatly that it should be so much in request as it is: for whereas some fruits are sweet and pleasant in taste, and therefore desired; others beautiful to the eye, and in that regard draw chapmen : pepper hath neither the one nor the other. A fruit or berry it is (call it whether you will) neither acceptable to the tongue nor delectable to the eye : and yet for the biting bitterness that it hath, we are pleased therewith, and we must have it fet forsooth from as far as India. What was he, gladly would I know, that ventured first to bite of pepper and use it in his meats? Who might he be, that to provoke his appetite and find himself a good stomach, could not make a shift with fasting and hunger only? Surely ginger and pepper both, grow wild in those countries where they do like, and yet we must buy them by weight, as we do gold and silver.

WHY INCENSE IS SO EXPENSIVE

Setting this people of the Sabeans aside, there be no Arabians that see an incense tree from one end of the year to another: neither are all these permitted to have a sight of those trees. For the common voice is, that there be not above three thousand families which can claim and challenge by right of succession that privilege, to gather incense. And therefore all the race of them is called sacred and holy : for look when they go about either cutting and splitting the trees, or gathering the incense, they must not that day come near a woman to know her carnally; nay, they must not be at any funerals, or approach a dead corpse, for being polluted. By which religion, and ceremonious observation, the price is raised, and the incense is the dearer.

THE MORAL EFFECT OF RELIGION

The whole wood or forest is divided into certain portions: and every man knoweth his own part: nay, there is not one of them will offer wrong unto another, and encroach upon his neighbours. They need not to set any keepers for to look unto those trees that be cut, for no man will rob from his fellow if he might, so just and true they be in Arabia. But believe me, at Alexandria where frankincense is tried, refined, and made for sale, men cannot look surely enough to their shops and work-houses, but they will be robbed. The workman that is employed about it, is all naked, save that he hath a pair of trousers or breeches to cover his shame, and those are sewed up and sealed too, for fear of thrusting any into them. Hood-winked he is sure enough for seeing the way to and fro, and hath a thick coif or mask about his head, for doubt that he should bestow any in mouth or ears. And when these workmen be let forth again, they be stripped stark naked, as ever they were born, and sent away. Whereby we may see, that the rigour of justice cannot strike so great fear into our thieves here, and make us so secure to keep our own, as among the Sabaeans, the bare reverence and religion of those woods.

ARABIA FELIX

Neither cinnamon nor cascia do grow in Arabia, and yet it is named Happy: unworthy country as it is, for that surname, in that it taketh itself beholden to the gods above therefore, whereas indeed they have greater cause to thank the infernal spirits beneath. For what hath made Arabia blessed, rich, and happy, but the superfluous expense that men be at, in funerals? employing those sweet odours to burn the bodies of the dead, which they knew by good right were due unto the gods. And verily it is constantly affirmed by them who are acquainted well with the world, and know what belongeth to these matters, that there cometh not so much incense of one whole year's increase in Saba, as the Emperor *Nero* spent in one day, when he burnt the corpse of his wife *Poppaea*. Cast then, how many funerals every year after were made throughout the world: what heaps of odours have been bestowed in the honour of dead bodies; whereas we offer unto the gods by crumbs and grains only.

THE THIRTEENTH BOOK

describeth strange and foreign trees

WHY PERFUME WAS INVENTED

BUT THE truth is, the Persians and none but they ought to be reputed the inventors of precious perfumes and odoriferous ointments. For they to palliate and hide the rank and stinking breath which cometh by their surfeit and excess of meats and drinks, are forced to help themselves by some artificial means, and therefore go evermore all to be perfumed and greased with sweet ointments.

THE FOLLY OF WEARING SCENT

At this day there is not in Rome anything wherein men more exceed, than in these costly and precious ointments: and yet of all others, they are most superfluous and may be best spared. True it is, that much money is laid out upon pearls and precious stones; but these are in the nature of a domain and inheritance, and fall to the next heir in succession. Again, rich and costly apparel stand us in a great deal of coin; howbeit they are durable and last a long time: but perfumes and ointments, are soon done and gone; they exhale and breathe away quickly, they are momentary, they serve but for the present, and die suddenly. The greatest matter in them, and their commendation is this, to cause a man (what business soever he hath otherwise) to cast his eye and look after a gentlewoman as she passeth by perfumed in the streets, and sendeth a smell from her as she goeth. This is all the good they do: and yet forsooth a pound of this ware must cost 400 deniers: so dear is the pleasure that passeth from ourselves and goeth to another: for the party himself that carrieth the perfume about him, hath little or no delight at all in it: others they be that reap the benefit and pleasure thereof.

*   *   *   *   *

Well known it is, that *L. Plotius,* brother to *L. Plancus,* a man of great credit and authority, as having been twice Consul, and Censor besides, being outlawed and proclaimed a banished person by the decree of the Triumvirs, was discovered within a certain cave at Salernum, where he lay close hidden and sure enough otherwise, by the very smell only of a precious ointment that he had about him: and so by that means (besides the shame and disgrace that he received, thus to detect himself and be found of his enemies) the rigour of the act and arrest that passed against him, was executed and performed upon his body. And who would ever pity such persons, and not judge them worthy to come to so bad an end?

DATE-TREES

Moreover, it is constantly affirmed, that the females be naturally barren, and will not bear fruit without the company of the males among them to make them for to conceive: yet grow they will nevertheless and come up of themselves, yea and become tall woods: and verily a man shall see many of the females stand about one male, bening and leaning in the head full kindly toward him, yielding their branches that way as if they courted him for to win his love. But contrariwise, he a grim sir and a coy, carrieth his head aloft, beareth his bristled and rough arms upright on high: and yet what with his very looks, what with his breathing and exhalations upon them, or else with a certain dust that passeth from him, he doth the part of an husband, insomuch as all the females about him, conceive and are fruitful with his only presence. It is said moreover, that if this male tree be cut down, his wives will afterwards become barren and bear no more dates, as if they were widows. Finally, so evident is the copulation of these sexes in the date trees, and known to be so effectual, that men have devised also to make the females fruitful, by casting upon them the blooms and down that the male beareth, yea and otherwhiles by strewing the powder which he yieldeth, upon them.

* * * * *

Now to conclude this treatise, I think it not amiss to set down for an example, what did betide the soldiers that were of *Alexander's* army, who with eating of green dates new ripe, were choked, and so died. In the Gedrosians' country, this accident befell unto them, only by the nature of the fruit itself, eat they of it as moderately as they could : but in other parts, their greedy and over-liberal feeding upon them, was their bane. For surely new dates as they come from the tree, are so exceeding pleasant and delicious, that a man can hardly forbear and make an end in good time, before he surfeit of them and catch a shrewd turn.

NERO'S OINTMENT

Nero Caesar the Emperor in the beginning of his Empire, gave great credit unto thapsia : for using (as he did) to be a night-walker, and to make many riots and much misrule in the dark, he met otherwhiles with those who would so beat him, as that he carried away the marks black and blue in his face : but (as he was subtle and desirous to avoid the speech of the people) an ointment he made of thapsia, frankincense, and wax, wherewith he would anoint his face, and by the next morning come abroad with a clear skin, and no such marks to be seen; to the great astonishment of all men that saw him.

THE FOURTEENTH BOOK

sheweth of vine-plants

VINES

IN THE country of Campaine about Capua, they be set at the
roots of poplars, and (as it were) wedded unto them: and so
being suffered to wind and clasp about them as their husbands,
yea, and with their wanton arms or tendrils to climb aloft, and
with their joints to run up their boughs, they reach up to their
head, yea, and overtop them: insomuch as the grape-gatherer in
time of vintage, putteth in a clause in the covenants of his bargain when he is hired, that in case his foot should fail him, and
he break his neck, his master who sets him awork should give
order for his funeral fire and tomb at his own proper cost and
charges.

*   *   *   *   *

But the greatest voice and speech of men was of *Rhemnius
Palaemon* (who otherwise by profession was a famous and renowned grammarian) for that he by the means and help of the
foresaid *Sthenelus*, bought a farm within these twenty years for
600,000 sesterces in the same territory of Nomentum, about ten
miles distant from Rome, lying somewhat out of the highway.
Now it is well known far and near, of what price and account
all such farms are, and how cheap such ware is lying so near
to the city side: but among the rest, this of *Palaemon's* in that
place was esteemed most cheap and lowest priced, in this regard
especially, that he had purchased those lands, which through the
carelessness & bad husbandry of the former owners, lay

neglected and fore-let, and were not of themselves thought to be of the best soil, chosen and picked from among the worst. But being entered once upon these grounds as his own livelode and possession, he set in hand to husband and manure them, not so much of any good mind and affection that he had to improve and better anything that he held, but upon a vainglory of his own at the first, whereunto he was wonderfully given : for he makes fallows of his wine-plots anew, and delveth them all over again, as he had seen *Sthenelus* to do with his before : but what with digging, stirring, and meddling therewith, following the good example and husbandry of *Sthenelus*, he brought his vineyards to so good a pass within one eight years, that the fruit of one year's vintage was held at 400,000 sesterces, and yielded so much rent to the lord : a wonderful and miraculous thing, that a ground should be so much improved in so small a time! And in very truth, it was strange to see what numbers of people would run thither, only to see the huge and mighty heaps of grapes gathered in those vineyards of his : and all idle neighbours about him, whose ground yielded no such increase, attributed all to his deep learning, and that he went to it by his book, & had some hidden speculation above other men; objecting against him, that he practised art magic and the black science.

THE WINE OF POMPEII

As for the wine of Pompeii, a town in the kingdom of Naples, neither it nor the wine whereof it cometh, will last above ten years at the most : after which term, the elder they both be, the worst they are. Besides, they are found by experience to cause the headache, insomuch, as if a man drink thereof overnight, he shall be sure not to have his head in good tune until noon the morrow after.

WINE AND WOMEN

In ancient time, women at Rome were not permitted to drink any wine. We read moreover in the chronicles, that *Egnatius Mecennius* killed his own wife with a cudgel, for that he took her drinking wine out of a tun; and yet was he cleared by

Romulus, and acquit of the murder. *Fabius Pictor* in his Annals reporteth, that a certain Roman dame, a woman of good worship, was by her own kinsfolk famished and pined to death, for opening a cupboard, wherein the keys of the wine-cellar lay. And *Cato* doth record, that hereupon arose the manner and custom, that kinsfolk should kiss women when they met them, to know by their breath whether they smelled of Temetum : for so they used in those days to term wine : and thereof drunkenness was called in Latin Temulentia. *Cn. Domitius* (a judge in Rome) in the like case pronounced sentence judicially against a woman defendant, in this form, THAT IT SEEMED SHE HAD DRUNK MORE WINE WITHOUT HER HUSBAND'S KNOWLEDGE, THAN WAS NEEDFUL FOR THE PRESERVATION OF HER HEALTH, and therefore awarded definitely, that she should lose the benefit of her dowry.

PITCH-PLASTERS

But I am abashed and ashamed to report, how in these days the same pitch whereof we speak, should be in so great account as it is, for making of pitch-plasters, to fetch off the hair of men's bodies, and all to make them more smooth and effeminate.

LUMPS OF WINE

I will tell you a strange wonder, yet true and to be verified, not by hearsay, but pain insight. There were seen upon a time whole heaps and huge lumps of wine congealed into ice, by occasion that the hoops of the hogsheads burst that contained the wine : and this was held for a prodigious token. For indeed wine of its own nature will not congeal and freeze, only it will lose the strength, and become appalled in extremities of cold.

THE FOLLY OF HARD DRINKING

If a man mark and consider well the course of our life, we are in no one thing more busy and curious, nor take greater pains, than about wines : as if Nature had not given to man the liquor of water, which of all others is the most wholesome drink, and wherewith all other creatures are well contented. But we thinking it not sufficient to take wine ourselves, give it also to our horses, mules, and labouring beasts, and force them against Nature to drink it. Besides, such pains, so much labour, so great cost and charges we are at, to have it; such delight and pleasure we take in it; that many of us think, they are born to nothing else, and can skill of no other contentment in this life : notwithstanding, when all is done, it transporteth and carrieth away the right wit and mind of man, it causeth fury and rage, and induceth, nay, it casteth headlong as many as are given thereto, into a thousand vices and misdemeanours. And yet forsooth, to the end that we might take the more cups, and pour it down the throat more lustily, we let it run through a strainer, for to abate and geld (as it were) the force thereof : yea, and other devices there be to whet our appetite thereto, and cause us to quaff more freely. Nay, to draw on their drink, men are not afraid to make poisons, whilst some take hemlock before they sit down, because they must drink perforce them, or else die for it : others, the powder of the pumice stone, & such like stuff, which I am abashed to rehearse and teach those that be ignorant of such lewdness. And yet we see these that be the stoutest and most redoubted drinkers, even those that take themselves most secured of danger, to lie sweating so long in the bains and brothel-houses for to concoct their surfeit of wine, that otherwhiles they are carried forth dead for their labour. Yet shall have some of them again when they have been in the hot house, not to stay so long as they may recover their beds, no not so much as to put on their shirts : but presently in the place, all naked as they are, puffing and labouring still for wind, catch up great cans and huge tankards of wine (to show what lusty and valiant champions they be) set them one after another to their mouth, pour the wine down the throat without more ado, that they might cast it up again, and so take more in the place; vomiting and revomiting twice or thrice together that which they have drunk, and still make quarrel to the pot : as if they had been born into this world for no other end but to spill and mar good wine : or, as if there were no way else to spend and waste the same, but through man's body. And to this purpose, were taken up at Rome these foreign exercises, of vaulting and dancing the Morris; from hence came the tumbling of wrestlers in the dust and mire together;

for this, they show their broad breasts, bear up their heads, and carry their necks far back. In all which gesticulations, what do they else but profess that they seek means to procure thirst, and take occasion to drink? But come now to their pots that they use to quaff and drink out of : are there not graven in them fair portraits think you of adulteries? as if drunkenness itself were not sufficient to kindle the heat of lust, to prick the flesh, and to teach them wantonness. Thus is wine drunk out of libidinous cups : and more than that, he that can quaff best and play the drunkard most, shall have the greatest reward. But what shall we say to those (would a man think it?) that hire one to eat also as much as he can drink, and upon that condition covenant to yield him the price of his wine drinking, and not otherwise. Ye shall have another that will enjoin himself to drink every denier that he hath won at dice. Now when they are come to that once, and be thoroughly whitled, then shall ye have them cast their wanton eyes upon men's wives; then fall they to court fair dames and ladies, and openly bewray their folly even before their jealous and stern husbands; then (I say) the secrets of the heart are opened and laid abroad. Some ye shall have in the midst of their cups, make their wills, even at the very board as they sit : others again cast out bloody and deadly speeches at random, and cannot hold but blurt out those words which after-wards they eat again with the sword's point : for thus many a man by a lavish tongue in his wine, hath come by his death and had his throat cut. And verily the world is now grown to this pass, that whatsoever a man saith in his cups, it is held for sooth; as if truth were the daughter of wine. But say they escape these dangers : certes speed they never so well, the best of them all never seeth the sun rising, so drowsy and sleepy they are in bed every morning : neither live they to be old men, but die in the strength of their youth. Hence cometh it, that some of them look pale, with a pair of flaggy blabd cheeks; others have bleared and sore eyes : and there be of them that shake so with their hands, that they cannot hold a full cup, but shed and pour it down the floor. Generally they all dream fearfully (which is the very beginning of their hell in this life) or else have restless nights : and finally, if they chance to sleep (for a due guerdon and reward of their drunkenness) they are deluded with imaginary conceits of *Venus'* delights, defiled with filthy and abominable pollutions : and thus both sleeping and waking they sin with pleasure. Well, what becomes of them the morrow after? they belch sour, their breath stinketh of the barrel, and telleth them what they did overnight; otherwise they forget what either they did or said, they remember no more, than if their memory were utterly extinct and dead. And yet our jolly drunkards give out and say, that they alone enjoy this life, and rob other men of it. But who seeth not, that ordinarily they lose not only the yesterday past, but the morrow to come?

A STRONG HEAD

But to return again to noble *Torquatus,* herein consisted his excellency, that he did it according to art (for this you must take withal, there is an art of drinking, grounded upon certain rules and precepts). *Torquatus* (I say) drank he never so much, was not known at any time to falter in his tongue, never eased himself by vomiting, never let it go the other way under board : how late soever he sat up at the wine overnight, he would be sure to relieve the morning watch and sentinel. He drank most of any man at one entire draught before the pot went from his head; and for smaller draughts besides, he went beyond all other in number; his wind he never took while the cup was at his mouth, but justly observed the rule of drinking with one breath; he was not known to spit for all this : and to conclude, he would never leave a drop behind in the cup, not so much as would dash against the pavement, & make the least sound to be heard : a special point & precise law to prevent the deceit of those that drink for a wager. A singular glory no doubt in him, and a rare felicity.

THE FIFTEENTH BOOK

comprehendeth all fruitful trees

OLIVE OIL

THE PROPERTY of oil, is to warm the body, and to defend it against the injuries of cold: and yet a sovereign thing it is to cool and mitigate the hot distemperature of the head. The Greeks, whom we may count the very fathers and fosters of all vices, have perverted the true and right use thereof, to serve for all excess and superfluity; even as far as to the common anointing of their wrestlers with it, in their public place of exercise. Known it is for certain, that the governors and wardens of those places, have sold the oil that hath been scraped from the bodies of the said wrestlers for 80 sesterces at a time.

MYRTLE

Furthermore, it is said, that if a wayfaring man that hath a great journey for to go on foot, carry in his hand a stick or rod of the myrtle tree, he shall never be weary, nor think his way long and tedious.

BAY

It is reported, that *Tiberius Caesar* the Emperor used ever to wear a chaplet thereof when it thundered, for fear of being strucken with lightning.

* * * * *

Moreover, certain strange and memorable events as touching the bay tree, have happened about *Augustus Caesar*. For *Livia Drusilla* (who afterwards by marriage with the said *Augustus*, became Empress, and was honoured with the title of *Augusta*), at what time she was affianced and espoused to *Caesar*, chanced as she sat still, to have an exceeding hot hen to light into her lap (which an eagle flying aloft, let fall from on high) without any harm at all to the said pullet. Now when this lady or princess advised and considered well the hen, without being astonished and amazed at so strange and miraculous a sight, she perceiveth that the hen held in her bill a laurel, branched full of bay berries. The wizards and soothsayers were consulted withal about this wonderful occurrent, and gave advice in the end to preserve the bird and the brood thereof: likewise to set in the ground the foresaid branch, and duly to tend and look unto it. Both the one and the other was done and executed accordingly, about a certain house in the country belonging to the *Caesars*, seated upon the river *Tiberis*, near the causey or portway Flamina, about nine miles from Rome: which house thereupon was called, Ad Gallinas, as a man would say, The sign of the hens. Well, the foresaid branch mightily prospered, and proved afterwards to be a grove of laurels, which all came from that first stock. In process of time, *Augustus Caesar* when he entered in triumph into Rome, carried in his hand a branch of that bay tree, yea, and wore a chaplet upon his head of the same: and so did all the emperors and *Caesars* his successors after him.

THE SIXTEENTH BOOK

describeth unto us all wild trees

THE LOW COUNTRIES

WE HAVE shewed heretofore, that in the east parts verily toward the main ocean, there be many countries in that estate, to wit, altogether destitute of trees. In the north also I myself have seen the people called Cauchi, as well the greater as the less (for so they be distinguished) where there is no show or mention at all of any tree. For a mighty great compass, their country lieth so under the ocean and subject to the tide, that twice in a day & night by turns, the sea overfloweth a mighty deal of ground when it is flood, and leaveth all dry again at the ebb & return of the water: insomuch, as a man can hardly tell what to make of the outward face of the earth in those parts, so doubtful it is between sea and land. The poor silly people that inhabit those parts, either keep together on such high hills as Nature hath afforded here and there in the plain: or else raise mounts with their own labour and handiwork (like to tribunals cast up and reared with turf, in a camp) above the height of the sea, at any spring tide when the flood is highest; and thereupon they set their cabins and cottages. Thus dwelling as they do, they seem (when it is high water, & that all the plain is overspread with the sea round about) as if they were in little barks floating in the midst of the sea: again, at a low water when the sea is gone, look upon them, you would take them for such as had suffered shipwreck, having their vessels cast away, and left lying ato-side amid the sands: for ye shall see the poor wretches fishing about their cottages, and following after the fishes as they go away with the water. They have not a four-footed beast among them : neither enjoy they any benefit of milk, as their neighbour nations do : nay, they are destitute of all means to chase wild beasts, and hunt for venison; in as much as there is neither tree nor bush to give them harbour, nor any near unto them by a great way. Sea-weeds or rack, rushes and reeds growing upon the washes and meres, serve them to twist for cords to make their fishing nets with. These poor souls and silly creatures are fain to gather a slimy kind of fatty mud or oase, with their very hands, which they dry against the wind rather than the sun : and with that earth, for want of other fuel, they make fire to seethe their meat (such as it is) and heat the inward parts of their body, ready to be stark and stiff again with the chilling north wind. No other drink have they but rain water, which they save in certain ditches after a shower, and those they dig at the very entry of their cottages. And yet see! this people (as wretched and miserable a case as they be in) if they were subdued at this day by the people of Rome, would say (and none soner than they) that they lived in slavery. But true it is, that fortune spareth many men, to let them live still in pain and misery.

THE ASH

Moreover, they be excellent good, and nothing so sovereign can be found against the poison of serpents, if the juice thereof be pressed forth, & given to drink; or to cure old ulcers, if they be applied and laid thereto in manner of a cataplaster : nay, so forcible is their virtue, that a serpent dare not come near the shadow of that tree, either morning or evening, notwithstanding at those times it reachest farthest; you may be sure then they will not approach the tree itself, by a great way. And this am I able to deliver by the experience which I have seen, that if a man do make a round circle with the leaves thereof, and environ therewith a serpent and fire together within, the serpent will choose rather to go into the fire, than to fly from it to the leaves of the ash. A wonderful goodness of dame Nature, that the ash doth bloom and flourish always before that serpents come abroad; and never sheddeth leaves, but continueth green, until they be retired into their holes, and hidden within the ground.

WHY THE LEAVES FALL

Timaeus (the great astrologer and mathematician) is of opinion, that when the sun is in the sign Scorpio, he causeth leaves to fall, by a certain venomous and poisoned infection of the air, proceeding from the influence of that malign constellation. But if that were true, we may well and justly marvel, why the same cause should not be effectual likewise in all other trees. Moreover, we see that most trees do let fall their leaves in autumn : & some are longer ere they shed, and continue green until winter be come. Neither is the timely or slow fall of the leaf long of the early or late budding; for we see some that burgeon and shoot out their spring with the first, and yet with the last shed their leaves and become naked : as namely the almond trees, ashes, and elders. And contrariwise, the mulberry tree putteth forth leaves with the latest, and is one of them that soonest sheddeth them again. But the cause hereof lieth much in the nature of the soil : for the trees that grow upon a lean, dry and hungry ground, do sooner cast leaf than others : also old trees become bare before younger : and many of them also lose their leaves ere that their fruit be fully ripe : for in the fig-tree, that cometh and beareth late, in the winter pyrrie, and pomegranate, a man shall see in the latter end of the year, fruit only and no leaves upon the tree.

SPRING

The manner and order of Nature year by year, holdeth in this wise : first, trees and plants do conceive by the means of the western wind Favonius, which commonly beginneth to blow about six days before the Ides of February : for this wind is instead of a husband to all things that grow out of the earth, and of it they desire naturally to be conceived, like as the mares in Spain, of which we have written heretofore. This wind is that spirit of generation which doth breathe life into all the world; which the Latins call thereupon Favonius, a *favendo,* (i.e. of cherishing and nourishing everything) as some have thought. It bloweth directly from the equinoctial sun-setting, and evermore beginneth the spring. This time, our rustical peasants call the seasoning, when as Nature seemeth to go proud or assaut, and is in the rut and furious rage of love, desirous to conceive by this wind, which indeed doth vivify and quicken all plants and seeds sown in the ground. Now all of them conceive not at once, but in sundry days: for some are presently sped in a moment, like as living creatures: others are not so hasty to conceive, but long it is first ere they retain, and as long again before their vital seed doth put forth, and this is thereupon called their budding time. Now are they said to bring forth and be delivered, when in the spring they bloom, and that blossom breaketh forth of certain matrices or ventricles. After this, they become nurses all the while they cherish and bring up the fruit: and this time also the Latins call germinatio (i.e. the breeding season). When trees are full of blossoms, it is a sign that the spring is at the height, and the year become new again. The blossom, is the very joy of trees, and therein standeth their chief felicity: then they shew themselves fresh and new, as if they were not the same, then be they in their gay coats; then it seemeth they strive avie one with another in variety of colours, which of them should excel and exceed in beautiful hue. But this is not general, for many of them are denied this pleasure, and enjoy not this delight; for all trees blossom not: some are of an heavy and sad countenance, neither cheer they at the coming of this new season and gladsome spring: for the mast-holm, the pitch tree, the larch, and the pine, do not bloom at all, they are not arrayed in their robes, they have not ther liveries of divers colours to fore-signify (as messengers and vantcourriers) the arrival of the new year, or to welcome and solemnize the birth of new fruits.

WHEN TO HAVE ONE'S HAIR CUT

Beware thou meddle not with timber trees but either at the change or full of the moon. And in no hand, neither stork it up then, nor hew it hard to the ground. But within four days after the full moon, pluck up trees hardly, for that is the best time.

Item, be well advised, that thou neither fell, square, nor touch with the axe, any timber that is black, unless it be dry. And meddle not with it, if either it be frozen, or full of dew. *Tiberius* the Emperor abovenamed, observed likewise the change of the moon, for cutting the hair both of head and beard. And yet *M. Varro* gave a rule, that to prevent baldness and the shedding of hair, the barber should be sent for always after the full moon.

THE ELM

The elm, of all kinds of wood, will keep straight and stiff best, and not warp at all : and because it twineth and casteth not, it is passing good for hinges and hooks, for sawn boards, for ledges in doors and gates : so as this regard be had of exchange, that the upper end of the board which grew toward the head of the tree, be fitted to the nether hinge or hook of the door; and contrariwise the butt end serve the higher.

MODERN EXTRAVAGANCE

Lo, from whence first came the superfluous expense to cover and seal one wood with another ! See how those trees which for their very wood were of no price, are become more costly and dearer, when they serve as a bark to clad others ! that one tree forsooth by this means, should be sold many and sundry times at a several price. Thus have been devised (I would not else) thin leaves of wood, like gold or silver foil. And yet that is not all : for there is come up of late a device, to paint and dye in sundry colours the horns of beasts, to cut and saw their teeth into thin plates : and whereas at first there was fret-works only inlaid and set out with ivory here and there, soon after it came to pass, that the wood was covered all over therewith. Neither hath the ryot and wasteful prodigality of the world stayed there, but proceeded farther, even to search into the deep sea for that, which might serve instead of wood and timber. Thus the tortoise shell hath been cut into flakes and leaves, for want forsooth of wood upon dry land. And now of late days, certain monstrous spirits, during the Empire of *Nero*, have found out a device to disfigure the tortoise shell also with paintings, that it might be sold the dearer when it looked like wood. Thus means are wrought, that the price of beds should be raised and set up by this means: thus they would have the terebinth wood to be excessive dear and above the worth: thus must the citron wood be enhanced to an higher rate: and thus the maple is counterfeited, tortoise shells are foisted in the place and bought for it. To conclude, of late days the curiosity of men was such, that they could not content themselves with rich and costly wood; and now for to beautify and set out their wood, tortoise shells must needs be bought, there is no remedy.

A LOVE AFFAIR

There is a little hill named Carne within the territory of Tusculum, not far from Rome city side, clad and beautified with a goodly grove and tuft of beech trees, so even and round in the head, as if they were curiously kept, cut, and shorn artificially with garden shears: which grove was consecrated in old time to *Diana*, by the common consent of all Latium, which did their devotions there. In it there was one especial fair tree above the rest, which *Passenus Crispus*, a man in our days of great authority (as having been twice Consul in his time, and reputed an excellent orator, who also afterward mounted to higher place of reputation by marrying *Agrippina* the Empress, by which match became father-in-law to *Nero* the Emperor), cast a fancy and extraordinary liking unto: insomuch as he was wont not only to take his repose and lie under it, to sprinkle and cast wine plentifully upon it, but also to clip, embrace, and kiss it otherwhiles.

THE SEVENTEENTH BOOK

containeth tame trees within hortyards

HOW TO TELL GOOD SOIL

WELL, TO speak at a word, surely that ground is best of all
other, which hath an aromatic smell and taste with it. Now if
we list moreover to be better instructed, what kind of savour
and odour that should be, which we would so gladly find in
the earth; we may oftentimes meet with that scent, even when
she is not stirred with the plough, but lieth still and quiet, namely,
a little before the sun-setting, especially where a rainbow seemeth
to settle and pitch her tips in the horizon : also, when after
some long and continual drought, it beginneth to rain; for then
being wet and drenched therewith, the earth will send up a
vapour and exhalation (conceived from the sun) so heavenly and
divine, as no perfume (how pleasant soever it be) is comparable
to it. This smell there must be in it when you ere it up with the
plough : which if a man find once, he may be assured it is a
right good ground; for this rule never faileth : so as (to say a
truth) it is the very smell and nothing else, that will judge best
of the earth : and such commonly are new broken grounds, where
old woods were lately stocked up : for all men by a general
consent, do command such for excellent.

MUCK

As for muck, there be divers sorts thereof, and in old time
much use there was of it : for in *Homer* we read, that long ago
the good old king (*Laertes*) was found laying soil and dung upon

his land with his own hands. The first that devised mucking of grounds, was (by report) *Augeas*, a king in Greece : but *Hercules* divulged the practice thereof among the Italians, who in regard of that invention immortalized their king *Stercutius* the son of *Faunus*. *M. Varro* esteemeth the dung of blackbirds (gathered out of their bartons where they be kept in mew) above all others. He highly magnifieth and extolleth it also, for that it bringeth forth so good forage to feed kine, oxen, and swine withal : avouching for certain, that they will become fat beef and pork with no meat sooner. We must think well therefore and hope the best of the world nowadays, since that our ancestors and forefathers so long ago had so great bartons and pens, that the dung of fowls there kept, was sufficient to help their hard and hungry grounds. In the second degree of goodness, *Columella* rangeth pigeons' dung gathered out of dovecotes : the third place he giveth to that of hens, and other land pullen, rejecting altogether the dung of waterfowl. Howbeit all other authors (setting these two aside) attribute with one voice and consent unto the excrements of man's body, the greatest praise for this purpose. Some of them prefer man's urine, and namely when the hairs of beast-hides have been soaked therewith and quick-lime together in the tanners' pits. Others use urine alone by itself, only they mingle water with it again, but in greater quantity a good deal, than they (whose urine it was) did put to the wine when they drank it : and good reason too; for more need there is now to correct and repress the malice thereof, considering that besides the native malignity of the wine itself, man's body hath given and imprinted into it, a strong and unsavoury quality. Thus you may see how men labour, strive, and try conclusions, to feed and enrich the very ground, the best way they can devise. Next unto the ordure and urine of man's body, the filthy dung of swine is most commended : only *Columella* condemneth it. Some praise the muck of any four-footed beasts whatsoever, so they were fed with tree-trifoly, called cytisus. Others prefer the dung of pigeons before any other; in the second place that of goats; thirdly of sheep, then of kine and oxen; and lastly of cart-jades, mules, asses, and such like. Thus you see as well what difference there was in past times, between this dung and that; as also what were the rules (so far as I can guess and learn) whereby they went, in the use and ordering thereof : for, to say a truth, the old way is best, even herein as well as in other matters. Over and besides, the practice hath been already seen in some of our provinces (where there is so great store of cattle bred) to riddle and sift their dung over their ground through sieves, in manner of meal; and so in process of time it loseth not only the stinking scent and ill-favoured sight that it had, but also turneth into a pleasant smell, and looketh lovely withal.

WHEN THE EARTH IS IN LOVE

Like as therefore there be three seasons of planting trees, so there are as many wherein they bud and put forth new shoots; to wit, the spring, the rising of the Dog star, and the apparition of Arcturus. And verily this is a thing worthy to be noted, that not only beasts and other living creatures have an appetite to engender, but the earth also, and all the plants thereupon, are much more lusty and hot that way. And therefore to make them to conceive in due season, the time would be well observed, when they be as it were in love, and desire the act of generation. And not only in the earth and trees therein planted, is this to be seen, but in grafts and stocks also particularly by themselves, since that they have a mutual and respective appetite, one to join and incorporate with the other.

THE NATURE OF THE VINE

In one word, hold a vine down as much as you can, never cocker and cherish her, but rather repress her fruitfulness; for of this nature is the vine, rather than her life, she would be always bearing; neither taketh she such pleasure to live long, as to bear much : and therefore the more you take away of her rank and superfluous wood, the better will she employ her radical sap and moisture to fructify and yield good store of grapes : yet by her good will she would be ever putting forth branches for new plants rather than busy in bearing fruit; for well wotteth she, that fruit will fall and is but transitory. Thus to her own undoing and overthrow, while she thinketh to spread and gain more ground, she spends her strength, herself and all.

L

THE IMPORTANCE OF HOLIDAYS

Over and besides, the manner is otherwhiles to untie the vine, and for certain days together to give it liberty for to wander loosely, and to spread itself out of order, yea, and to lie at ease along the ground, when all the year besides it only beheld from on high : in which repose it seemeth to take no small content- ment and refreshing; for like as draught horses, when they be out of their gears, and hackneys unsaddled, like as oxen when they have drawn in the yoke, yea, and greyhounds after they have run in chase, love to tumble themselves and wallow upon the earth; even so the vines also, having been long tied up and restrained, liketh well now to stretch out her limbs and loins, and such easement and relaxation doth her much good. Nay, the tree itself findeth some comfort and joy thereby, in being dis- charged of that burden which it carried continually as it were upon the shoulders, and seemeth now to take breath and heart again. And certes, go through the whole course and work of Nature, there is nothing, but by imitation of day and night, desireth to have some alternative ease and play-days between. And it is by experience found very hurtful, and therefore not allowed of, to prune and cut vines presently upon the vintage or grape-gathering, whiles they be still weary and over-travailed with bearing their fruits so lately : ne yet to bind them (thus pruned) in the same place again, where they were tied the year before : for surely vines do feel the very prints and marks which the bonds made, and no doubt are vexed and put to pain there- with, and the worse for them.

VINES AND RADISHES

The nature of some plants is, not to kill and destroy trees out of hand, but to hurt and offend them only, either with their smell, or else with the mixture and intermingling of their own juice with their sap. Thus the radish and the laurel do harm to the vine if they grow near unto it : for surely the vine is thought to have the sense of smelling, and wonderfully to scent any odours : and therefore it is observed in her by experience, that if she be near unto radish or laurel, she will turn away and withdraw herself backwards from them, as if she could not abide their strong breath, but utterly abhorred it as her very enemy. And upon the observation of this secret in Nature, *Androcydes* the physician devised a medicine against drunkenness, and prescribed his patients to eat radish if they would not be overcome with wine.

THE GARDEN THAT CROSSED THE ROAD

But above all the prodigies that were ever seen or heard, there is one that passeth, and the same happened in our age, about the very time that *Nero* the Emperor came to his unhappy end and fall: for in the Marrucine territory there was an olive garden belonging to *Vectius Marcellus*, a right worshipful knight of Rome, which of itself removed all and whole as it stood over the broad highway, to a place where lay tillage or arable ground; and the corn lands by way of exchange, crossed over the said causey again, and were found in lieu of the olive plot or hortyard aforesaid.

THE EIGHTEENTH BOOK

treateth of the nature of corn, and all sorts thereof,
together with the profession of husbandmen, and
agriculture

IN DEFENCE OF THE EARTH

BUT BEFORE that I enter into this discourse, very willing I am to
take in hand the cause of the Earth (the common mother of us
all) and to assist her against all slanderous imputations, notwithstanding I have in the beginning of this my work pleaded once
already in her defence. For when we look into the matter within
her contained, we are set on fire inwardly to find fault with her
for breeding and bearing noisome things, charging upon her our
own faults, and imputing unto her that, for which we of right
ought to be blamed. Set case she hath brought forth poison and
venom, who hath searched them out but man? As for the fowls
of the air and wild beasts, it is sufficient that they touch them
not, nay they know how to beware and avoid them. For say that
the elephants do file their teeth sharp against hard trees, say
that the rhinocerotes whet their horns against the rocks, and the
wild boars sharpen their edge tusks against both stock and stone;
say that all creatures know well enough how to prepare and
frobish their weapons to do mischief, which of them all yet infect
them with poison, but man alone? We have the cast to envenom and poison arrows; we can tell how to put something to
our darts of iron and steel, more hurtful and mischievous than
they be. It is ordinary for us to poison rivers also; yea and the
very elements whereof the world doth stand, are by us infected:
for even the air itself, wherein and whereby all things should

live, we corrupt to their mischief and destruction. Neither can we truly say or think, that other creatures besides us are ignorant of these poisons; for we have already shewed, that they are not to seek either what defensatives to provide against they should fight with serpents, or what remedies to find for their cure after they have fought and are hurt. Moreover, setting man aside, there is no creature furnished or armed with any other venom, but their own. We cannot choose therefore but confess our great fault and deadly malice, in that we rest not contented with natural poisons, but betake ourselves to many mixtures and compositions artificial, made even with our own hands. But what say you to this? Are not some men themselves mere poisons by nature? for these slanderers and backbiters in the world, what do they else but launch poison out of their black tongues, like hideous serpents? what do these envious persons, but with their malicious and poisonful breath singe and burn all before them that they can reach or meet with, finding fault with everything whatsoever? Are they not well and fitly compared to these cursed fowls flying in the dark, which albeit they sequester themselves from birds of the day, yet they bewray their spite and envy even to the night and the quiet repose thereof, by their heavy groans (the only voice that they utter) disquieting and troubling those that be at rest: and finally, all one they be with those unlucky creatures, which if they happen either to meet or cross the way upon a man, presage always some ill toward, opposing themselves (as it were) to all goodness, and hindering whatsoever is profitable for this life. Neither do these monstrous and abominable sprites know any other reward of this their deadly breath, their curst and detestable malice, but to hate and abhor all things. Howbeit, herein may we acknowledge and see the wonderful majesty of dame Nature: for like as she hath shewed herself more fruitful and liberal in bringing forth profitable and wholesome plants, in greater plenty than hurtful and noisome; so surely hath she furnished the world better with good men and virtuous for the weal public.

"THIS ONLY IS THE WITCHCRAFT I HAVE USED"

And here I cannot hold and rule myself, but I must needs

allege one example out of ancient histories, whereby it may be understood, how it was an ordinary matter to commence actions and to maintain pleas in open court before the body of the people in the case of husbandry: as also in what sort those good husbandmen of old time were wont to defend their own cause when they were brought into question. And this was the case. There was one *C. Furius Cresinus*, late a bondslave, and newly enfranchized, who after that he was set at liberty, purchased a very little piece of ground, out of which he gathered much more commodity than all his neighbours about him out of their great and large possessions: whereupon he grew to be greatly envied and hated, insomuch, as they charged him with indirect means, as if he had used sorcery, and by charms and witchcraft drawn into his own ground that increase of fruits, which should otherwise have grown in his neighbours' fields. Thus upon complaint and information given, he was presented and indicted, by *Spurius Albinus*, and Aedile Curule for the time being: and a day was set him down peremptorily for his personal appearance to answer the matter. He therefore fearing the worst, and doubting that he should be cast to pay some grievous fine; at what time as the tribes were ready to give their voices, either to acquit or condemn him, brought into the common place his plough with other instruments and furniture belonging to husbandry: he presented likewise in the open face of the court, his own daughter, a lusty strong lass and big of bone; yea, and (as *Piso* telleth the tale) well fed, and as well clad: he shewed himself (I say) his tools and plough irons of the best making, and kept in as good order; main and heavy coulters, strong and tough spades, massy and weighty plough-shares, and withal his draught oxen, full and fair. Now, when his course came to plead his own cause before the people, and to answer for himself, thus he began and said:

"My masters" quoth he "you that are citizens of Rome, behold, these are the sorceries, charms, and all the enchantments that I use" (pointing to his daughter, his oxen, and furniture abovenamed;) "I might besides" (quoth he) "allege mine own travail and toil that I take, the early rising and late sitting up so ordinary with me, the careful watching that I usually abide, and the painful sweats which I daily endure; but I am not able to represent these to your view, nor to bring them hither with me into this assembly." The people no sooner heard this plea of his, but with one voice they all acquit him and declared him un-guilty, without any contradiction. By which example verily, a man may soon see, that good husbandry goeth not all by much expense : but it is painstaking and careful diligence that doth the deed.

THE COUNTRYMAN'S CLOCK

And verily there is not a plant growing upon the earth (I mean of such as are sown of seed) more admirable than the lupin, in regard of the great amity and sympathy between the earth and it. Look how the sun keepeth his course in our horizon above, so doth it turn and go withal; insomuch as the husbandmen of the country go by no other clock to know how the day passeth, in close and cloudy weather, than this observation.

AN AGRICULTURAL DISCOVERY

And here I cannot overpass one invention more as touching earing and ploughing the ground, devised in Piemont and those parts beyond the Po, by occasion of some hard measure and wrong offered to the people and peasants of that country during the wars. And thus stood the case. The Salassians making roads into the vale lying under the Alps, as they forayed and harried the country all over, essayed also to overrun their fields of panicke and millet being now come up and well grown, meaning thereby to destroy it : but seeing the nature of that grain to be such, as to rise again and to check this injury, they set ploughs into it, and turned all under furrow, imagining by that means to spoil it for ever. But see! what ensued thereupon? those fields thus misused (in their conceit) bare a two-fold crop, in propor-tion to other years; and yielded so plentiful an harvest, as that thereby the peasant aforesaid learned the device of turning corn in the blade into the ground, which I suppose in those days when it new came up, they called Aratrare.

ASTRONOMY FOR PLOUGHMEN

Now, as these men have no regard at all to the speculation of Nature, and the course of the stars; so the other beforenamed, are given too much thereto, and rapt they are so high among the stars and planets, that their own eyes be dazzled therewith : and besides, their subtleties and quiddities doe blind others, considering that the practice of these matters must pass through the hands of rustical peasants, who are so far from conceiving astronomy, & the constellations above, that they know not one letter of the book, nor never learned their A.B.C. Howbeit, we cannot choose but confess, that the true reason and knowledge of agriculture, dependeth principally upon the observation of the order in heavenly bodies : for *Virgil* saith very well, that before all other things, a husbandman should be skilful in the winds, and have the foreknowledge and prediction of them : also to have an insight into the nature and influence of the stars : and in one word, to observe both the one and the other, as well as the sailors and mariners at sea. Certes, a hard piece of work it is, and infinite; and small hope I have that ever I shall be able to drive into their heads that are so ignorant and gross of conceit, this high learning and heavenly divinity, as touching the planets, the fixed stars, together with the reason of their orderly motions and celestial powers : howbeit considering the great profit that may arise and grow thereupon to mankind, I will cast a proffer and give the attempt to make ploughmen astrologers, or astronomers likewise, if it may be.

SIGNS OF SPRING

But now to come more particularly to the signs which foretoken the spring : some there be that go by the butterfly, and hold that their brood coming abroad, is an assured token that the spring is come, for that these creatures so feeble, are not able to abide any cold : howbeit, this was checked that very year, wherein I wrote this book or history of Nature's work : for seen it was and marked very well, that three flights of them one after another were killed with the cold weather that surprised them thrice, for that they were stirring too early, and came abroad oversoon. Yea, and the very birds who are our guests in warm weather, visited us five or six days before February, and made a goodly show of a timely spring, putting us in good hope, that all cold weather was gone : howbeit, there ensued a most bitter after-winter straight upon it, that nipped and killed them in manner every one.

THE STARS IN THE GRASS

Nature contented not herself to assemble a troop of stars together in a knot (I mean the brood-hen Vergiliæ, whereby it is a sign in heaven above, conspicuous enough already, and of great mark) but she would needs give the husbandman other stars beneath upon the earth, as signs to shew him the true seasons and times when and how to go to work : as if she cried out and spake unto him after this manner : Why shouldest thou look up to the heavens, thou that art to till thy ground? Why keepest thou a-seeking among the stars for thy country work? Take thy rest and repose thy wearied limbs good man, for the nights be now shorter than they were : to bed therefore, for thou hast but a while to sleep : Behold I scatter and spread here and there among thy very weeds and grass growing upon the ground, other especial shining stars, and those I represent unto thine eyes in the evening, & when thou doest unyoke and give over thy day's work : and that thou shouldst not either plead ignorance, or neglect the same, I provoke thee to regard and look thereat, as a strange wonder. Seest thou not these flies or glow-birds aforesaid cover their bright and glittering light, resembling sparkles of fire, when they keep their wings close together, and carry fire-light about them even in the night? More than so, I have given thee certain herbs to tell thee what is a clock, and how the day goes : and to ease thee more, that thou needest not pain to avert thine eyes away from the earth where thy work lieth, and cast them so much as up to the sun; lo the herb heliotropium and the lupin, turn about with him. What standest thou staring still into the sky, and holdest up thy nose aloft into the air? why are thou amused upon the course of the stars, and searchest into heaven? Hast thou not I pray thee another brood hen star, other Vergiliæ, I say, even before and under thy very feet, I mean those pretty glow-worms? Surely these come duly at their set days: these keep time just with those of the heaven, and so long as they appear and shine above, these glow and glitter beneath: as if they were linked to that star by some near alliance and affinity: in such sort, as a man may resolve and hold for certain that engendered they be no otherwise but by the influence thereof, and are the very chickens and brood of the foresaid hen.

A PHILOSOPHER GOES INTO BUSINESS

It is reported of *Democritus*, the first philosopher who understood himself, and afterwards showed unto the world, the great affinity and agreement that was between heaven and earth (which sundry of his the richest and wealthiest citizens where he lived, seemed to scorn and despise) foreseeing by the course of the stars, & namely, by the rising that would be of the Vergiliæ or brood-hen (according as I have showed already, and will anon declare more at large) that olives would fail that year, and consequently a dearth ensue of oil; bought up all the oil in that tract and country, which as then for the hope of great plenty of olives, bare no price: whereat the great merchants of the city (who dreamed of nothing less than of a scarcity of oil, considering the olives made so fair a show upon the trees) were astonished and marvelled much, that *Democritus* so learned a philosopher, & a man who they knew, was wont by his profession to content himself with poverty, to set his mind upon nothing so much as a quiet life, & wholly to busy his brains in attaining of knowledge and learning, was now on a sudden become a merchant. In the end they perceived what the cause was, & acknowledged the divine skill in foreseeing & preventing a dearth: and he for his part showed plainly, that it was not avarice and desire of lucre that moved him to take this course, but to let the world know, that if he were so disposed, he could by the means of his learning only, be soon a rich man (as indeed he grew hereby to exceeding wealth;) for presently of his own accord he restored again unto the former owners, who God wot were displeased with themselves for that they had done, & wished with all their hearts, that they had met with the like bargain;

he remitted (I say) all this commodity which he had gotten into his own hands, at their own price: resting herein, that he had made good proof, how soon and easily he could be rich whensoever he would.

A MECHANICAL REAPER

As touching the manner of cutting down or reaping corn, there be diverse and sundry devices. In France where the fields be large, they use to set a jade or an ass unto the tail of a mighty great wheelbarrow or cart made in manner of a van, and the same set with keen and trenchant teeth sticking out on both sides: now is this car driven forward before the said beast upon two wheels, into the standing ripe corn (contrary to the manner of other carts that are drawn after) the said teeth or sharp tines fastened to the sides of the wheelbarrow or car aforesaid, catch hold of the corn ears, and cut them off: yet so, as they fall presently into the body of the wheelbarrow.

A CORNER IN WINE

Howbeit in these days I have seen those that for want of vessels have gone in hand to tun up their wine in the beginning of January: yea I have known when the vintage hath been so great, that wines newly pressed have been kept in fish cisterns: and for default of other pipes and tuns, when the wine cellars have been full already, I have seen them that would let the old run out into such cisterns, for to make room for the new, and such as a man would say were neither made nor unmade. And yet this is not so often practised by occasion of the exceeding store of new wine that lieth upon men's hands, as of a wicked and covetous mind that some carry to gather a deal together for to set up a monopoly, thinking thereby to make a dearth and to raise the price of their wines, to the great detriment and hindrance of a common-weal. But a good and honest-minded householder will rest contented to furnish himself with a competent provision of wine, and lay up no more than he shall spend every year: and this is found also by experience the most profitable way for his purse.

ADVICE FOR SHEPHERDS

Thou shepherd, thou herdsman whatsoever, when thou perceivest in summer-time by the shadow growing short, that noonstead is at hand, drive thy sheep and cattle out of the sun, into some worm-stall and place of shade. More yet I have to say to thee, if thou keep sheep or other beasts at their pasture in summer-time, lead them or drive them before thee all the morning into the west, before midday : but after noon turn thy face eastward with thy flock and thy herd. Otherwise, and at other seasons, as namely, all winter and in the spring, thou shouldst do thy cattle hurt, to conduct or lead them after this manner out of the warm sun into moist places, and where the dew falleth. As chary also and heedful must thou be to drive thy cattle northward from the sun, and there to let them graze : for mark what I say, in so doing, they will not be able to hold open their eyes; this wind will make them bleared and bloodshot; nay, it will drive them into a gurrie or flux of the belly, which will soon make an end of them. Howbeit, if thou wouldst have the beasts conceive and bring forth females, force them when they be leaped and covered, to stand with their heads into this wind, and thou shalt see the proof hereof.

THE NINETEENTH BOOK

discourseth of Flax, Spart, and Gardenage

FLAX

WHAT SAY we to line or flax, so commonly sowed as it is? yet may it not be ranged either among the fruits of the field, or herbs of the garden. But what region (I pray you) or part of the earth is without it? And what is there so necessary for this life of ours in all respects? Again, is there anything in the whole world more wonderful and miraculous, than that there should be an herb found of this virtue and property, as to bring Egypt and Italy together? insomuch, as *Galerius*, Lord Deputy in Egypt under the Romans, was known to set sail from the firth of Messina in the straits of Sicily, and in seven days to arrive at Alexandria: *Babilius* also Governor there likewise, in six: and that by the means of the said herb? Moreover, what say you to this, which was seen no longer since than the summer past; when *Valerius Marianus*, a Senator of Rome, and late Lord Praetor, embarked and took ship at Puteoli, and in nine days sailed to the said Alexandria, and yet he had but a very mild and still wind to help him in that voyage? Is not this a strange and sovereign herb think you, that in a seven-night space can fetch Gades from as far as the straits of Gibraltar or Hercules' pillars, into the harbour of Ostia in Italy? can shew (I say) the kingdom of Catalogne in Spain before the said port-town in four days, Provence in three, and Barbary in twain? For *C. Flaccus*, lieutenant under *Vibius Crispus* the Pro-consul, did as much as I speak of, and that with no great fore-wind, but a most gentle and mild gale. Oh the audacious boldness of this world, so rash,

so full of sin and wickedness, that man should sow and cherish
any such thing, as might receive and swallow the winds, storms,
and tempests; as if the float and tide alone were not sufficient to
carry so proud a creature! But now are we grown moreover
to this pass, that sails bigger than the ships themselves, will not
serve our turns. For albeit one mast be sufficient to carry the
biggest cross-yard that can be devised, yet are not we content
with a single main-sail thereupon, unless we set up sail upon sail,
top and top-gallant: unless (I say) we have fore-sails and sprit-
sails in the prow, mizens also hoisted up and displayed in the
poop; besides other trinkets and more cloth still: and all to set
us more forward upon our death, and to hasten our end. Finally,
is there aught again so admirable, as that of so small a grain as
is the line-seed, there should grow that which is able to carry
to and fro in a moment, this round globe of the earth; the same
being so slender a stalk as it is, and not growing high from the
ground? considering withal, that twisted it is not entire and
whole in the stem: but before it can be occupied, it must be
watered, dried, braked, tew-tawed, and with much labour driven
and reduced in the end to be as soft and tender as wool: and
all to do violence to nature and mankind most audaciously even
in the highest degree, in such sort, as a man is not able to proceed so far in execration as is due unto this invention. The first
deviser whereof I have inveighed against in convenient place
elsewhere, and not without desert: as who could not be content,
that a man should die upon the land, but he must perish upon
the sea, to feed haddocks there, without the honour of sepulture.

GARDENS

The invention to have gardens within a city, came up first
by *Epicurus* the doctor and master of all voluptuous idleness,
who devised such gardens of pleasance in Athens: for before his
time, the manner was not in any city, to dwell (as it were) in
the country, and so to make city and country all one, but all
their gardens were in the villages without. Certes at Rome, a
good garden and no more, was thought a poor man's chievance;
it went (I say) for land and living. The garden was the poor
commoner's shambles, it was all the market place he had for to

provide himself of victuals. O what a blessed, what a secure, and harmless life was that, so long as men could be content to take up with such a pittance, and stay themselves so! but better it is I trow, for to satisfy the appetite of our wanton gluttons and bellygods, to search into the bottom of the deep sea: for to get (I say) oysters and all sorts, to fear no tempest nor shipwreck: for to meet with dainty fowl, to send out one way as far as beyond the river Phasis for those birds, which a man would think were sure enough and secured from the fowler, by reason of the fearful tales that go of them, and of the danger of those that approach near unto them (and yet why say I so, considering they are the better esteemed and more precious, the farther they be fet and dearer bought:) to have purveyors another way in Numidia and Aethyopia, for the rare birds there about the sepulchres; among those sepulchres (I say) where instead of meeting with game, they stumble otherwhiles upon their own graves and never come home again: and lastly to have others to chase the wild and savage beasts of the forest, yea and to maintain fight with them, in danger to be devoured as a prey, by those which soon after must serve as venison for other men to eat.

DEATH THE LEVELLER

O the monstrous bellies that be nowadays! O the excessive gluttony and gourmandise which now reigneth in the world! Is it any marvel that poor asses and such dumb beasts may not feed upon thistles, when the commons of Rome are restrained and forbidden to eat thistles and dare not once touch them? And yet here is not all: our waters also be distinguished and set apart for some persons; even the very elements whereof this world consisteth are distinct, severed, and ranged into sundry degrees, and all at the pleasure of moneyed men: for some you shall have to drink snow, others ice: and will you see in one word their folly and vanity? the very misery that high mountains are punished and plagued with, they make their pleasure of, and therewith content and delight the throat. These men lay for to be provided of chilling cold against the heat of summer, and seek by all means that they can possible, to have snow

M

remain white still and frozen (as it first was) out of winter season, even in the hottest months of the year, which are most opposite unto the nature of snow. Some there be, who first seethe their water, and anon let it congeal again to ice, after it was once scalding hot. Whereby we may see, how man never contenteth himself in Nature's works, but cross he will be always and peevish; and look what pleaseth her, shall displease him : for whoever would have thought that any one herb should have grown for the rich, and not as well for the poor? Well, let no man for all this, cast about and look toward mount Sacer, or Aventine hill, that the commoners again should by way of insurrection rise, and in the heat of their blood depart aside thither, as sometimes they did in a mutinous fit of theirs, in high discontentment with the nobility. For what needs that, since they may be sure that death shortly will bring them together, and make equal, between whom now for a while riches hath put a bar, and made distinction of place and degree.

CUCUMBERS

A wonderful thing in their nature : they cannot abide oil in any wise, but water they love well; insomuch, as if they be cut off, or fallen from the place where they grew, they wind and creep thereinto, if it be but a little way off : contrariwise, fly they will as fast from oil, if a man set it by them; and in case anything be in their way to let them, or that they hang still upon their plant, a man shall perceive how they will turn up and crook, to shun and avoid it. This amity to the one, and enmity to the other, may be seen even in one night's space : for if a man set under them, four fingers off where they grow, a vessel with water overnight, he shall see by the morning that they will come down unto it : contrariwise, let oil stand the like distance from them, shrink they will from it, and hook upward.

RADISHES

All radishes breed wind wonderful much, and provoke a man that eateth them to belch. A base and homely meat therefore it is, and not for a gentleman's table, especially if it be eaten with other worts, as beets: marry if a man take them with unripe olives condite, he shall neither belch nor rift wind so much, ne yet so sour and stinking will his breath be afterwards.

GARLIC AND ONIONS

Moreover, if you would have garlic, onions, and such like, not to smell strong and stink so as they do, the common opinion and rule is, that they should not be set or sown, but when the moon is under the earth, nor yet be gathered and taken up but in her conjunction with the sun, which is the change. But *Menander*, a Greek writer, saith, that there needs none of all these ceremonies for the matter: for if a man would not have his breath stink with eating of garlic, let him do no more (quoth he) but take a beetroot roasted in the embers, and eat it after, it shall extinguish that hot and strong flavour, and cause the breath to continue sweet.

CANKERWORMS

And generally, no cankerworms shall do harm to any herbage in the garden, if a man pitch upon the pales about a garden the bones of a mare's head; but he must be sure it was of a mare, for a horse head will not serve.

A SPECIAL USE FOR GOATS

But that you may know how diligent and curious men have been to search into the secrets of everything, I will tell you what I have found contrived in certain verses of a poet, namely, that if a man take the round treddles of a goat, and make in every one of them a little hole, putting therein the seed either of leeks, rocket, lettuce, parsley, endive, or garden cresses, and close them up, and so put them into the ground, it is wonderful how they will prosper, and what fair plants will come thereof.

THE TWENTIETH BOOK

*sheweth of garden herbs, good to serve both the kitchen
for meat, and the Apothecary's shop for medicine*

PREFACE

SINCE WE are come thus far, as to treat of the greatest and
principal work of Nature, we will begin from henceforward at
the very meats which men put into their mouths, and convey
into their stomachs, and urge them to confess a truth, that
hitherto they have not well known those ordinary means whereby
they live. And let no man in the meantime think this to be a
simple or small piece of knowledge and learning, going by the
base title and bare name that it carrieth : for so he may be soon
deceived. For in the pursuit and discourse of this argument, we
shall take occasion to enter into a large field as touching the
peace and war in nature; we shall handle I say a deep secret,
even the natural hatred and emnity of dumb deaf and senseless
creatures. And verily, the main point of this theme, and which
may ravish us to a greater wonder and admiration of the thing,
lieth herein, that this mutual affection which the Greeks call
sympathy, whereupon the frame of this world dependeth, and
whereby the course of all things else doth stand, tendeth to the
use and benefit of man alone. For to what end else is it, that
the element of water quencheth fire? For what purpose doth the
sun suck and drink up the water, as it were to cool his heat and
allay his thirst? and the moon contrariwise, breed humours and
engender moist vapours? and both planets eclipse & abridge the
light one of the other? But to leave the heaven and those celestial
bodies in their majesty; what is the cause that as the magnet or

load stone draweth iron unto it, so there is another stone ab-
horreth the same and drives iron from it? What should the
reason be of the diamond, that peerless stone, the chief jewel
wherein our rich worldings repose their greatest joy and delight :
a stone otherwise invincible, and which no force and violence
besides can conquer, but that it remaineth still infrangible; and
yet that the simple blood of a poor goat is able to burst it in
pieces? Besides many other secrets in nature, as strange, yea
and more miraculous. All which we purpose to reserve unto their
several places, and will speak of them in order.

ROCKET

As touching rocket, the seed cureth as well the venomous sting
of scorpions, as the biting of the hardy shrew. The same chaseth
all vermin that be apt to engender in man's body. A liniment
made therewith, and honey together, taketh away all the spots
that blemish the skin of the face: and with vinegar, represseth the
red pimples whatsoever. The black or swert scars remaining after
wound or sore, it reduceth to the former fair white, if it be
applied with a beast's gall. It is said moreover, that a potion
thereof made with wine, and given to those who are to receive
punishment by the whip, will harden them in such sort, that
they shall feel little or no smart at all by any scourging.

WHAT TO TAKE BEFORE A PARTY

Is a man disposed to drink freely, and to sit square at it? let
him before he begin take a draught of the decoction of rue
leaves, he shall bear his drink well, and withstand the fumes that
might trouble and intoxicate his brains.

MINT

In the time of *Pompey* the Great, it was known by experience,
that the leaves of wild mint chewed and applied outwardly,
cured the leprosy: by occasion, that a certain leper minding to
disguise himself, that he might not for very shame be known,
chanced to anoint and besmear his face all over with the juice

of wild mints. But fortune was better mistress unto him than
he expected, for beyond his expectation or intent, his good hap
was to be rid of his leprosy by that means.

* * * * *

Moreover, the wiser sort of people save the dry leaves of wild
mints to be reduced into a powder, as a very counterpoison
against all venom whatsoever. For being strewed in the house,
or burnt, the very air and perfume thereof chaseth away scorpions. A drink made therewith purgeth and purifieth women
passing well, such I mean as be newly delivered of childbirth :
but it killeth the fruit within the womb of as many as use it
while they go with child. There is not a medicine in the world
so effectual as it is for those, who are so strait-winded, that they
cannot take their breath unless they sit upright : for such also
as in the choleric passion, never give over casting upward and
purging downward. It appeaseth also the pain of the loins, and
easeth the gout, if it be applied to the place affected. The juice
thereof is good to be dropped into ears that have worms within
them. It is usually taken in drink for the jaundice. A liniment
made thereof, helpeth the king's evil; besides, it is a singular
remedy for them that by a strong imagination of *Venus* in their
dreams, defile and pollute themselves in their sleep. If one drink
it with vinegar, it excludeth the flat broad worms in the belly.
To scourge away the foul dandruff, an embrocation of it and
vinegar upon the head in the sun is counted singular.

* * * * *

The juice of mints is excellent for the scour the pipes and clear
the voice, being drunk a little before that a man is to strain
himself either in the choir, or upon the stage, or at the bar; and
not otherwise.

* * * * *

The branches of mint and pennyroyal both, are usually put
into glass vials with vinegar, for to be infused therein : and a
man would not think how good this vinegar is for faintings of
the heart; so great is the society that these two herbs have one
with the other in this behalf. For which cause, I remember upon

a time when divers learned physicians were met together to confer in my chamber, they resolved and concluded definitely, that a chaplet of pennyroyal was without comparison far better for the giddiness and swimming of the head, than one of roses; for a garland of pennyroyal, if it be worn only upon the head, allayeth (by report) the ache thereof.

CUMIN

But the garden cumin is of singular use in physic, but principally for the pain in the stomach. It dispatcheth the gross vapours arising from fleame; it dissolveth also ventosities, if it be either bruised and eaten with bread, or drunk with water and wine : in which sort it assuageth the wringing torments and other pains of the guts : howbeit, it maketh folk look pale as many as drink of it. Certes by that device, namely, by ordinary drinking of cumin (as it is reported) the scholars and followers of *Porcius Latro* (that famous and great rhetorician) procured themselves pale faces because they would look like their masters; who indeed came to that colour by continual study & plying his book. Thus likewise not long since, *Iulius Vindex*, being desirous to be affranchized by *Nero*, pretending by his pale visage and poor look, that he had not many days to live, made fair semblance unto *Nero* by his will and testament, that he should shortly be his heir; (which cheat the said *Nero* gaped after;) and so by that means *Vindex* entered so far within him, as he obtained whatsoever he would at his hands.

PEPLIUM

There is a wild purslane also, which they call peplium : more effectual, though not much, than the garden purslane; for there be strong and wonderful properties reported thereof for sundry uses. First it is holden for certain, that this herb if it be eaten as meat, dulleth the poison of venomous arrows, of serpents also called hæmorrhoids and presters : and being laid to the hurt place, draw forth the said poison. The juice also of this herb pressed forth and drunk in wine cuit, is a remedy for those that be poisoned with henbane. Now if the herb itself is not to be gotten, the seed hath the like effect. Moreover, it is thought to be singular good for the acuosities gathered within the body, and the diseases caused thereby, as dropsies, etc.; for the head-ache; for rheumatic ulcers also, if it be bruised and applied with wine. All other sores likewise it healeth, if it be chewed and laid to with honey. After the same manner prepared, it is good to be applied to children's heads for to temper the heat of the brain, as also to their navels when they bear out more than they should. For all vehement distillations of watery humours into the eyes, as well of old folk as small infants, it is counted singular; for to be applied to the forehead & temples, together with barley groats: but if it be laid unto the very eyes, then would the same be tempered with milk and honey. Now if it chance that the eyes be ready to fall out of the head, the leaves stamped with the shells of bean cods, and applied thereto, is an excellent remedy. A cataplasm made of it, with barley groats, salt, and vinegar, cureth angry weals and blisters that break the skin. The same being chewed raw, represseth the cankers in the mouth, and the smelling of the gums: likewise, it assuageth the toothache. The juice of it being well sodden, cureth the sores of the amygdales, if the mouth and throat be washed therewith. And some put to this collution a little powder of the stone murra. And no marvel, for the very chewing only thereof doth fasten the teeth that be loose in the head. It doth mitigate the incon-venience of crudity and indigestion, it strengtheneth the voice, and putteth by thirst. A cataplasm made therewith, having gall nuts and linseed among, of equal quantity, allayeth the pains and cricks in the nape or chine of the neck. Tempered with honey and white fullers' clay, it is singular for the accidents that befall to women's breasts. The seed taken with honey, is very wholesome for such as be short winded. Eaten in salads, it strengtheneth the stomach. If it be laid as a cataplasm (to the belly and hypochondrial region) it allayeth the heat of ardent and burning fevers: yea, and in other cases the very chewing of it cooleth the heat of the guts and entrails. It stayeth vomits, eaten in vinegar: or taken in drink with cumin, it is good for the bloody flux and other inward impostumes and filthy sores. Being first sodden and then eaten, it is singular for those that strain hard upon the stool, and notwithstanding many provocations and proffers, deliver nothing. And whether it be taken in meat or drink, it is a sovereign thing for the falling sickness. For a shift or immoderate course of women's terms, it is given with great success, the quantity of one acetable measure in wine cuit. A liniment made with it and salt, is good for the hot gout and *S. Anthony's* fire. The juice if it be drunken, helpeth the reins and the bladder. It expelleth worms and suchlike vermin out of the belly. A good mitigative, it is of pain, if it be applied as a cataplasm to wounds with oil and barley groats. It mollifieth the stiffness and hardness of the sinews. *Metrodorus* in his book entitled the Abridgement or Breviary of those roots that are to be cast up or gathered; gave counsel to give this herb to women, newly laid upon childbirth, for the immoderate and excessive purgation that many times followeth them. It cooleth the heat of lust, and represseth dreams of wantonness. I know myself a great signor in Spain, father unto a great personage, and one who had been advanced to the dignity of a praetor, who carried ever about him a root of this peplium hanging at his neck by a lace or small thread, and that for the intolerable pains of the uvula, whereto he was subject : and never would he leave it off, but when he went into the stove or bain : whereby he found such ease, that he was never troubled afterward with the said disease. Moreover, I have read in some writers, that if the head be anointed or well rubbed therewith, a man shall not for a year together find any inconvenience of a rheum distilling from the brain. Howbeit, it is thought that the use thereof will make the eyes dim.

HOW TO CREATE A THIRST

The root either of thistle or artichoke, sodden in water and so eaten, is as good as a shoeing-horn to draw on pot after pot, for these great bibbers that desire nothing more than to be thirsty and make quarrel to the cup.

THE ONE AND TWENTIETH BOOK

treateth of flowers and garlands

FLOWERS

Cato IN his Treatise of Gardens, ordained as a necessary point, that they should be planted and enriched with such herbs as might bring forth flowers for coronets and garlands. And in very truth, their diversity is such, that impossible it is to decipher and express them accordingly. Whereby we may see that more easy it was for dame Nature to depaint and adorn the earth with sundry pictures, to beautify the fields (I say) with all manner of colours, by her handiwork (especially where she hath met with a ground to her mind, and when she is in a merry humour and disposed to play and disport herself) than for any man in the world to utter the same by word of mouth. Wherein certes her admirable providence she hath shewed, principally in this, that whereas she hath given unto those fruits of the earth which serve for necessities and the sustentation of man, long life and a kind of perpetuity, even to last years, and hundreds of years; these flowers of pleasure and delight, good only to content the eye or please the sense of smelling, she would have to live and die in one day. A great document and lesson for us men in general to learn, how all things whatsoever that flourish most lovely and be gayest in show, soonest fade and are gone suddenly.

THE ARTIST AND THE FLOWER-GIRL

And (to say a truth) the Sicyonians passed in this feat of sorting together one with another flowers of sweet savour and

187

pleasant colour, in making of garlands and posies. Howbeit, the example of *Pausias* the cunning painter, and *Glycera* the artificial maker of such chaplets set them first a-work. This painter was wonderfully enamoured upon the said *Glycera*, and courted her by all means that he could devise : among the rest, he would seem to counterfeit and represent lively with his pencil in colours, what flowers soever she wrought and set with her fingers into garlands; and she again strived avie to change and alter her handiwork every day, for to drive him to a non-plus at the length, or at leastwise, to put him to his shifts; insomuch, as it was a very pleasant and worthy sight, to behold of one side the works of Nature in the woman's hand, and on the other side the artificial cunning of the foresaid painter. And verily there are at this day to be seen diverse painted tables of his workmanship : and namely, one picture above the rest, entitled Stephanoplocos, wherein he painted his sweetheart *Glycera*, twisting and braiding coronets and chaplets, as her manner was.

CLEOPATRA'S JOKE

As for the Greeks verily, they have written also several treatises concerning flowers and garlands : and namely, *Mnestheus* and *Callimachus*, two renowned physicians, have compiled books of those chaplets that be hurtful to the brain and cause headache. For even herein also lieth some part of the preservation of our health, considering that perfumes do refresh our spirits, especially when we are set at table to drink liberally and to make merry, while the subtle odour of flowers doth pierce to the brain secretly ere we be aware. Where, by the way, I cannot choose but remember the device of Queen *Cleopatra*, full of fine wit, and as wicked and mischievous withal : for at what time as *Antonie* prepared the expedition and journey of Actium against *Augustus*, and stood in some doubt and jealousy of the said Queen; for all the fair show that she made of gratifying him and doing him all pleasure, he was at his taster, and would neither eat nor drink at her table without assay made. *Cleopatra* seeing how timorous he was, and minding yet to make good sport and game at his needless fear and foolish curiosity, caused a chaplet to be made for *M. Antonius*, having before dipped all the tips and edges of

the flowers that went to it in a strong and rank poison, and being
thus prepared, set it upon the head of the said *Antonie*. Now,
when they had sitten at meat a good while, and drunk themselves merry, the Queen began to make a motion and challenge
to *Antonie*, for to drink each of them their chaplets; and withal
began unto him in a cup of wine seasoned and spiced (as it were)
with those flowers which she wore her own self. Oh the shrewd
and unhappy wit of a woman when she is so disposed! who
would ever have misdoubted any danger of hidden mischief
herein? Well, *M. Antonie* yielded to pledge her: off goeth his
own garland, and with the flowers minced small, dresseth his
own cup. Now when he was about to set it to his own head,
Cleopatra presently put her hand between, and stayed him from
drinking, and withal uttered these words, "My dear heart and
best beloved *Antonie*, now she what she is whom so much thou
dost dread and stand in fear of, that for thy security there must
wait at thy cup and trencher extraordinary tasters; a strange
and new fashion ywis, and a curiosity more nice than needful:
lo, how I am not to seek of means and opportunities to compass
thy death, if I could find in my heart to live without thee."
Which said, she called for a prisoner immediately out of the gaol,
whom she caused to drink off the wine which *Antonie* had prepared for himself. No sooner was the goblet from his lips again,
but the poor wretch died presently in the place.

ROSES

And to say a truth, all the said roses, unless it be this coroneola,
and that which groweth upon the brier or eglantine beforenamed,
have no smell with them in the whole world naturally, but are
brought to it by many devices and sophistications: yea, & the
very rose itself, which of the own nature is odoriferous, carrieth
a better smell in some one soil than in another. For at Cyrene
they pass all other for sweetness and pleasant savour: which is
the reason, that the oil rosat, and ointment compounded thereof,
is most excellent there of all other places. And at Cartagena in
Spain there be certain timely or hasty roses that blow and flower
all winter long. The climate also and temperature of the air
maketh for the sweetness of the rose: for in some years ye shall

have them less odoriferous than in others. Over and besides, the place would be considered: for the roses be ever more sweet growing upon dry than wet grounds. And indeed the rose bush loveth not to be planted in a fat and rich soil, ne yet upon a vein of clay, no more than it liketh to grow near unto rivers where the banks be overflowed, or in a waterish plot; but it agreeth best with a light and loose kind of earth, and principally with a ground full of rubbish, and among the ruins of old houses.

DYEING THE LILY

But such are the monstrous devices of some fantastical spirits, that they invented forsooth a new kind of artificial colouring and dyeing of lilies: for which purpose, in the month of July they gather their stems, when they begin to wither, and hang them up in the smoke to dry. Now when the knobs or heads of their roots look once bare and are shot out from the said stalks (which commonly falleth out in the month of March), they infuse & steep them in the lees of deep red wine, or some Greekish wine, for to suck and drink in the colour thereof: which done, they set them in little trenches, whereinto they pour certain hemines or pints of the said wine: and by this means become the lilies aforesaid, purple. A strange and wonderful matter, that any root should take a tincture so deep, as to bring forth a flower of the same dye and colour.

THE SCENTS OF FLOWERS

Some flowers, the farther they be off, the more pleasant is their smell: come nearer unto them, their scent is more dull and weaker than it was, as namely violets. A fresh and new gathered rose casteth a better smell afar off than near at hand; let it be somewhat withered and dry, you shall scent it better at the nose than farther off. Generally, all flowers be more odoriferous and pleasant in the spring, than at any other season of the year; and in the morning they have a quicker and more piercing scent, than at any hour of the day besides: the nearer to noon, the weaker is the smell of any herb or flower. More-

over the flowers of new plants are nothing so sweet as those
of an old stock; and yet I must needs say, that flowers smell
strongest in the mids of summer. As for roses and saffron-flowers,
they cast the pleasanter smell, if they be gathered in clear
weather, when it is fair and dry above head : and in one word,
such as grow in hot countries, be ever sweeter to smell unto,
than in cold climates. Howbeit, in Egypt the flowers have no
good scent at all, by reason that the air is foggy and misty, with
the dews rising from the river Nilus. Moreover, certain flowers
there be which are sweet and pleasant enough, yet they stuff
and fill the head.

FLOWER-DYES

The excessive riot and prodigal superfluity of men is grown
to this pass, that having taken no small pleasure in surmounting
the natural savour of simple flowers, by their artificial odours
and compound perfumes; they cannot rest so, but must proceed
also in the craft and mystery of dyeing cloth, to challenge the
fairest flowers in the garden, and to match, if not to surpass, the
lively colours of Nature's setting. Of these tinctures, I find that
there be three principal : the one in grain, which striveth with
that bright orient colour in roses : and there is not a more
pleasant thing to the eye, than to see the scarlet or purple of
Tyros, or to behold the double-dyed dibapha, or the Laconian
purple. The second rich dye, standeth upon the amethyst colour,
and resembleth the March violet : this also beareth much upon
that purple, which of the said violet is called Ianthinus : for now
I handle dyes and colours in general terms, which nevertheless
may be subdivided into many other special sorts. The third, is
ordinarily made of the purple and porcellane shell-fishes, and
that in divers and sundry manners; for of this tincture there are
cloths which incline much to the colour of tornsoll; and of these,
some be many times of a deeper and fuller dye than others.
Also there is another sort that standeth much upon the mallow
flower, inclining to a purple : and a third sort which resemble
the violet that cometh late in the year (called the purple stock-
gillofre) and indeed this is the freshest and richest colour that
can be dyed out of those fishes aforesaid. Certes, the tinctures

and dyes nowadays are so lively, as well for simple colours as mixed and compound (such artificial means are devised by our sumptuous gallants) that in this strife of Nature and Art together, a man shall hardly judge whether of them have the better hand.

FLOWERS OF SUMMER AND AUTUMN

Now succeed and come after in their rank, the summer flowers, to wit, lychnis, *Iupiter's* flower or columbine, and a second kind of lily : likewise iphyon, and that amaracus or marjoram, which they call the Phrygian. But of all others, the flower pathos is most lovely and beautiful : whereof there be two kinds, the one with a purple flower like unto the hyacinth : the other is whiter, and groweth commonly in churchyards among graves and tombs, and the same holdeth on flowering better, and liveth longer. The flower de luce also is a summer flower. These have their time, fade, and are soon gone. And then come other flowers for them in their place in autumn, to wit, a third kind of lily, and saffron : but of both these, the one is of a dull or no scent at all : the other is very odoriferous. But all of them break out and shew abroad with the first shower of rain in autumn. Our chaplet-makers use the flowers also of bedegnar or white thistle in their garlands : and no marvel, since that our cooks dress the young tendrils and crops thereof, for to make a dainty dish for to content our taste and go pleasantly down the throat. Thus you see the order and manner of beyond-sea flowers, how and when they come abroad. In Italy it is somewhat otherwise : for the rose followeth immediately after the violets : and when the rose is in the mids of his ruffe, in comes the lily to bear him company. No sooner hath the rose played his part, but the blue-blaw entereth the stage : and after him the passeveleur or flower-gentle. As for the pervincle, it continueth fresh and green all the year long.

NOMAD BEES

As touching their food and nourishment, I will tell you a wonderful and memorable thing upon mine own knowledge.

There is a town or burgade called Hostilia situate upon the river Po. The inhabitants of this village, when they see that their bees' meat goeth low thereabout, and is like to fail, take me their hives with bees and all, and set them in certain boats and barges, and in the night row up the said river Po, against the stream five miles forward. The morrow morning out go the bees to seek food and relief. Now when they have met with meat, and fed themselves, they return again to the vessel aforesaid : and thus they continue daily, although they change their place and haunt; until such time as their masters perceive that the hives be full, by the settling of their boats low within the water with their weight, and then they return home again down the stream, and discharge the hives of the honey within.

POISONOUS HONEY

At Heraclea in Pontus, in some years, all the honey that the bees do make, is found to be venomous, and no better than poison; and yet the same bees in other years gather good and wholesome honey. Howbeit, those authors who have delivered thus much in writing, have not set down what flowers they be that yield this hurtful honey : and therefore I think it not amiss to write what I have found and known as touching this point. There is an herb called aegolethron in Greek, which killeth horses verily, but goats most of all, feeding thereupon; and therefore it took that name : the flowers of this herb, if it chance to be a wet and rainy spring, do conceive and engender within them a certain deadly venom which doth corrupt and rot them. This may be a probable reason, that the foresaid mischief and bane is not always felt alike. This poisonous honey may be known by these signs : first it will never thicken but continue liquid still; secondly, the colour is more deep and reddish than ordinary; thirdly, it carrieth a strange scent or smell with it, and will cause one to sneeze presently; last of all, it is more ponderous and heavy than the good and harmless honey. The symptoms or accidents that ensue upon the eating of this honey, are these, they that have tasted thereof, cast themselves upon the ground and there fall a tumbling : they seek by all means they can to be cooled : and no marvel, for they run all to sweat, that one drop

N

overtakes the other. Howbeit, there be many remedies for this poison, which I will show in place convenient. Meanwhile, because a man would not be without some good thing ready at hand, since the world is so full of villainy and set upon such secret mischief, I must needs put down one good receipt, and that is this: take honeyed wine that is old, mingle and incorporate it with the best honey you can meet withal, and rue together: use this confection at your need. *Item*, eat much of salt-fish, although it came up again, and that your stomach do cast it. Moreover, this honey is so pernicious, that the very dogs if they chance to lick up any excrement that pass from the party so infected (either by reaching, spitting, vomit, or seege) they are sure to be sped therewith, and to feel the like torments. Howbeit, the honied wine that is made therewith, if it may have age enough and be stale, is known for a certainty to do no creature harm. And there is not a better medicine in the world, either to fetch out spots in women's faces, and make their skin fair and clear (if it be applied with costus;) or to take out the black and blue marks remaining after stripes in eye or elsewhere, so it be tempered with aloe. Another kind of honey there is in the same region of Pontus, and namely among the Sanni (a people there inhabiting) which because it driveth folk into a fit of rage and madness, they call in Greek maenomenon. Some attribute the occasion thereof to the flower of the oleander, whereof the woods and forests there be full. This nation selleth no honey at all, because it is so venomous and deadly: notwithstanding they do pay for tribute a huge mass of wax unto the Romans every year. Moreover, in the kingdom of Persis, and in Getulia, which lieth within Mauritania Caesariensis, a country confining and bordering upon the Massaesuli, there be venomous honey-combs; yea, you shall have in one hive some honey-combs full of poisoned honey, whereas others be sound and good: a dangerous thing no doubt, and than which, there could be no greater deceit to poison a number of people; but that they may be known from the rest by their leaden and wan hue that they have. What should we think was Nature's meaning and intent by these secret sleights and hidden mischiefs, that either the same bees should not every year gather venomous honey; or not lay the same up in all their combs differently? Was it not enough that she had bestowed upon us a thing, wherein poison might be soonest given and least perceived? Was she not content thus to endanger our lives, but she must proceed farther, even to incorporate poison herself in honey, as it cometh from the bee, for to enpoison so many living creatures? Certes, I am of this mind, and believe verily, that she had no other purpose herein, than to make men more wary what they eat, and less greedy of sweetmeats to content and please the tooth.

BEEHIVES

As touching beehives, they ought to stand on the open side upon the equinoctial sun rising, that is to say, when the days and nights be equal. And in any wise, regard would be had, that they open not into the north-east, and much less the full west. The best beehives be made of barks and rinds of trees: the second in goodness be those of ferula or fennel-giant. In the third place are such as be wrought of osier twigs. Many have made them of talc, which is a kind of transparent glass stone, because they would see through them how the bees do work and labour within. Daubed they should be if they were well served, both without and within with ox dung. The cover and lid thereof ought to be movable and have liberty to play up and down behind, that it may be let down far within-forth, in case either the hive be too large and of greater receipt in proportion than the bees are in number; for fear they should slack their work and give over their travail, despairing ever to fill the same, seeing it so big and of so great capacity: and being thus let down (to make the hive seem the less) it must be gently drawn up again by little and little, that the bees may be deceived thereby, and not perceive how their work grows upon them.

THE OPINION OF SOPHOCLES

Moreover, I know full well that divers authors renowned and of great credit, have delivered in their books, that five and twenty grains of that trefoil, which we called menianthes, is sufficient for a preservative and antidote against all poisons whatsoever:

besides many other medicinable virtues which be ascribed to this herb. For mine own part, I am induced by the authority of the most grave and reverend poet *Sophocles*, to stand against their opinion : for he affirmeth plainly, that trefoil is venomous.

HELENIUM

Helenium, an herb which sprang first from the tears of lady *Helena*, as I have already shewed, is thought to have a special virtue to preserve beauty, and to maintain the skin fair, pure, and delicate, as well in the face of women, as in other parts of their body. Moreover, a deep opinion there is of this herb, that whosoever use it shall prove amiable and gracious : they shall, I say, win love and favour wheresoever they come. Also there is attributed and prescribed to this herb, if it be taken in wine, a mighty operation to procure mirth and make the heart merry : and it is thought to be as effectual that way, as was that noble drink Nepenthes (so highly commended in *Homer*) so called, for that it puts away all heaviness, sorrow, and melancholy. And in faith the juice of helenium is passing sweet and pleasant. The root of helenium taken in water upon an empty stomach when a man is fasting, is very good for them that are strait-winded, and cannot take their breath but upright. Now is this root white within and sweet also as is the herb. The same is given to drink in wine against the sting of serpents. To conclude, being beaten into powder, it is said to kill mice.

THE HYACINTH

The hyacinth loveth France very well, and prospereth there exceedingly. The French use therewith to dye their light reds or lusty-gallant, for default of grain to colour their scarlet. The root is bulbous and onion-like, well known to these slave-coursers, who buy them at best hand; and after, tricking, trimming, and pampering them up for sale, make gain of them : for being reduced into a liniment, they use it with wine to anoint as well the share of youths, as the chin and cheeks; to keep them for ever being under-grown, or having hair on their face, that they may appear young still and smooth.

A DANGEROUS HERB

The third kind of strychnos or solanum, hath leaves like to basil: but I must but lightly touch this herb, and not stand long about the description either of it or the properties which it hath; since my purpose is to treat of wholesome remedies to save folk, and not of deadly poisons to kill them: for certes, this herb is so dangerous, that a very little of the juice thereof is enough to trouble a man's brain, and put him besides his right wits. And yet the Greek writers have made good sport with this herb, and reported pretty jests of it: For (they say) whosoever taketh a dram of this juice, shall have many strange fantasies appearing evidently unto them in their dreams; if they be men, that they dally with fair women; if women, that they be wantons playing and toying with men, without all shame and modesty; and a thousand such vain illusions: but in case they take this dose double, then they shall prove foolish indeed, broad waking, yea and go besides themselves: let them take never so little more, it is mortal, and no remedy then but death. This is that poison, which the most harmless and best minded writers that ever wrote, called simply dorycnion: for that soldiers going to battle, used to anoint and envenom therewith the heads of their arrows, darts, and spears, growing as it did so commonly in every place. But other writers, who had not sought so far into the matter, nor advisedly considered of it, gave it the name of manicon. But those that of a naughty mind, cared not secretly to empoison the whole world, have hidden the danger thereof, and term it by a name pretending no harm; some calling it neuris, others perisson. But as I protested before, I think it not good to be too curious and busy about the description of this herb, nothwithstanding I might seem to give a good caveat of it, by further particularizing thereof.

THE HERB OF PROPHECY

Indeed, the root of halicacabus they use to drink and make no bones at it, who would be known for great prophets to foretell future things: and therefore it is alone for them, to be seen furious and raging, the better to colour their knavery and lead the world by the nose in a superstitious conceit and persuasion of their divine gift of prophecy, and so to feed men still in their folly. But what is the remedy, when a man is thus overtaken? (for surely I am better content to deliver that). Even to give the party thus intoxicated, a great quantity of mead or honeyed water, and to cause him to drink it off as hot as he can.

THE TWO AND TWENTIETH BOOK

*containeth the chapters and medicines
made of herbs*

COSMETICS

CERTES, I do find and observe, that there be foreign nations, who time out of mind, have been ever accustomed to anoint their bodies with the juice of certain herbs, for to embellish and beautify them, as they thought. And verily in some of these barbarous countries, ye shall have the women to paint their faces, some with this herb, and other with that: yea, and among the Dakes and Samatians, in Transylvania, Walachia, Tartaria, and those parts, the men also mark their bodies with certain characters. But to go no farther than into Gaul, there groweth an herb there like unto plantain, and they call is glastum (i.e. woad) with the juice whereof the women of Britain, as well the married wives, as young maidens their daughters, anoint and dye their bodies all over: resembling by that tincture the colour of Moors and Aethyopians: in which manner they use at some solemn feasts and sacrifice, to go all naked.

HERBS FOR DYEING

And now of late days we know there hath been taken up a strange and wonderful manner of dyeing and colouring clothes. For (to say nothing of grain brought out of Galatia, Africa, and Portugal, whereof is made the royal scarlet, reserved for princes only and great captains to wear in their rich mantles of estate and coat of arms:) behold, the French inhabiting beyond the

Alps have invented the means to counterfeit the purple of Tyrus, the scarlet also and violet in grain; yea, and to set all other colours that can be devised, with the juice only of certain herbs. These men are wiser (believe me) than their neighbours of other nations before them: they hazard not themselves to sound and search into the bottom of the deep sea for burrets, purples, and such shell-fishes. These adventure not their lives in strange coasts and blind bays, where never ship hath rid at anchor, offering their bodies as a prey to feed the monstrous whales of the sea, while they seek to beguile them of their food in fishing for the said burrets: and all to find that, whereby as well unchaste dames of light behaviour might set out themselves and seem more proper, to allure and content adulterous ruffians: as also those gallants again, squaring and ruffling thus in their colours, might court fair ladies and wedded wives, yea, and with more ease entrap and compass them to yield unto their pleasure. But these men stand safe upon dry land, and gather those herbs for to dye such colours, as an honest minded person hath no cause to blame, nor the world reason to cry out upon. Nay, our brave minions and riotous wantons, it might beseem also to be furnished therewith; if not altogether so glorious to the eye, yet certainly with less offence and harm.

A FRIVOLOUS PIECE OF WORK

But what man is there well given and honestly minded, who can contain and hold his peace, having so just cause to reprove and rebuke the manner of the world in these our days? First and foremost, our life was never so costly as now it is, in regard of the dainties, delights and superfluities, which must be maintained, if we will live to the fashion of the time: and for to enjoy these pleasures only, we hold our lives more sweet and precious. Never were men more desirous of long life, and never less careful to entertain the means of long life. The government of our health we commit to the charge of others, and strangers we credit with our own bodies, and yet slack enough and negligent are they, to ordain according to our trust & confidence, that which indeed should do us good. Thus the physicians are provided well for: they thrive alone and go away with the gains by this means.

Oh good God, to see the folly and vanity of man! Nature having put so many good things into our own hands as she hath, and willing that we should enjoy them for our health and pleasure: yet we (to our great shame and rebuke be it spoken) are so unhappy, as to commit ourselves to other men's tuition, and live under their warrantize and assurance. Full well I know, that I for my part also, shall have but small thanks of many a one for all my pains taken in writing this history of the world and Nature's works: nay, I am assured that I make myself a laughing stock, and am condemned of them for spending and losing my time in such a frivolous piece of work as this is. Howbeit, this is yet my comfort and no small contentment I take herein, that my labours and travels (excessive and infinite though they be) cannot be despised, but the contempt will rebound likewise to dame Nature herself.

ERYNGION

Certes, there be wonders reported of this herb, namely, that the root of this white eryngion, (which is very geason and hard to be found) resembleth one while the male sex, and otherwhiles the female, of our kind. But if it chance that a man do meet with that eryngion which is like unto that member which distinguisheth him from a woman, he shall be very amiable and beloved of women. Which was the reason (men say) that lady *Sappho* was so enamoured upon the young knight *Phao* of Lesbos. And verily, as touching this herb, not only the magicians, but the disciples also and followers of *Pythagoras*, tell us many vain and foolish tales.

THE NETTLE

Applied in a liniment to the bare and naked places of the head, it causeth the hair to grow again, and bringeth all to the former beauty. Many do use to make a cataplasm of nettle-seed and old oil; or else stamp the leaves together with bear's grease, for the pain of the gout: and verily for that purpose, as also for the spleen, the root pouned with vinegar, is no less effectual. Being boiled in wine, it discusseth and driveth down rising in the groin, and such like emunctories, so it be laid to with old hogs' grease salted. But the same root dry, is a very depilatory, and fetcheth hair off.

ASPHODEL

Some say, that if one take the asphodel root, and lay one part thereof to those swelling kernels called the king's evil, & remove it upon the fourth day, letting the other part to hang in the smoke; the said kernels will dry away, even as the root doth in the chimney. *Sophocles* (for the gout) used the root both ways, as well raw as boiled. In case of humble-heels he applied it sodden in oil: but to them that were fallen into the jaundice or dropsy, he gave it in wine. Some writers have set down in their books, that if either the members of generation be anointed with a liniment made therewith and wine and honey together, or if the same be taken in drink, it will mightily provoke fleshly lust. *Xenocrates* affirmeth, that a decoction of the root in vinegar taketh away the ringworms, tettars, and running scabs. *Item*, if the root be boiled with henbane and tar, and therewith the arm-holes and parts between the legs be well rubbed, it will rid away the strong and rank savour which cometh from thence: and if the head be first shaven, & afterwards rubbed with the said root, the hair coming afterwards will curl and frizzle the better.

ANTHRISCUS

And verily I would say that anthriscus were the same herb, if it had smaller, tenderer, and sweeter leaves: This peculiar praise and commendable property it hath, that if the body be overlaid and wearied with the use of women, it restoreth the spirits, and refresheth them again: yea, and such as be well stepped in years and begin to droop, it maketh lusty and able to perform the act of generation youthfully.

THE ARTICHOKE

Also, by the testimony of *Hesiodus* and *Alcaeus*, if it be taken in wine, it inciteth to wantonness and fleshly pleasures. These poets do write, that when this herb doth flourish and is at the best, then grasshoppers chant loudest and sing most shrill: and as women at such a time be most desirous of men's company and hottest in lust, so contrariwise men are most loth to turn unto them, and least able to content their appetite: as if Nature to satisfy the pleasure of these good wives, had provided against that faint season the help of the artichoke, as a viand most powerful at this time to set their husbands in a heat, and to enable them to that business.

LASER

I would not give counsel (as many writers do prescribe) for to put it in the concavity or hole of a rotten tooth, and so to stop up the place close with wax, for fear of that which might ensue thereupon: for I have seen the fearful sequel of that experiment, in a man, who upon the taking of that medicine, threw himself headlong from an high loft and brake his neck; such intolerable pains he sustained of the toothache: and no marvel, for do but anoint the muffle or nose of a bull therewith, it will set him on a fire and make him horn-mad: and being mingled with wine, if serpents (as they are most greedy of wine) chance to lap or lick thereof, it will cause them to burst. And therefore I would not advise any to be anointed with it and honey of Athens incorporat together; howsoever there be physicians who set down such a receipt.

HONEYED WINE

The honeyed wine is very nutritive and breedth good flesh. Many have held out a long time fresh and lusty in their old age, with the nourishment of honeyed wine alone, without any other food: whereof we have one notable example of *Pollio Romilus,* who being above a hundred years old, bare his age passing well: whereat the Emperor *Augustus* of famous memory, marvelled much; and being upon a time lodged as a guest in his house, he demanded of him, what means he used most to maintain that fresh vigour both of body and mind? unto whom *Pollio* answered, by using honeyed wine within, and oil without.

A CURE FOR GOUT

Sextus Pompeius, who in his days was one of the principal peers of high Spain, and a son behind him, who afterwards was lord Praetor of Rome, sitting upon a time before his barn doors to see his corn winnowed, was surprised suddenly with a fit of the gout, and whether it were by chance, or in a rage for the extremity of pain, thrust his legs above the knees into the heap of wheat, lying thereby : but finding his legs mightily dried hereby, and himself wonderfully eased of his pain by that means, he never used any other remedy afterwards, but so soon as he felt a fit of his gout coming, he plunged his feet and legs into a heap of wheat.

FAR

As for this bearded wheat far, there is a certain worm breeding in it like to a moth or the grub that eateth wood, which is singular good to make rotten teeth to fall out of the head; for if the same be lapped within wax, and so put into the hole of the faulty tooth, it will drop out : or if the sound teeth be but rubbed therewith, they will shed and fall forth of the head.

BREAD

For singing men and choristers who are desirous to have a clear voice, for such also as be subject to rheums falling from the head, it is the wholesomest thing in the world, to eat dry bread in the beginning of meals. The sitanian bread, that is to say, which is made of three months' corn, being incorporat with honey, is a fair medicine to cure either the black prints remaining after strokes, or the skalling and pilling of the face. White bread crumbs soaked either in hot or cold water, yield unto sick men a meat of light digestion. The same being applied with wine, cureth swelling eyes. And so it healeth the breaking out in the head, especially if dried myrtles be put thereto. It is an ordinary thing to prescribe unto them that are given to shaking, for to eat fasting bread soaked in water, presently after they come forth of the bath. The perfume of bread burnt, taketh away all other evil smells that may be in a bed chamber.

A CURE FOR WARTS

Some there be, who for to be rid of all kinds of warts, take as many chick peas as there be warts, and with every one of them touch a wart, and that, upon the first day after the change of the moon : which done, they tie the foresaid peas or chicks in a little linen rag, and fling them away backward behind them : and they are persuaded that the warts will be gone by this means.

MALT LIQUORS

Thus much as touching all kinds of grain, as far forth as they concern physic. But this moreover is to be noted, that of corn there be certain drinks made; as namely, zythus, in Egypt; coelia and ceria, in Spain; ale and beer and many more sorts, in Gaul and other provinces. Now the froth or barm that riseth from these ales or beers, have a property to keep the skin fair and clear in women's faces. But for the operation that ale and beer hath in them who drink thereof, I mean to pass them over here.

THE THREE AND TWENTIETH BOOK

sheweth the medicinable virtues of wine, and tame
trees growing in hortyards

IN PRAISE OF WINE

AND BECAUSE we are entered into this theme, note thus much
moreover, that the drinking of milk nourisheth the bones: of
beer and ale, and such like, made with corn, feedeth the sinews
and nervous parts: but of water, maintaineth the flesh and
brawny muscles only. Which is the cause, that such nations as
drink either milk, ale, beer, etc., or sheer water, are nothing so
ruddy of colour, nor so strong and firm to undergo painful
travail, as those, whose ordinary and familiar drink is wine. And
in truth, as the moderate use of wine doth comfort the sinews
and help the eyesight; so the over-liberal taking thereof doth
offend the one, and enfeeble the other. Wine doth recreate and
refresh the stomach : wine stirreth up the appetite to meat : wine
allayeth sorrow, care and heaviness: wine provoketh urine, and
chaseth away all chilling cold out of the body. Finally, wine
induceth sleep and quiet repose. Moreover, this good property
hath wine, to stay the stomach and repress vomits, taken into the
body : and without forth applied with wool embrued and bathed
therein, to dissipate and resolve all swelling apostemes.
Asclepiades was so addicted to the praise of wine, that he bashed
not to make comparisons and pronounce, that the power and
puissance of the gods was hardly able to match and countervail
the might and force of wine.

WINE BEFORE MEALS

To drink wine upon an empty stomach fasting, is a new found device lately come up, and it is most unwholesome for the body, and namely for those who are to get into the field for to fight a battle : for it hindereth the forecast of the mind, and dulleth the vigour and quickness of the spirit : fitter indeed to bring and lull men asleep in the bed of security. Certes, it was a practice long ago among such as desired rest and peace, and who loved to sleep in a whole skin, for to drink wine fasting : for so we read in *Homer*, how *Helena* that fair lady, presented a cup of wine before meat. And hereupon came the proverb, that wine doth overshadow and darken the light of wisdom & understanding. Verily we that are men have this property above all other living creatures, and we may thank wine for it, that we drink many times when we be not dry or a-thirst. And therefore passing good it is to drink fair water otherwhiles between. In like manner such as use ordinarily to be drunk, and are lightly never sober, shall not do amiss to take a good draught of cold water presently upon their liberal pouring in of wine : for it will forthwith dispatch and discuss those fumes which cause drunkenness.

WINE : CONTRA-INDICATIONS

In like sort, those are forbidden to drink wine, who are given to yexing : and much more they, who in an ague labour for breath, and draw their wind hardly. But most of all must the sick be kept from wine when their eyes be set in their head, and their eyelids stand stiff and stark, with their eyes broad open : or be shut, by reason that they are weak and heavy. Also, they must avoid wine (if they be wise) who in their sickness, as they wink or twinkle with their eyes, do imagine that they sparkle and glitter again : like as those who cannot lay their eyes together and close their lids, but sleep open-eyes. And even so they ought to fly from drinking of wine whose eyes be red and bloodshot, or otherwise given to be full of viscous and gummy matter. Neither are they permitted to drink any wine, who eftsoons stut and cannot pronounce their words perfectly, whether it be, that their tongue be over-light and spongeous, or otherwise dull and heavy : no more than those, who hardly and with much difficulty, make water : who are affright suddenly at every little thing that they hear or see : who are given to cramps and cricks : such also as otherwhiles lie benumbed, as if they were dead asleep. And last of all, as many as shed their sperm involuntarily in their sleep. True it is, and no man maketh any doubt, that the only hope and right way to cure them, who in the cardiac disease, for very faintness are troubled with the trembling and shaking of the heart and given unto diaphoretical sweats, consisteth in the drinking of wine. And yet in the manner thereof, physicians are not agreed : for some are of advice, not to give it but in the very fit and extremity of the disease : others again prescribe it at no time else, but when the violence of the fit is past, and the patient at some ease. They who are of the former opinion, have a regard to their sweat, for to repress it : but these have an eye to the danger of the patient, being of this mind, that it is a more safe course to give wine when the violence of the sickness doth abate. And indeed of this judgement I see that most physicians are. As touching the time to drink wine, this is certain, that good it is not but at meat : neither presently after sleep, nor immediately upon any other drink, which is as much to say, as never but when a man is dry and thirsty. Neither must a sick man be allowed it, but in case of necessity or desperate extremity. In sum, we grant it to men rather than to women : to aged persons sooner than to young folk : and yet to a lusty young man, before a child : in winter oftener than in summer : and to conclude, to such as be accustomed thereto more than to those who have not drunk thereof beforetime.

VINEGAR

The physicians were ignorant heretofore of the sovereign virtue that vinegar had against the sting of the serpent called aspis, until by a mere chance they came to the knowledge thereof. And thus stood the case : It fortuned that a certain fellow carrying about him a bottle of vinegar, trod upon the said adder or serpent, which turned upon him again and stung him : howbeit he felt no harm at all so long as he carried the vinegar : but

o

so often as he set the bottle down out of his hands, the sting put him to sensible pain. By which experiment it was found and known that vinegar was the only remedy: and so with a draught thereof he had help out of hand, and was cured. But behold another proof and trial thereof: They that use to suck out the poison of venomed wounds given by serpents and such like, use no other collution to wash their mouths withal, but only vinegar.

*   *   *   *   *

And to knit up and close this discourse of vinegar, I cannot forget nor overpass one rare and singular accident that befell of late: *M. Agrippa* in his later days was much troubled and afflicted with a grievous gout of his feet; and being not able to endure the intolerable pains thereof, took counsel of a certain lewd leech, some bold and venturous empiric, who made great boast of his deep skill and admirable knowledge (for the Emperor *Augustus Caesar*, whose daughter he had espoused, he made not acquainted with the matter); who gave him counsel to bathe his legs with hot vinegar, and to sit therein above his knees, at what time as his disease tormented him most: True it is indeed, that he was eased of his pain by this means, for he lost the very feeling of his feet. Howbeit, *Agrippa* chose rather to be paralytic in some sort, and to want both use and sense of his legs, than to abide the extremity of his gout.

THE POMEGRANATE

The first knitting of this fruit, when the tree beginneth to flower, is called by the Greeks cytinus. Of which there be observed strange properties, approved by the experience of many men: For if any person, man or woman; unbraced, unlaced, unpointed, and unbuttoned, with girdle loose, hose ungartered, and shoe unbuckled, and have not so much as a ring about any finger, come and gather one of these tender buds or knots, with two fingers only, to wit, the thumb and the fourth ring-finger of the left hand; and after this ceremony proceed forward to another, namely, to touch light with the same bud the compass of the eyes round about, as if the priest should sacre or hallow them; and withal, when this is done, convey the same into the mouth, and swallow it down whole, so as a tooth touch it not:

there goeth an opinion, that he or she for certain shall feel no impediment or infirmity of the eyes that year throughout.

* * * * *

And here before I proceed any farther, I cannot sufficiently admire and wonder at the careful industry and diligence of our ancients beforetime, which they employed in the consideration of Nature's works, searching as they did into every secret, and left nothing behind them unassayed and untried : insomuch, as they took regard of those little pretty flowers appearing upon these knots or buds beforesaid, such I mean as break forth and spring, before the pomegranate itself is formed, and maketh any appearance; which small blossoms as I said before, are called balaustium. For even these, as little as they be, our ancestors have found by their experiments to be adverse unto scorpions.

A CURE FOR SCROFULA

Moreover, it is commonly said, that if one come to a fig tree, bend a bough or branch thereof downward to the ground, and bearing up his head without stooping, reach and catch hold of a knot or joint with his teeth, and so bite it off, that no man see him when he is doing of it; and then lap the same within a piece of fine leather, tied fast by a thread, and hang it about his neck, it will dispatch the king's devil and swelling kernels or inflammations behind the ears.

WALNUTS

As for walnuts, the Greeks have given them a name importing as much as the heaviness of head; and not without good cause, for the very shade of the tree and the scent of the leaves, do pierce and enter into the head : so do the kernels also in less while, if they be eaten : now the newer they be, the more pleasant taste they have : the dry are more oily and unctuous, hurtful to the stomach, hard of digestion, causing headache, naught for them who have a cough, and for such as would vomit in a morning fasting : good only in that troublesome running to the stool and straining for naught, by reason of their property to evacuate fleame. The same being eaten before meat, do dull the force of any poisons : they help the squinancies also, applied with rue & oil. Adverse and contrary they are to the nature of onions, and do keep down and repress their strong smell which riseth from them, after a man hath eaten them. Applied with a little honey, they are thought to be very good for the inflammation of the ears; and with rue, for the breasts and paps; as also for dislocations and parts out of joint. But if they be used with onions, salt and honey, they are singular for the biting both of dog and man. The shell of a walunt, is thought to be of a caustic quality, and good to burn or sear an hollow tooth : the same being burnt, pulverized, and incorporat with oil or wine, serveth to anoint the heads of young babes for to make the hair grow thick : and in that manner it is used to bring the hair again of elder folk, when through some infirmity it is shed.

THE FOUR AND TWENTIETH BOOK

declareth the properties of wild trees serving in physic

MODERN MEDICINE

GUMS ARE sooner dissolved and more easily tempered with vinegar than with anything else; & ink with water : besides an infinite number of other such, which I shall have occasion to write of continually in their due places. And indeed, this is the very ground and foundation of all our physic. For (to say a truth) nature ordained at the first such things and none but such, for to be the remedies of our diseases, which we feed and live daily upon; even those which are soon found and as soon prepared, which be ready at hand, common everywhere, and cost us little or nothing at all. But afterwards the world grew to be so full of deceit and cousenage, that some fine wits and nimble heads devised to set up apothecary shops, promising and bearing us in hand, that every man might buy his life and health there for money. Then anon a sort of compositions, mixtures, & confections were set on foot, then there was no talk but of strange and intricate receipts, and these were bruited abroad for the only medicines, of wonderful and unspeakable operations. So that nowadays we use no other drugs but those that come from Arabia and India. And if a man ail never so little, or have the least push or weal about him, he must have some costly physic forsooth for it : and a plaster that came from as far as the Red Sea : whereas in truth, the right remedies appropriate for every malady, be no other than such as the poorest man that is feedeth upon every night ordinarily at his supper. But if we went no farther than to the garden for medicines, and sought after herbs, shrubs, and plants only, for to cure our sickness or maintain our health, certes there was not a baser occupation in the world than the profession of physic, and physicians would be nought set by. But will you have the truth? To this pass are we come, the old world we have bidden farewell unto : the ancient manners and rites of Rome city are dead and gone : our state is grown so much in greatness, as there is no goodness left. Our victories and conquests be these, and nothing else, which have vanquished and subdued us : for subject we must acknowledge ourselves to strangers and foreign nations, so long as physic (one of their arts) is able to command our commanders, and overrule our Emperors.

A HAIR-RESTORER

As for the little round balls or apples found upon the oak robur, if they be incorporate with bear's grease, they cause the hair to come thick again, where it is shed, in case the bare or bald place be anointed therewith.

CEDAR-OIL

The great cedar, called by the Greeks cedrelate, as one would say, the fir-cedar, yieldeth a certain pitch or paraffin named cedria, a singular medicine for the toothache; for it breaketh them, fetcheth them out of the head and easeth all their pain. As touching the liquor that runneth from the cedar, and the manner how it is made, I have written already. This kind of pitch were excellent for the eyes but for one discommodity, in that it causeth headache. It preserveth dead bodies from corruption, a world of years : contrariwise, living bodies it doth putrify and corrupt : a strange and wonderful property, thus to mortify the quick, and quicken (as it were) the dead. It marreth and rotteth apparel, as well linen as woollen : and it killeth all living creatures. And therefore I would not advise as some have done, to taste this medicine and take it inwardly for the squin-ancie or crudities of the stomach : neither would I be bold, but fear rather, to prescribe it in a collution with vinegar to wash the mouth withal for the toothache, or to drop it into their ears who be hard of hearing or otherwise have vermin within them. But a monstrous and beastly thing it is which some report of it. That if a man do anoint therewith the instrument or part serving for generation, at what time as he is minded to know a woman carnally, it will bring her to an abortive slip, if she were conceived before; or hinder conception, if she were clear. Howbeit, I would not make doubt to anoint therewith the head and other parts, for to kill lice, or to rid away the scurf and scaly dandruff among the hair, either in head or face.

THE SCENT OF PINE-WOODS

The leaves of the pitch tree have a particular property respective to the liver, and the infirmities thereof, if one take a dram weight of them and drink it in mead or honeyed water. It is well known and resolved upon, that to take the air of those woods and forests only where these trees be cut, lanced, and scraped, for to draw pitch and rosin out of them, is without all comparison the best course which they can take who either be in a consumption of the lungs, or after some long and languishing sickness, have much ado to recover their strength. Certes, such an air is far better, than either to make a long voyage by sea into Egypt, or to go among the cottages in summer-time for to drink new milk coming of the fresh and green grass of the mountains.

ROSINS

For salves to heal wounds, as also for emollitive plasters, rosins ought to be dissolved in oil: for drinks or potions, with bitter almonds. As touching their medicinable virtues, they be good to cleanse and close up wounds: to discuss and resolve any apostemes which be in gathering. Moreover, they be used in the diseases of the breast (and namely true turpentine) by way of liniment; for then it is singular good, especially if it be applied hot: also for the pains of the limbs, and for those that be plucked with the cramp, in case the grieved parts be well rubbed therewith in the sun; which they know well enough who buy slaves and sell them for gain, after they have trimmed and set them out for sale : for they especially are very curious to anoint their bodies all over with this turpentine, for to loosen the skin when they be hide-bound, lank, and carrion lean, to give more liberty and space for every part to receive nutriment, and so to make their body seem fat and fair liking.

MASTIC

Moreover, this mastic, which is the gum of the lentisk tree, is used ordinarily to lay the hairs of the eyelids even, and to extend or make plain and smooth the riveled skin of the face : therefore it is used in soap, and wash-balls. Moreover, there is good use thereof, for spitting and reaching up of blood, & for an old cough. In one word, it serveth all those turns whereto the gum ammoniac is used. It healeth all places galled and chafed, where the skin is rubbed or fretted off : and if the cods and members of generation be fomented either with the oil made of the seed of the mastic tree mixed with wax, or with a decoction of the leaves boiled in oil or else in water, it will skin any raw part thereof. To knit up this discourse, I am not ignorant that *Democritus* the physician, who had in cure *Considia* the daughter of *M. Servilius* late consul of Rome, for an infirmity or malady of hers, (for that this damosel could not abide to hear of any unpleasant physic) caused her to be fed a long time with the milk of goats which were kept with the lentisk tree leaves, and did eat nothing else, and so he cured her of her malady.

AN INSECTICIDE

The tendrons of the elder, incorporat with goat's tallow, and reduced into a liniment, are singular good for the gout, if they be applied to the grieved place. The water of their infusion, if it be cast or sprinkled with the decoction of the leaves, it will not leave a fly alive.

AGNUS CASTUS

There is a kind of tree named vitex, not much different from the willow, in regard of the use that the twigs be put unto, as also of the leaves which resemble those of the willow in outward show, but their smell is more pleasant and odoriferous: the Greeks, some call it lygos others agnos, i.e. chaste; for that the dames of Athens, during the feasts of the goddess *Ceres*, which were named Thesmophoria, made their pallets and beds with the leaves thereof, to cool the heat of lust, and to keep themselves chaste for the time. And two sorts there be of it ...

There is neither of them both, but as well the seed as the leaves, reduced into a liniment, be singular good for the prick of spiders. And there is not any venomous creature that will come near those who are but anointed therewith: and they will fly from the very perfume thereof, or the couch which is made of the leaves. They abate the heat of wanton lust: and in that regard especially they be contrary to the venomous spiders phalangia, which by their sting do prick a man forward that way, and cause his flesh to rise. The flower and young tendrils of agnus castus, incorporat in oil rosat, do allay the headache, occasioned by drinking overliberally. But if the said headache be exceeding great, it is good to foment the head with a decoction of the seed of the said agnus: for it will resolve and dispatch the extremity thereof ...

It is said, that whosover beareth in his hand a twig of agnus, or gird himself about the middle therewith, shall not be galled or fretted between the legs.

TAMARISK

To come now to tamarisk, which the Greeks call myrice, *Lenaeus* affirmeth, that it is used in manner of the Amerian willow for besoms: and more than so, that if it be sodden in wine, stamped and reduced into a liniment with honey, it healeth cankerous ulcers. And in very truth, some hold, that the myrice and tamarisk be both one. But doubtless, singular it is for the spleen, in case the patient drink the juice pressed out of it, in wine. And by report, there is that wonderful antipathy and contrariety in nature between tamarisk and this one part alone of all the other bowels, that if the troughs out of which swine drink their swill, be made of this wood, they will be found when they are opened, altogether without a spleen. And therefore some physicians do prescribe unto a man or woman also diseased in the spleen, and subject to the opilations thereof, both to drink out of cups and cans of tamarisk, and also to eat their meat out of such treen dishes as be made of that wood. One renowned writer above the rest, and for knowledge in great credit and authority among physicians, hath affirmed and avouched constantly, that a twig of tamarisk slipped or broken from the plant, so as it touched neither the ground, nor any iron tool, assuageth all belly-ache, in case the patient wear it about him so, as that his girdle and coat hold it fast and close to the body.

* * * * *

The ashes of the very wood of the tree, is good in all those cases beforesaid : which if they be mingled in the stall of an ox, and so taken of man or woman, either in meat or drink, it will disable them for having any mind to the sports of *Venus* ever after. And a burning coal of this wood, when it is quenched in that stale or beasts' piss, they use to save and lay up in the shade for that purpose : but if one list to kindle lust, then they set it on fire again. To conclude, the magicians say, that it would do as much, if the urine only of a gelded man were taken for the said purpose.

SELAGO

Much like unto this herb savin, is that which they call selago. Many ceremonies are to be observed in the gathering of this herb : First and foremost, the party who is to gather it, must be apparelled all in white, as it were in a surplice; go barefoot he must, and have his feet washed in fair water : before he cometh to gather it, he ought to do sacrifice unto the gods with bread and wine : moreover, no knife or iron tool is to be used here about : neither will any hand serve but the right, and that also must do the deed not bare and naked, but by some skirt or lappet of his coat between, which was done off with the left hand, and so closely besides, as if he came to steal it away secretly : last of all, when it is gathered, wrapped it must be, and carried in a new linen napkin or towel. The Druidae of France have a great opinion of this herb thus gathered, and have prescribed it to be kept as the only preservative against all hurtful accidents and misfortunes whatsoever, saying, that the fume thereof is singular good for all the infirmities and diseases of the eye.

HOLLY

As touching the holly or hulver tree, if it be planted about an house, whether it be within a city or standing in the country, it serveth for a countercharm and keepeth away all ill spells or enchantments. *Pythagoras* affirmeth, that the flower of this tree will cause water to stand all upon an ice : also that a staff made thereof, if a man do fling it at any beast whatsoever, although it chance to light short for default of strength in his arms who flung it, will notwithstanding edge forward and roll from the place where it fell upon the earth, and approach near to the beast aforesaid; of so admirable a nature in this holly tree.

A TRUTH-SERUM

He writeth moreover, that in a country of India inhabited by the Tardistiles, there is another herb named Achaemenis, growing without leaf, and in colour resembling amber : of the root of which herb there be certain trochiskes made : whereof they cause malefactors and suspected persons to drink some quantity with wine, in the daytime, to the end they should confess the truth : For in the night following they shall be so haunted with spirits and tormented with sundry fancies and horrible visions, that they shall be driven perforce to tell all, and acknowledge the fact for which they are troubled and brought in question.

ACCORDING TO DEMOCRITUS

He proceedeth moreover, to another, known by the name adamantis, growing only in Armenia and Cappadocia : which if it be brought near unto lions, they will lie all along upon their backs, and yawn with their mouths as wide as ever they can.

*   *   *   *   *

Over and besides, he speaketh of the plant ophiusa, found in a country of the same Aethyopia, named elephantine : Of a leaden hue it is, and hideous to see to : whosoever drink thereof, shall be so frighted with the terrors and menaces of serpents represented unto their eyes, that for very fear they shall lay violent hands on themselves : and therefore church robbers are enforced to drink it. Howbeit, if a man take after it a draught of date wine, he shall not be troubled with any such fearful visions and illusions.

Moreover, there is found (saith *Democritus*) the herb thalassegle about the river Indus, and thereupon is known by another name potamantis : which if men or women take in drink, transporteth their senses so far out of the way, that they shall imagine they see strange sights.

As for Theangelis, which by his saying groweth upon mount Libanon in Syria, and upon Dicte, a mountain in Candie; also about Babylon and Susis in Persia; if the wise philosophers (whom they term Magi) drink of that herb, they shall incontinently have the spirit of prophecy, and foretell things to come.

There is besides in the region called Bactriana and about the river Borysthenes, another strange plant named gelotophyllis, which (by his report) if one do drink with myrrh and wine, it will cause many fantastical apparitions : and the party shall thereupon fall into a fit of laughter without ceasing and intermission, and never give over, unless it be with a draught of date wine, wherein were tempered the kernels of pine nuts together with pepper and honey.

ANACAMPSEROS

A famous grammarian of late days made mention of another herb anacampseros, of this virtue, that if a man touched a woman therewith, were she departed from him in all the hatred that might be, she would come again and love him entirely. The same benefit also should the woman find thereby, in winning the love of a man.

ERIPHIA

Many writers have made mention of eriphia. This herb hath

within the straw of the stem a certain fly like a beetle, running up and down, and by that means making a noise like unto a young kid, whereupon it took the foresaid name. There is not a better thing in the world for the voice, than this herb, as folk say.

A CURE FOR DISLOCATION

The grass or herb near unto which a dog lifts his leg and pisseth, if it be plucked out of the ground without touching a knife or iron instrument, cureth any dislocation or bone out of joint, most speedily.

INTERNATIONAL MEDICINE

Touching the tree (in manner of an opiet or poplar) called rumbotinus, I have described it in my treatise of hortyards and tree-plots. Near to one of these (and namely, when there is no vine coupled or married to it) there groweth a certain herb, which in France they call rhodora: it riseth up with a stem pointed and knotted in manner of a figtree rod or wand; beareth leaves resembling nettles, somewhat whitish in the midst, but the same in process of time become red all over; and a flower of silver colour: This herb stamped and mixed with old hog's grease, maketh a sovereign liniment for all swellings, inflammations, and impostumes gathering to an head; provided always that no edge tool come near to touch it, and that the party who is dressed or anointed therewith turn the head to the right hand, and spit thrice upon the ground on that side. And the operation of this medicine will be the more effectual, if three sundry men of three divers nations, stand on the right hand when they anoint the patient.

THE FIVE AND TWENTIETH BOOK

*treateth of the herbs in the field coming up of their
own accord*

BOOKS ABOUT HERBAL REMEDIES

AND AMONG the rest, *Evax* a King of the Arabians, wrote a book
as touching the virtues and operation of simples, which he lent
unto the Emperor *Nero*. *Cratevas* likewise, Dionysius also, and
Metrodorus, wrote of the same argument after a most pleasant
and plausible manner (I must needs say;) yet so, as a man could
pick nothing almost out of all their writing, but an infinite difficulty of the thing : for they painted every herb in their colours,
and under the portraits they couched and subscribed their several
natures and effects. But what certainty could there be therein ?
pictures (you know) are deceitful; also, in representing such a
number of colours, and especially expressing the lively hue of
herbs according to their nature as they grow, no marvel if they
that limned and drew them out, did fail and degenerate from the
first pattern and original. Besides, they came far short of the
mark, setting out herbs as they did at one only season (to wit,
either in their flower, or in seed time) for they change and alter
their form and shape every quarter of the year. Hereof it came,
that all the rest laboured to describe their forms and colours, by
words only. Some without any description at all of their figure
or colour, contented themselves (for the most part) with setting
down their bare names, and thought it sufficient to demonstrate
and shew their power and virtue afterwards, to whosoever were
desirous to seek after the same : and verily, the knowledge thereof
is no hard matter to attain unto. For mine own part, it hath

been my good hap to see growing in the plant, all these medicinable herbs (excepting very few) by the means of *Antonius Castor* (a right learned and most renowned physician in our days) who had a pretty garden of his own well stored with simples of sundry sorts, which he maintained and cherished for his own pleasure and his friends', who used to come and see his plot, as indeed it was worthy the sight. This physician was then above an hundred years old, and in all his life never found what sickness meant; neither for all this age of his, was his fit decayed or memory any whit impaired, but continued as fresh still as if he had been a young man.

THE POWER OF HERBS

In sum, so far were men in old time ravished with the admiration of herbs and their virtues, that they bashed not to avouch even incredible things of them. *Xanthus* an ancient chronicler, writeth in the first book of his histories, of a dragon, which finding one of her little serpents killed, raised it to life again by a certain herb, which he named balis: and with the said herb, a man also named *Thylo*, whom the dragon had slain, was revived and restored to health again. Also King *Iuba* doth report, that there was a man in Arabia, who being once dead, became alive again by the virtue of a certain herb. *Democritus* said, and *Theophrastus* gave credit to his words, that there is an herb, with which a kind of fowl (whereof I have made mention before) is able to make the wedge or stopple to fly out of the hole of her nest, into which the shepherds had driven it fast, in case she bring the same herb and but once touch the foresaid wedge therewith. These be strange reports and incredible, howbeit they draw men into a wonderful opinion of the thing, and fill their heads with a deep conceit, forcing them to confess, that there is some great matter in herbs, and much true indeed which is reported so wonderfully of them.

A CURE FOR HYDROPHOBIA

But the most dishonest and shameful cause why so few simples in comparison be known, is the naughty nature and peevish disposition of those persons who will not teach others their skill, as if themselves should lose for ever that which they imparted unto their neighbour. Over and besides, there is no certain way or means to direct us to the invention and knowledge of herbs and their virtues: for if we look upon these herbs which are found already, we are for some of them beholden to mere chance and fortune: and for others (to say a truth) to the immediate revelation from God. For proof hereof, mark but this one instance which I will relate unto you. For many a year until now of late days, the biting of a mad dog was counted incurable: and look who were so bitten, they fell into a certain dread and fear of water: neither could they abide to drink, or to hear talk thereof, and then were they thought to be in a desperate case. It fortuned of late, that a soldier, one of the guard about the Praetorium was bitten with a mad dog, and his mother saw a vision in her sleep, giving (as it were) direction unto her for to send the root unto her son for to drink, of an eglantine or wild rose (called cynorrhodon) which the day before she had espied growing in an hortyard, where she took pleasure to behold it. This occurrent fell out in Lacetania, the nearest part unto us of Spain. Now, as God would, when the soldier beforesaid upon his hurt received by the dog, was ready to fall into that symptom of hydrophobia, and began to fear water; there came a letter from his mother, advertising him to obey the will of God, and to do according to that which was revealed unto her by the vision. Whereupon he drank the root of the said sweet briar or eglantine, and not only recovered himself beyond all men's expectations: but also afterwards as many as in that case took the like receipt, found the same remedy. Before this time, the writers of physic knew of no medicinable virtues in the eglantine, but only of the sponge or little ball, growing amid the pricky branches thereof, which being burnt and reduced into ashes, and incorporate with honey into a liniment, maketh hair to come again where it was shed by any infirmity.

THE POOR ESTATE OF MAN

So unfortunate is our condition, and so much exposed are we to manifold calamities, that the earth is not pestered with wicked beasts only for to do us harm: but also there be otherwhiles venomous waters and pestilent tracts to work us more woe and misery. In that voyage or expedition which prince *Caesar Germanicus* made into Germany, after he had passed over the river Rhine, and had given orders to advance forward with his army, he encamped upon the sea coasts along Friseland, where there was to be found but one spring of fresh water; and the same so dangerous, that whosoever drunk of that water, within two years lost all their teeth, and were besides so feeble and loose jointed in their knees, that unneth they were able to stand. These diseases the physicians termed stomacace and sceletryrbe: as one would say, the malady of the mouth, and palsy of the legs. Yet they found a remedy for these infirmities, and that was a certain herb called brittannica, which is very medicinable, not only for the accidents of the sinews and mouth, but also for the squinancie and stinging of serpents. It hath leaves growing somewhat long, and those inclining to a brownish or dark green colour, and the root is black; out of which, as also from the leaves, there is a juice drawn and pressed. The flowers by a peculiar name be called vibones: which being gathered before any thunder be heard, and so eaten, do assure and secure the parties together from that infirmity. The Frisians, near unto whom we lay encamped, shewed our men this herb. But I muse much & wonder what should be the reason of that name, unless the Frisians bordering upon the narrow race of the Ocean, which lieth only between them and England (called in those days Brittania) should thereupon for the neighbourhood and propinquity of that island, give it the name Britannica. For certain it is, that it took not the name because there grew such plenty thereof in that country of England, that it should be transported over from thence to our camp; for as yet that island was not wholly subject unto us and reduced under the Roman signory. For an ordinary thing it was in old time practised by those that found out any herbs, to affect the adoption (as it were) of the same, and to call them by their own names, wherein verily men took no small contentment: according as I purpose to show by the example of certain kings and princes, whose names live and continue yet in their herbs; so honourable a thing it was thought in those days to find and it were but an herb that might do good unto man. Whereas in this age wherein we now live, I doubt not but there be some who will mock us for the pains taken in that behalf, and think us very simple for writing thus as we do of simples; so base and contemptible in the eyes of our fine fools and delicate persons, are even the best things that serve for the benefit and common utility of mankind. Howbeit, for all that, good reason it is and meet that the authors and inventors of them, as many as can be found, should be named and praised with the best; yea, and that the operations and effects of such herbs should be digested and reduced into some method, according as they be appropriate to every kind of disease. In the meditation whereof, I cannot choose nor contain myself, but deplore and pity the poor estate and miserable case of man: who over and besides the manifold accidents and casualties which may befall unto him, is otherwise subject to many thousands of maladies, which we have much ado to devise names for every hour of the day happening as they do, and whereof no man cannot account himself free, but every one is for his part to fear them. Of these diseases so infinite as they be in number, to determine precisely and distinctly which be most grievous, might seem mere folly, considering that everyone who is sick for the present, imagineth his own sickness to be worst and fullest of anguish. And yet our forefathers have given their judgement in this case, and by experience have found, that the most extreme pain and torment that a man can endure by any disease, is the strangury or pissing dropmeal, occasioned by the stone or gravel in the bladder. The next is the grief and anguish of the stomach: and the third, headache: for setting these three maladies aside, lightly there are no pains that can kill a man or woman so soon. And here by the way, I cannot for mine own part but marvel much at the Greeks, who have published in their writings venomous and pestilent herbs, as well as those that be good and wholesome. And yet there is an appearance and shew of reason, why some poisons should be known: for otherwhiles it falleth out that men live in such extremity, as better it were to die, than for to lie in anguish and torment, insomuch, as death is the best port and harbour of refuge that they have. Certes, *Marcus Varro* reporteth of one *Servius Clodius* a gentleman or knight of Rome, who for the extreme pain of the gout, was forced to anoint his legs and feet all over with a narcotic or cold poison, whereby he so mortified the spirits of the muscles and sinews, that he became paralytic in that part: and ever after unto his dying day, was rid as well of all sense, as of the pain of the gout. But say, that in these cases it might be tolerable to set down in their books some poisons: what reason, nay what leave had those Greeks to shew the means how the brains and understanding of men should be intoxicated and troubled? What colour and pretence had they to set down medicines and receipts to cause women to slip the untimely fruit of their womb, and a thousand such-like casts and devices that be practised by herbs of their penning? For mine own part, I am not for them that would send the conception out of the body unnaturally before the due time: they shall learn no such receipts of me. Neither will I teach any how to temper and spice an amatorious cup, to draw either man or woman into love, it is no part of my profession: For well I remember, that *Lucullus* a most brave general, and a captain of great execution, lost his life by such a love-potion. Much less then shall ye have me to write of magic, witchcraft, charms, enchantments and sorceries, unless it be to give warning that folk should not meddle with them, or to disprove those courses of their vanities, and principally to give an item, how little trust and assurance there is to be had in such trumpery. It sufficeth me and contenteth my mind, yea and I think that I have done well for mankind, in recording those herbs which be good and wholesome, found out by men of wit and learning for the benefit of prosperity.

HELLEBORE

Touching white hellebore, the best is that which most speedily provoketh sneezing: it is without comparison far more terrible than the black, especially if a man read what ado and preparation there went unto it in the old time, when they were to drink it against shiverings and shakings, against the rising of the mother and danger of suffocation: in case also of immoderate and extraordinary drowsiness, of excessive hiccoughs and yexing without intermission, and of continual sneezing: moreover, when they were troubled with weakness and feebleness of stomach: in like manner in case of vomits, when they came either too fast or over-slow, either too little or too much : for this was a rule observed among them, To give with hellebore some other drugs, for to cause it work the sooner, and to hasten vomit more speedily : also they used means to fetch away the very hellebore again if it lay over-long in the body, either by other purgative medicines, or by clysters : oftentimes also by opening a vein or blood-letting. And say that hellebore taken in manner aforesaid, wrought very well, yet they used to observe every vomit, the divers colours of humours that came away which many times were fearful to behold : yea and when the patient had done casting, they con-sidered also the ordure and excrements that passed away by the belly : they gave order besides, for bathing either before or after the taking of hellebore, as occasion best required; yea and they took great heed and regard of the whole body besides : and yet, did what they could, the terrible name and report that went of this medicine, passed all their care and circumspection whatso-ever : for it was an opinion generally held and received, that hellebore doth eat away and consume the flesh seething in the pot, if it be boiled therewith. But herein were the ancient physicians much to blame and greatly in fault, in that they were over-timorous, and for fear of such accidents ensuing upon this medicine, gave it in too small a dose : whereas indeed, the greater quantity that one taketh of it, the more speedily it worketh, and the sooner passeth out of the body, when it hath once done the errand. *Themison* used to prescribe two drams, and not above. The physicians who followed after, allowed the dose of four drams; grounding upon a notable and famous apophthegm or speech of *Herophylus*, who was wont to say, that hellebore was like unto a valiant and hardy captain : For when (quoth he) it hath stirred all the humours within the body, itself issueth forth first and maketh way before them.

* * * * *

And thus being used as is beforesaid, it is a most sovereign remedy for the falling sickness, the swimming or dizziness of the head : it cureth melancholic persons troubled in mind; such as be brainsick, mad, lunatic, frantic, and furious : it is singular good for the elephantie, the foul and dangerous morphew called leuce, the filthy leprosy, and the general convulsion whereby the body continueth stiff and stark, as if it were all one piece without any joint. It helpeth those that be troubled with trembling, shivering, and shaking of their limbs, with the gout, and the dropsy, and namely such as be entering into a tympanie : singular it is for those that have weak and feeble stomachs and can keep nothing that they take; for such as are given to spasms or cramps, lie bedrid of the ague, which will not be rid away by any other means; troubled with an old cough, vexed with ventosities and griping wrings and torments which be periodical, and use to come and go at certain set times : howbeit, physicians forbid the giving of hellebore to old folk and young children : *Item*, to such as be of a feminine and delicate body; as also to those that be in mind effeminate : likewise to those who are thin and slender, soft and tender : in which regards, we may not be altogether so bold to give it unto women as unto men. In like manner, this is a medicine that would not be ministered inwardly to fearful, timorous, and faint-hearted persons, neither to those who have any ulcer in the precordial region about the midriff, ne yet unto such as usually be given to swell in those parts; and least of all to those that spit or reach up blood; no more than to sickly and crazy persons who have some tedious and lingering malady, or phthisic, etc., hanging upon them, and namely, if they be grieved and diseased in their sides or throat. Nevertheless, applied without the body in manner of a liniment with salted hog's grease, it cureth the breaking forth of phlegmatic weals and pimples; as also healeth old sores remaining after impostumes suppurat and broken : mixed with parched or fried barley-groats, it is a very ratsbane, and killeth both them & mice. The Gauls or Frenchmen when they ride a-hunting into the chase, use to dip their arrow heads in the juice of hellebore, and they have this opinion, that the venison which they take will eat the tenderer; but they then cut away the flesh round about the wound made by the foresaid arrows. Furthermore it is said, that if white hellebore be beaten to powder and strewed upon milk, all the flies that taste thereof will die. To conclude, the said milk is good to rid away lice, nits, and such like vermin out of the head and other parts of the body.

HIBERIS

Of late days *Servilus Damocrates*, a famous practitioner in physic, brought to light an herb, which he termed hiberis, a devised and feigned name for his own pleasure, and nothing significant, as may appear by a certain poem that he made as touching the discovery of that herb. It cometh up most willingly about old tombs and sepulchres, decayed walls, and ruinate buildings, in untoiled and neglected places, and namely, common highways. It beareth flowers at all times, and is leaved like to cresses: the main stalk is a cubit high: but the seed so fine and small, that hardly they can discern it. The root also hath the very smell of cresses: it serveth to many good purposes, but with most success in summertime, and never but when it is green and fresh gathered. Much ado and trouble there is about the punning and stamping of it. Being tempered and incorporat with a little hog's grease, it is singular to be applied to the pain of the huckle-bone called sciatica as also to the gout of any joints whatsoever. If the patient be a man, it must lie bound fast unto the place four hours at the most: but women may abide it but half so long, provided always, that presently upon this medicine they go down into an hot bain, and after they have bathed, anoint their bodies all over with wine and oil. Thus must the patient do once every twenty days, so long as there remaineth any grudging or minding of the foresaid pain. And surely in this sort it drieth up and cureth all secret and inward rheums running near unto the bones. Howbeit, this caveat would be given, not to lay this plaster to in the very heat and fury of the pain or disease, but the time must be waited when the extremity is somewhat slaked and overpast.

THE CELANDINE

Moreover, other living creatures also there be besides men, unto which we are to attribute the invention of herbs: as first and principally, the great celandine, called in Greek chelidonia, for that the old swallows with the help of this herb help their young ones to see again, yea though their eyes were plucked out of their head, as some are of opinion.

THE SPITEFULNESS OF DOGS

Touching the dogs' grass canaria, it took that name in Latin, because dogs use therewith to discharge their gorge & whet their stomachs when their appetite to meat is gone. A strange thing of these dogs; we see them chew this herb in our sight ordinarily every day, yet so, as we never can tell which herb it is that they have bitten : for we may perceive it only when it is eaten down. But no marvel if this creature be so spiteful as to conceal from us a purgative herb, considering a greater malice that he sheweth in another : For it is said, that if a dog be bitten by a serpent, he hath recourse by and by to a certain herb that cureth him presently, but he will be sure that no man shall see him when he croppeth that herb.

ARISTOLOCHY

The round rooted aristolochy hath a special property against the poison of serpents. Yet there goeth the greatest name of the long, for this excellent quality, if it be true that is reported thereof : namely, that if a woman newly conceived with child, apply the root thereof to her natural parts within a morsel of raw beef, it will cause her to breed and form in her womb a man child. Our fishers hereby in Campaine, do term the round root, the poison of the earth. In very truth I have seen them with mine own eyes to stamp the said root, and incorporate it with lime into a paste, and so to cast it into the sea in small pellets or goblets, for to catch fishes : and I assure you they will scud amain, and make haste to this bait, and be very eager of bite : but no sooner have they tasted thereof, but they will turn up their bellies, and lie floating aloft upon the water stark dead.

BETONY

But of betony above all the rest there is made a most sovereign salve to be laid upon the place that is stung. And such a contrariety in nature or antipathy there is (by folks' report) between them and this herb, that if the leaves thereof be stewed in a circle round about them, the serpents within will never give over flapping with their tails, and beating their own sides, until they have killed themselves.

VERVAIN

But the wise men or sages called Magi, overpass themselves mightily in this herb, and show their foolery and vanity without all sense and reason : They would bear us in hand forsooth, that whosoever be rubbed all over the body therewith, shall obtain whatsoever their heart desireth, be able to cure and drive away all manner of agues, reconcile them that be fallen out, make friendship between whom they list, and in one word, give remedy to any disease whatsoever. They give moreover express order, that it be gathered about the rising of the great Dogstar, but so, as neither sun nor moon be at that time above the earth to see it; with this especial charge besides, that before they take up the herb, they bestow upon the ground where it groweth, honey with the combs, in token of satisfaction and amends for the wrong and violence done in depriving her of so worthy an herb. They rest not so, but when those ceremonious circumstances be performed, they enjoin them also who are to dig it up, for to make a circle round about the place with some instrument of iron, and then to draw and pluck it up with the left hand in any wise, and so to fling it aloft over their heads up into the air : which done, they appoint precisely that it be dried in the shade, leaves, stalks, and roots, every one apart by themselves. To conclude, they add moreover and say, that if the hall or dining chamber be sprinkled with the water wherein vervain lay steeped, all that sit at the table shall be very pleasant, and make merry most jocundly. Well, to leave these toys and fooleries, the truth is this, stamp and beat it, give the juice or powder thereof in wine, it is a good defensative against the poison of serpents.

FROGS AND TOADS

Moreover, frogs (such especially as keep in bushes and hedges, and be called in Latin rubetae, i.e. toads) are not without their venom : I myself have seen these vaunting mountebanks calling themselves Psylli as coming from the race of those people Psylli, who feared no kind of poison; I have seen them (I say) in a bravery (because they would seem to surpass all others of that profession) who eat those toads baked red hot between two platers; but what became of them? they caught their bane by it, and died more suddenly than if they had been stung by the aspis: but what is the help for this rank poison? surely the herb phrynion drunk in wine.

TO STOP DOGS BARKING

Vervain, which the Greek call peristereos, is an herb bearing one main stalk of a good height, furnished well with leaves, spreading forth toward the head into other branches, much sought unto by doves and pigeons, whereupon it took the foresaid name peristereos. They say, whosoever carry this herb about them, there dare not a dog bark at them.

SCALP-TREATMENT

There is an unseemly accident happening otherwhiles to the head, and disgraceth it much, called alopecia, when as the hair unnaturally falleth off. The cure of this inconvenience, is to make a liniment with the roots of nymphaea and helmock stamped together, and therewith to anoint the bald and naked places, for it will cause the hair to come up again and grow thick. Polytricha and callitricha (both capillare herbs) differ one from another; for that polytricha hath white benty filaments or threads, the leaves also be more in number & greater withal: besides, the very plant itself spreadeth and brancheth more than the other: This herb is singular to fasten the hair of the head at the root, and to make it bush and grow thick, being otherwise ready to shed. In like manner, there is an herb called in Latin lingulaca, which loveth to grow about springs or fountains, and is singular for the same imperfection of shedding hair, if the root together with the leaf burnt and beaten to powder, be incorporat with the grease of a black sow (but in any wise she must be a young guilt that never farrowed or had pigs) and so brought into a liniment, and the head rubbed and anointed therewith: with this charge besides, that after the anointing, the patient sit bare-headed in the sun; for that helpeth forward the cure very much. And in the same case there is the like use of the cyclamine or sowbread root.

Touching the scurf or branny scales called dandruff, the root of veratrum or hellebore, sodden either in oil or water, maketh a most excellent medicine to rid it away, and to cleanse the head thereof.

MANDRAGORA

The leaves moreover of mandrage are commonly kept and condite in a kind of pickle or salt brine : for otherwise the juice of them whiles they be fresh and green, is pestiferous and a very poison. And yet order them so well as you can, hurtful they be every way : the only smell of them stuffeth the head, and breedeth the murre and the pose. Howbeit, in some countries they venture to eat the apples or fruit thereof : for those they know not how to dress and order them aright, lose the use of their tongue thereby, and prove dumb for the time, surprised and overtaken with the exceeding stronger savour that they have. And verily if they be so bold as to take a great quantity thereof in drink, they are sure to die for it. Yet it may be used safely enough for to procure sleep, if there be a good regard had in the dose, that it be answerable in proportion to the strength and complexion of the patient : one cyath thereof is thought to be a moderate and sufficient draught. Also it is an ordinary thing to drink it against the poison of serpents : likewise, before the cutting, cauterizing, pricking or lancing of any member, to take away the sense and feeling of such extreme cures. And sufficient it is in some bodies to cast them into a sleep with the smell of mandrake, against the time of such chirurgery.

HEMLOCK

The leaves also of hemlock do keep down all tumours, appease pains, and cure watering eyes. *Anaxilaus* mine author saith, that if a pure maiden do in her virginity anoint her breasts with this juice, her dugs will never grow afterwards, but continue still in the same state. True it is indeed, that being kept unto the paps of women in child-bed, it drieth up their milk : as also extinguisheth natural seed, if the cods and share be anointed therewith. What remedies they should use to save themselves who are adjudged by law to drink it, I for my part purpose not to set down.

GROUNDSEL

There is an herb called groundsel, which the Greeks name erigeron, and we the Latins senecio : they say if a man make a circle round about it with some instrument of iron, and then dig it out of the ground, and therewith touch the tooth that is pained, three several times, and between every touching spit upon the ground, and then bestow the said herb root and all in the very same place where he drew it, so as it may live and grow again, the said tooth shall never ache afterwards.

FOR HALITOSIS

But since I have named a stinking breath, which is a foul and nasty disease, putting man or woman to shame, as no infirmity more; I will set down one or two compound receipts for that imperfection. Take myrtle and lentisk leaves, of each a like weight; of the gall nuts growing in Syria, half as much in quantity : stamp them all together, and in the stamping sprinkle them with good old wine : give the patient this composition in bowl to chew and eat in the morning, there is not the like medicine unto it for a sweet breath.

THE SIX AND TWENTIETH BOOK

sheweth of many new and strange maladies, the medicinable virtues also of certain herbs, according to sundry diseases

---

A NEW SKIN DISEASE

LONG IT is not since the face and visage of men began to be annoyed with certain new and strange diseases, unknown in our forefathers' days, and never heard of before in Italy, nor almost in any part of Europe. And even of late days when these maladies set first foot in these parts, they were not seen for to spread throughout all Italy, ne yet to range greatly in Illyricum, France, or Spain, although some little sprinkling there was in those countries: but about Rome only and those quarters adjoining, as they reigned first, so they raged most. These newcome diseases verily were nothing painful to the patients, nor dangerous anyways and deadly; but so foul and filthy, so loathsome and ugly, that a man would have chosen rather to die any death, than to be so disfigured. But of them all, the worst and most detestable was that, which by a Greek name they called lichenes, and in Latin (because ordinarily it began about the chin) mentagra. A term given unto it (I assure you) at the first by way of jest and in a merriment (as commonly we see many are disposed to play and make good game at other men's miseries) but afterwards it went current in every man's mouth: and by no other name than mentagra was it known, notwithstanding the disease possessed not the chin alone, but in many that had it, took up the whole visage, all save the eyes, yea, and ran downwards to the neck and breast, spreading also to the arms and the very

hands: and in such sort was the skin of the poor wretches be-
painted and berayed with foul scurf and filthy scales, as it would
have pitied one at the heart to see them. This contagious disease,
our fathers and ancestors in times past never heard of, nor knew
when it meant: for the first time that ever it crept into Italy, was
in the days of *Tiberius Claudius* late Emperor of Rome, even
about the middle of his reign; and that was by the means of a
certain knight or gentleman of Rome born at Perusium, who
being secretary or clerk unto the treasurer under the Romans in
Asia, and giving attendance according to his place, chanced
there to be infected, and so he brought the disease over with
him to Rome. But will you hear the strange nature of this foul
evil? women were not subject unto it; no more were slaves,
base and poor commoners, no nor citizens of mean state and condition: the greatest gentlemen and those of the nobility, it made
choice of, and picked them from among the rest: very catching
it was, and soon passed from one to another, especially by the
mouth, and by the means of a kiss were it never so short: foul
and ill-favoured enough was the disease itself, but the scar,
remaining after it was healed (for many there were who came
under the chirurgians' hand and endured the cure) looked a
hundred times worse: and why? no way there was to rid it, but
by caustic medicines or potential cauteries, and unless the flesh
were eaten away to the very bones, it was not possible to kill
and root it out clean, but it would revive and spring again. And
verily there came physicians and chirurgians out of Egypt (a
country apt to breed the like diseases and where they be common) such as professed only the skill in this kind of cure, who
filled their purses well, and mightily enriched themselves by their
practice at Rome: for well known it is, that *Manilius Cornutus*
(late L. Praetor, and lieutenant general for the state in the
province of Guienne or Aquitane in France) dealt with one of
these Egyptian leeches for to be cured of this disease, and agreed
to pay him 200,000 sesterces for his pain. And thus much of
mentagra.

ELEPHANTIASIS

As touching the white leprosy, called elephantiasis (according as I have before shewed) it was not seen in Italy before the time of *Pompey* the Great. This disease also began for the most part in the face, and namely it took the nose first, where it put forth a little speck or pimple no bigger than a small lentil; but soon after, as it spread farther and ran over the whole body, a man should perceive the skin to be painted and spotted with divers and sundry colours, and the same uneven, bearing out higher in one place than another, thick here but thin there, and hard everywhere; rough also, like as if a scurf or scab overran it, until in the end it would grow to be blackish, bearing down the flesh flat to the bones, whiles the fingers of the hands, and toes of the feet were puffed up and swelled again. A peculiar malady is this and natural to the Aegyptians; but look when any of their kings fell into it, woe worth the subject and poor people : for then the tubs and bathing vessels wherein they sat in the bain, filled with men's blood for their cure. But surely this disease continued not long in Italy, before it was quite extinguished : like as another before it, in old time called Gemursa, which began between the toes : and so long ago it is since any have been troubled therewith, that the very name also is forgotten and grown out of use. Where by the way, this is to be noted as a strange and wonderful thing, that some of our diseases should have an end and lose their course for ever; and others again continue still : as for example, the colic passion; which came among us no longer ago than in the days of *Tiberius Caesar* the Emperor : and the first that ever felt it, was the prince himself; whereupon arose no small question throughout the whole city of Rome : for when as the said emperor published a certain proclamation, wherein he excused himself for not coming abroad to manage the affairs of the State, because he was sick of the colic; the Senate and people reading this strange name of an unknown malady, entered into a deep discourse with themselves, what to think and make of it? But what should we say of all these kind of diseases? and what an anger and displeasure of the gods this is, thus to plague and punish us? Was it not enough to have sent amongst men into the world a certain number of maladies otherwise, and those not so few as three hundred, but we must be in fear and danger still every day of new? And yet see! as many as there be of them coming by the hand of God, yet men through their own excess and disorders, bring as many more upon themselves, and be causes still of farther troubles and miseries.

A FASHIONABLE DOCTOR

What cunning means soever these new physicians could devise to overthrow the ancient manner of working by simples, yet it maintained still the remnants of the former credit, built surely upon the undoubted grounds of long experience; and so it continued until the days of *Pompey* the Great, at what time *Asclepiades* a great orator and professor of rhetoric went in hand to pervert and reject the same : for seeing that he gained not by the said art sufficiently, and was not like to arise by pleading causes at the bar, to that wealth which he desired (as he was a man otherwise of a prompt wit and quick spirit) he resolved to give over the law, and suddenly applied himself to a new course of physic. This man having no skill at all, and as little practice, considering he neither was well studied in the theoric part of this science, nor furnished with knowledge of remedies which required continual inspection and use of simples, wrought so with his smooth and flowing tongue and by his daily premeditat orations gained so much, that he withdrew men's minds from the opinion they had of former practice, and overthrew all. In which discourses of his, reducing all physic to the first and primitive causes, he made it a mere conjectural art; bearing men in hand, that there were but five principal remedies which served indifferently for all diseases; to wit, in diet, abstinence in meat, forbearing wine otherwhiles, rubbing of the body, and the exercise of gestations. In sum, so far he prevailed with his eloquent speech, that every man was willing to give ear & applause unto his words : for being ready enough to believe those things for true, which were most easy; and seeing withal, that whatsoever he commended unto them, was in each man's power to perform, he had the general voice of them : so a⸺ by this new doctrine of his, he drew all the world into a singular admiration of him, as of a man sent and descended from heaven above, to cure their griefs and maladies. Moreover, a wonderful dexterity and artificial grace he had to follow men's humours and content their appetites in promising and allowing the sick to drink wine, in giving them eftsoons cold water when he saw his time, and all to gratify his patients. Now for that *Herophylus* before him had the honour of being the first physician who searched into the causes of maladies : and because *Cleophantus* had the name among the ancients, for bringing wine into request and setting out the virtues thereof : this man for his part also, desirous to grow into credit and reputation by some new invention of his own, brought up first the allowing of cold water beforesaid, to sick persons; and (as *M. Varro* doth report) took pleasure to be called the Cold-water Physician. He had besides other pretty devices to flatter and please his patients, one while causing them to have hanging litters or beds like cradles, by the moving and rocking thereof to and fro, he might either bring them sleep, ar ease the pains of their sickness; otherwhiles ordaining the use of bains, a thing that he knew folk were most desirous of : besides many other fine conceits very plausible in hearing, and agreeable to man's nature. And to the end that no man might think this so great alteration and change in the practice of physic, to have been a blind course and a matter of small consequence, one thing above the rest that won himself a great fame, and gave no less credit and authority to his profession, was this, that meeting upon a time by chance with one he knew not, carried forth as a dead corpse in a bier for to be burned, he caused the body to be carried home from the funeral fire, and restored the man to health again. Certes this one thing, we that are Romans may be well ashamed of and take in great indignation, that such an odd fellow as he, coming out of Greece (the vainest nation under the sun) and beginning as he did of nothing, should only (for to enrich himself) lead the whole world in a string, and on a sudden set down rules and orders for the health of mankind, notwithstanding many that came after him, repealed as it were and annulled those laws of his. And verily, many helps had *Asclepiades*, which much favoured his opinion and new physic, namely, the manner of curing diseases in those days, which was exceeding rude, troublesome, and painful; such ado there was in lapping and covering the sick with a deal of clothes, and causing them to sweat by all means possible : such a work they made sometime in chafing and frying their bodies against a good fire, but every foot in bringing them abroad into the hot sun, which hardly could be found within a shady and close city as Rome was. In lieu whereof, not only there but throughout all Italy (which now commanded the whole world and might have what it list) he followed men's humours in approving the artificial bains and vaulted stoves and hot-houses, which then were newly come up and used excessively in every place by his approbation. Moreover, he found means to alter the painful curing of some maladies, and mainly of the squinancie; in the healing whereof, other physicians before him went to work with a certain instrument which they thrust down into the throat. He condemned also (and worthily) that dog-physic which was in those days so ordinary, that if one ailed never so little, by and by he must cast and vomit. He blamed also the use of purgative potions, as contrary and offensive to the stomach; wherein he had great reason and truth on his side : for to speak truly, such drinks are by most physicians forbidden, considering our chief care and drift is in all the course of our physic, to use those means which be comfortable and wholesome for the stomach.

* * * * *

Above all other things, the superst..ious vanities of magicians made much to the establishing of *Asclepiades* his new physic; for they in the height of their vanity, attributed so strange and incredible operations to some simples, that it was enough to discredit the virtues of them all. First, they vaunted much of aethiopus, an herb which (by their saying) if it were but cast into any great river or pool, it would draw the same dry; and was of power (by touching only) to open locks, or unbolt any door whatsoever. Of achoemenius also another herb, they made this boast, that being thrown against an army of enemies ranged in battle array, it would drive the troops and squadrons into fear, disorder their ranks, and put them to flight. Semblably, they gave out and said, that when the King of Persia dispatched his ambassadors to any foreign States and Princes, he was wont to give them an herb called latace, which so long as they had about them (come where they would) they should want nothing, but have plenty of all they desired : besides a number of such fooleries wherewith their books be pestered. But where, I beseech you, were these herbs when the Cimbrians and Teutons were defeated in a most cruel and terrible battle, so as they cried and yelled again? What became of these magicians and their powerful herbs, when *Lucullus* with a small army consisting of some few legions, overthrew and vanquished their own kings? If herbs were so mighty, what is the reason (I pray you) that our Roman captains provided evermore above all things how to be furnished with victuals for their camp, and to have all the ways and passages open for their purveyors? In the expedition of Pharsalia, how came it to pass that the soldiers were at the point to be famished for want of victual, if *Caesar* by the happy having of one herb in his camp, might have enjoyed the abundance of all things? Had it not been better (think ye) for *Scipio Aemilianus* to have caused the gates of Carthage to fly open with the help of one herb, than to lie so many years as he did in leaguer before the city, and with his engines and ordnance to shake their walls & batter their gates. Were there such virtue in Asthiopus aforesaid, why do we not at this day dry up the Pontine lakes, and recover so much good ground unto the territory of Rome? Moreover, if that composition which *Democritus* hath set down and his books maketh praise of, be so effectual, as to procure men to have fair, virtuous and fortunate children, how happeneth it that the kings of Persia themselves could never attain to that felicity? And verily we might marvel well enough at the credulity of our ancestors in doting so much upon these inventions (howsoever at the first they were devised and brought in, to right good purpose) in case the mind and wit of man knew how to stay and keep a mean in anything else besides : or if I could not prove (as I suppose to do in due place) that even this new leech-craft brought in by *Asclepiades* which checketh those vanities, is grown to farther abuses and absurdities than are broached by the very magicians themselves. But this hath been always and ever will be, the nature of man's mind, to exceed in the end and go beyond all measure in everything which at the beginning arose upon good respects and necessary occasions.

FOR A COUGH

Foalfoot, called in Greek bechion, that is to say in Latin tussilago, doth appease the violence of the cough. Two kinds there be of this herb: the wild, which wheresoever it is seen to grow, sheweth that there is water under it: a thing that they know well enough who seek for springs, for they take it to be an assured sign and direction to water: it beareth leaves like to ivy, but somewhat bigger, either five or seven in number, which underneath or toward the ground be somewhat whitish, but above in the upper side, of a pale colour, without flower, stem or seed, and the root is but small. Some would have it and Chamaeleuce both, to be one and the same herb called by divers names. Take this herb, leaf and root together when they be dried, set all on fire and receive the smoke by a pipe, as if you would suck or drink it down, it is (they say) a notable medicine to cure an old cough; but between every pipe you must sip a pretty draught of sweet wine.

THE BELLY

Touching the paunch or belly, much ado there is with it : and although most men care for nothing else in this life, but to content and please the belly, yet of all other parts it putteth them to most trouble: For one while it is so costive, as that it will give no passage to the meat; another while so slippery, as it will keep none of it: one time you shall have it so peevish, as that it can receive no food; and another time so weak and feeble, that it is able to make no good concoction of it. And verily nowadays the world is grown to that pass, that the mouth and paunch together are the chief means to work our death. The womb (I say) the wickedest vessel belonging to our bodies, is evermore urgent, like an importunate creditor, demanding debt, and oftentimes in a day calleth unto us for victuals : For the belly's sake especially we are so covetous to gather good; for the belly, we lay up so many dainties and superfluities; to content the belly, we stick not to sail as far as the river Phasis; and to please the belly, we seek and sound the bottom of the deep seas : and when all is done, no man ever thinketh how base and abject this part of the body is, considering that filthy odour and excrement which passeth from it in the end. No marvel then if physicians be much troubled about it, and be forced to devise the greatest number of medicines for the help and cure thereof.

INVISIBLE INK

It is commonly said, that with the milk or juice of these tithy-mals, a man may write upon the skin of the body : for draw any letters therewith and strew ashes or dust thereupon, when they be dry, they will appear very legible. And this is a trick practised by those that make court unto other men's wives their mistresses, delivering their minds secretly unto them by this means, which they dare not set down in paper or missive letters.

PONTIC WORMWOOD

And *Cato* affirmeth, that whosoever have the pontic worm-wood about them, shall not be galled between their legs.

FOR BILES AND BOTCHES

Panaces made into a cataplasm with honey, healeth the flat biles and botches that arise in the emunctories of the share : and the like effect hath plantain, applied with salt, five-leaf, and the root of the great clot-bur, like as in case of the king's evil : even so is damasonium to be used. As for taperwort or mullen, if leaf root and all be stamped, with some sprinkling of wine among, and be afterwards lapped within a leaf of the own, and so heat under the embers & laid to the grieved place hot, it is very good for the same purpose. And some affirm upon their own know-ledge, by the experience that they have seen, that this cataplasm will work much more effectually, if a young maiden all naked have the applying of it to the said bile; provided always, that both she and he the patient be fasting : also that she touch the sore or impostume with the back-side of her hand, and in so doing say these words following, *Negat Apollo pestem posse crescere quam nuda virgo restinguat* : that is to say, *Apollo* will never suffer, that a botch which a naked virgin thus cureth, shall possibly grow farther : which charm she must pronounce thrice, after she hath withdrawn her hand back; and withal, both he and she are to spit as often upon the floor, that is to say, every time that she repeateth the foresaid spell.

APHRODISIACS AND ANTAPHRODISIACS

Nymphaea, which also is named heraclea, if it be but once taken in drink, disableth a man altogether for the act of generation (as I have said before) forty days after: the same if a man drink fasting, or eat with his meat, freeth him from the dreams of imaginary *Venus*, which cause pollution. The root applied in a liniment to the genitoirs, doth not only cool lust, but also keep down and repress the abundance of natural seed: in which regard it is thought good to nourish the body and maintain a clear voice. On the contrary side, the upper root of glader given to drink in wine, kindleth the heat of lust: like as the herb which they call sampier savage: as also wild clary, being stamped and incorporat with parched barley meal. But in this case wonderful is the herb orchis both male and female, and few be like unto it, for two kinds there be of it: the one beareth leaves like unto the olive, but that they are longer, riseth up with a stem four fingers high, carrying purple flowers, a double bulbous root formed like to a man's genitoirs, whereof the one swelleth and the other falleth by turns each other year, and ordinarily it groweth near the seaside. The other is known by the name of Orchis Serapias, and is taken to be the female: the leaves resemble leek blades, the stalk is a span or hand-breadth high, and the flowers be purple; the root likewise is bulbous and twofold, fashioned like to a man's stones or cullions; of which, the bigger, or (as some say) the harder, drunk in water, provoketh the desire to venery: the lesser or the softer taken in goat's milk, represseth the foresaid appetite. Some say it is leafed after the manner of squilla or sea-onion, save that the leaves be smoother and smaller, and it putteth up a stalk full of pricks or thorns: the roots whereof, do heal the sores in the mouth, and discharge the chest of phlegm; but drunk in wine, do stop a lask. A power it hath also to stir up fleshly lust, like as satyrion; but this herb differeth from the other in that it is divided by joints or knots, and besides busheth more, and is fuller of branches: the root is thought to be good for sorcery and witchcraft: the same also, either by itself alone reduced into powder, or else stamped and incorporat with fried barley groats into a liniment, is singular good for the tumours and other risings and impostumes in the said privy parts or members of generation. The root of the former orchis given to drink in the milk of an ewe bred up at home of a cade lamb, causeth a man's members to rise and stand; but the same taken in water, maketh it to go down again and lie. As for the Greeks, they describe satyrion with leaves like unto the red lily, but that they be smaller, and no more in number than three, which spring directly from the root: the stem smooth, a cubit high, naked and bare without leaves, and it hath withal two bulbous roots; of which the nethermore, which also is the bigger, serveth to get boys; the upper (and that is the less) is good to engender girls. They have likewise another kind of satyrion, which they name erythraicon, and it beareth certain grains or seeds resembling that of chaste-tree, or Agnus Castus, but that they be bigger and smooth: the root is hard and white within, the rind whereof is red, and in taste is somewhat sweetish: an herb ordinarily found (as they say) upon mountains: and by their saying, the root is of that virtue, that if it be held only in a man's hand, it will cause the flesh to rise and incite him to the company of women; but much more will it set him in a heat if he drink it in some hard and green wine: in regard of which property, the manner is to give it in drink to goats and rams, if they be unlusty and nothing forward to leap the females. The Sarmatians likewise ministered a drench made with this herb unto their stone-horses or stallions, when by reason that they are overtravailed and tired out of heart by continual labour, they perceive them to be slow and unapt to cover mares, which defect the Greeks call by a proper and fit term prosedamon. But say that one by taking of this root is over lusty and too much provoked that way, the means to abate and quench that heat and strength thereof, is to drink mead or the juice of lettuce. In sum, the Greeks generally when they would signify an extraordinary wanton lust or appetite to venery, have a pretty name for it and call is satyrion. And even so they have given a demomination to crataeogonon, which is an herb divided by knots or joints, busheth and spreadeth with a number of branches, the seed whereof is hot, and the root of no validity or use in physic: likewise they imposed upon others the names of arrhenogonum and thelygonum, the seeds or grains of which resemble cods or cullions. Moreover, it is said, that whosoever have about them the marrow or pith of the tithymal branches, shall be very prone and forward to the sports of *Venus*. *Theophrastus*, a renowned author, and otherwise a grave and modest writer, exceedeth in this point, and telleth of strange and incredible wonders, and namely, of a man who was able to company with women seventy times together, by touching or handling one only herb; but he hath not put down either the name or portraiture of that herb.

FOR INSOMNIA

Among the maladies which affect and infest the whole body, want of sleep, or an indisposition thereto, is by most physicians counted one : For which defect, they shew us these herbs following, to wit, panaces, water betony, and aristolochia, which they prescribe unto the patients both for to smell to, and also to anoint his head all over withal. Likewise houseleek called aeizoon and also sedum, giving direction to wrap it within a black cloth, and so to lay it under the pillow or bolster of the sick person, but in no wise to let him or her know so much. Likewise oenothera, otherwise named onuris, is effectual for this purpose : an herb good also in wine to make the heart merry. It groweth with leaves resembling those of the almond tree, and beareth flowers like unto roses. Store of branches it putteth forth, and hath a long root, which being dried, scenteth much of wine. Of such virtue is this herb, that if it be given in drink to the wildest beast that is, it will tame the same and make it gentle.

FOR SHINGLES

Now of this disease which we term *S. Anthony's* fire there be many kinds, whereof there is one more dangerous than the rest, which is called zoster, for that it coveteth to go round about the middle of a man or woman in manner of a girdle; and in case both ends meet together indeed, it is deadly and incurable. To meet with it therefore by the way and to prevent this extremity, plaintain is thought to be a sovereign remedy, if it be incorporat with fuller's earth.

SOME FORMS OF BEAUTY-TREATMENT

The grape called bumastos, taketh away the hairs about the nipples of nurses' breasts, which spring sometime after they have once borne children: which also otherwise is very good to cleanse the scales, and scurf in the face, and to scour away other spots and pimples arising upon the skin. Gentia, and nymphaea called heraclea, the root also of cyclamen, riddeth all such cutanean specks and blemishes. The grains of wild caraways, called cacalia, incorporated in wax melted or made liquid, lay the skin of the face plain and even, and smooth all wrinkles. The root of acorum, serveth likewise to purify the skin from all outward deformities. Herb willow giveth the hair of the head a yellow colour. Hypericon, which also is named corion, dyeth it black: likewise doth ophrys, an herb growing with two leaves and no more, like unto jagged beets or coleworts. Also polemonia setteth a black colour upon hair, if it be boiled in oil. As for depilatory medicines, which are to take away the hair from any part, the proper place to treat of them is indeed among those that pertain especially to women: but nowadays men also are come to it, and use such devices as well as women. The most effectual of all others be they accepted, that are made of the herb archezostis. The juice of tithymal is likewise very good to fetch off hairs: and yet there be some, who plucked them out first with pincers, and then the said juice incorporat with oil, rub the place often in the hot sun.

THE SEVEN AND TWENTIETH BOOK

goeth forward to certain other herbs and other medicines

PREFACE

CERTES, THE farther that I proceed in this discourse and history of mine, the more am I forced to admire our fore-fathers and men of old time: for, considering, as I do, what a number of simples there yet remain behind to be written of, I cannot sufficiently adore either their careful industry, in searching and finding them out; or their liberal bounty, in imparting them so friendly to posterity. And verily, if this knowledge of herbs had proceeded from man's invention, doubtless I must needs have thought, that the munificence of those our ancestors had surpassed the goodness of Nature herself. But now apparent and well known it is, that the gods were authors of that skill and cunning, or at leastwise there was some divinity and heavenly instinct therein, even when it seemed to come from the brain and head of man: and to say a truth, confess we must, that Nature, (the mother and nurse of all things) both in bringing forth these simples, and also in revealing them with their virtues to mankind, hath shewed her admirable power as much as in any other work of hers whatsoever. The herb scythica is brought hither at this day out of the great fens and meres of Mœotis, where it groweth: euphorbia cometh from the mountain Atlas, far beyond *Hercules'* pillars and the straits of Gibraltar, and those are the very utmost bounds of the earth: From another coast also, the herb brittannica we have, transported unto us out of Britain, and the islands lying without the continent, and divided from the rest of the world; like as Aethiopis out as far as Aethiopia, a climate directly under the sun, and burnt with continual heat thereof: Besides other plants and drugs necessary for the life and health of men, for which merchants pass from all parts to and fro, and by reciprocal commerce, impart them to the whole world; and all by the means of that happy peace which (through the infinite majesty of the Roman Empire) the earth enjoyeth: in such sort, as not only people of sundry lands and nations have recourse one unto another in their traffic and mutual trade, but high mountains also and the cliffs surpassing the very clouds, meet as it were together, and have means to communicate the commodities, even the very herbs which they yield, one to the benefit of another: Long may this blessing hold, I pray the gods, yea and continue world without end: for surely it is their heavenly gifts, that the Romans as a second sun should give light and shine to the whole world.

ACONITE

Aconite alone, if there were nothing else, is sufficient to induce any man to an endless admiration and reverence of that infinite care and diligence which our ancients employed in searching out the secrets of Nature; considering how by their means we know there is no poison in the world so quick in operation as it, insomuch as if the shap or nature of any living creature of female sex be touched therewith, it will not live after it one day to an end. This was that poison wherewith *Calphurnius Bestia* killed two of his wives lying asleep by his side, as appeareth by that challenge and declaration which *M. Cæcilius* his accuser framed against him. And hereupon it was, that in the end of his accusatory invective, he concluded with this bitter speech, that his wives died upon his finger. The poets have feigned a tale, that this herb should be engendered first, of the foam that the dog *Cerberus* let fall upon the ground, frothing so as he did at the mouth for anger when *Hercules* plucked him out of hell: and therefore it is forsooth, that about Heraclea in Pontus (where is to be seen that hole which leadeth into hell) there groweth aconite in great plenty. Howbeit, as deadly a bane as it is, our forefathers have devised means to use it for good, and even to

save the life of man : found they have by experience, that being
given in hot wine, it is a counterpoison against a sting of scorpions : for of this nature it is, that if it meet not with some
poison or other in men's bodies for to kill, it presently setteth
upon them and soon brings them to their end : But if it encounter
any such, it wrestleth with it alone, as having found within, a
fit match to deal with : neither entereth it into this fight, unless
it find this enemy possessed already of some noble and principal
part of the body; and then beginneth the combat : a wonderful
thing to observe, that two poisons, both of them deadly of themselves and their own nature, should die one upon another within
the body; and the man by that means only escape with life.
Our ancestors in time past, stayed not thus, but found out and
delivered unto us proper remedies also for wild beasts, and not
so contented, have shewed means how those creatures should be
healed which are venomous unto other : for who knoweth not,
that scorpions if they be but touched with aconite, presently
become pale, benumbed, astonied, and bound, confessing (as it
were) themselves to be vanquished and prisoners : contrariwise,
let them but touch the white hellebore, they are unbound and at
liberty again; they recover (I say) their former vigour and
virtue : whereby we may see, that the aconite also giveth the
bucklers to enemies twain, pernicious poisons both; the one, to
itself, and the other to all the world. Now if haply any man
should say, that the wit and head of man alone could possibly
compass the knowledge of these things; surely he should show
therein his ingratitude and impiety unto the gods, in not
acknowledging their beneficence. The people about Heraclea, for
to kill the panthers which breed in those parts, use to rub with
aconite certain gobbets of flesh, which they do lay about the
mountains as a bait and bane for them : and unless by this
means they did destroy them, no doubt they would fill the whole
country; which is the cause that some call it pardalianches, i.e.
libard bane. But they again on the other side, presently have
recourse to the excrements of a man, as I have before declared,
the only counterpoison whereby they save themselves. Who
doubteth now, but the knowledge of this secret came first to
them by mere chance ? and considering that it is not possible to
render a reason of the nature and usage of such wild beasts (and

whensoever we see the like to fall out, we count it still a new and strange accident) we must needs attribute the finding out thereof, to Fortune.

ANONYMOS

Anonymos, finding no name to be called by, got thereupon the name anonymos. A plant this is brought out of Scythia unto us; highly commended by *Hicesius* a physician of great name and authority, also by *Aristogiton*, for an excellent vulnerary, if it be bruised or stamped in water and so applied: but taken inwardly in drink, it is good for women's breasts and the precordial parts about the heart, if they have gotten a stripe, or be bruised: also for such as reach up blood. Some have ordained a vulnerary drink to be made thereof for those that be wounded. But what is said moreover as touching this herb, I hold mere fabulous: and namely, that if two pieces of iron or brass be put into the fire and burn together with this herb, fresh and new gathered, they will souder and join again.

TO PREVENT SEA-SICKNESS

Let a man or woman use to drink wormwood, they shall be not be sea-sick nor given to heaving, as commonly they be that are at sea.

NOT WORTH MENTIONING

Catanance is a mere Thessalian herb, and growing nowhere else but in Thessaly; and for as much as it is used only in amatorious matters, and for to spice love drinks withal, I mean not to busy myself in the description thereof: howbeit, thus much it would not be amiss to note, for to detect and lay open the folly and vanities of magicians, namely, that they went by this conjecture only, that it should be of power to win the love of women, because forsooth when it is withered, it draweth itself inward like a dead kite's foot. For the same reason also, I will hold my tongue and say never a word of the herb cemos.

A REMARKABLE RECOVERY

Concerning the fresh water sponge (for so I may more truly term it, than either moss or herb, so thick of shag hairs it is and fistulous withal) it groweth ordinarily within the rivers that issue from the foot of the Alps, and is named in Latin conferva, for that it is so good to conglutinate, in manner of a souder. Certes, I myself knew a poor labourer, who as he was lopping of a tall tree, fell from the top down to the ground, and was so piteously bruised thereby, that unneth he had any sound bone in all his body that was unbroken: and in very truth, lapped he was all over with this moss or sponge (call it whether you will) and the same was kept evermore moist and wet with sprinkling his own water upon it, whensoever it began to dry upon him with the heat of his body: seldom was it undone or removed, and never but when of necessity for very change fresh was laid to for default of the other: and by this manner of cure and no other, the poor wretch recovered perfectly, in so small a time, that it was wonderful and almost incredible.

PEONY

Of peony there be two kinds: the female is that thought to be, to the root whereof there stick eight long bulbs commonly, or six at least: the male hath more of them hanging to it, by reason it standeth not upon one single and entire root only, but of many, and those run down a span deep, and be white withal. These roots are found to be astringent and stypic at the tongue's end. As for the female, the leaves thereof do scent of myrrh, and grow somewhat thicker than those of the male. They love both, to grow in woods. It is commonly said, that the roots must be digged up in the night season, for fear that the wood speight or hickway should see them: for in the daytime the said bird would fly in their faces that carry it away, and be ready to job out their eyes. In the very drawing also of those roots out of the ground, there is some danger, least their fundament or tiwill fall out of their bodies who are employed about that business. But I suppose all this to be but a fabulous and vain invention, devised only to make folk believe it is an herb of wonderful operation.

A WONDERFUL PLANT

But of all herbs that be, there is none more wonderful than greimile: some call it in Greek lithospermon, others aegonychon, some diospyron, and others heracleos. It groweth ordinarily five inches high: and the leaves be twice as big as those of rue. The foresaid stalks or stems be no thicker than bents or rushes, and the same garnished with small and slender branches. It bringeth forth close joining to the leaves, certain little beards one by one, and in the top of them little stones white and round in manner of pearls, as big as chick peas, but as hard as very stones. Toward that side where they hang to their steles or tails, they have certain holes or concavities containing seed within. This herb groweth in Italy: but the best in the islands Candie. And verily of all the plants that ever I saw, I never wondered at any more: so sightly it groweth, as if some artificial goldsmith had set in an alternative course & order, these pretty beads like orient pearls among the leaves: and so rare a thing it is and difficult to be conceived, that a very hard stone should grow out of an herb. The herbarists who have written thereof, do say that it lieth along and creepeth by the ground: for mine own part, I never saw it growing in the plant: but shewed it was unto me plucked out of the ground. This is for certain known, that these little stones called gremil seed, drunk to the weight of one dram in white wine, break the stone, expel the same by gravel, and dispatch those causes that be occasions of strangury. Certes, a man no sooner seeth this herb, but he may presently know the virtues thereof, and for what it serveth in physic; a thing that he shall not observe again in any other whatsoever: for at the very first sight of those little stones, his eyes will tell him what it is good for, without information from any person at all.

A HOBGOBLIN-REPELLENT

There is an herb, which in Latin is named natrix, the root whereof being pulled out of the ground, hath a rank smell like unto a goat; with this herb they use in the Picene country to drive away those hobgoblins which they have a marvellous opinion to be spirits, called Fatui: for mine own part, I am verily persuaded they be nothing else but fantastical illusions of such as be troubled in mind and bestraught, the which may be chased and rid away by the use of this medicinable herb.

PHYTEUMA

As for phyteuma, somewhat else I have to do rather than to describe it, considering there is no use of it but in amatorious medicines to procure women's love.

TRACHINIA

As for trachinia, I find not in any writer what manner of herb it should be : and verily, I cannot believe that *Democritus* reporteth truly of it as he doth; for monstrous it is and incredible which he promiseth of it, namely, that in three days it will waste the spleen, if the patient do but wear it tied to any part of the body.

A DIVINE MYSTERY

Also there is no small difference to be considered between nation and nation : for, as I have heard them say who are of good credit, as touching worms and such like vermin, the people of Egypt, Arabia, Syria, and Cilicia, be troubled and infested with them : whereas contrariwise, some Grecians and Phrygians have none at all breeding among them. But less marvel there is of that, considering how among the Thebans and Boeotians (who confine upon Attica) such vermin is rife and common; and yet the Athenians are not given at all to engender and breed them : the speculation whereof, carrieth me away again unto a new discourse of living creatures, and their natures; and namely, to fetch from thence the medicines which Nature hath imprinted in them, of greater proof and certainty than any other for the remedy of all diseases. Certes, this great Mother of all things, intended not that any living creature should serve either to seed itself only, or to be food for to satisfy others; but her will was and she thought it good, to insert and engraff in their inward bowels, wholesome medicines for man's health, to counterpoise

R

those medicinable virtues which she had engraven and bestowed upon those surd and senseless herbs : nay her providence was such, that the sovereign and excellent means for maintenance of our life, should be had from those creatures which are endued with life : the contemplation of which divine mystery, surpasseth all others, and is most admirable.

THE EIGHT AND TWENTIETH BOOK

setteth down certain receipts of remedies in physic,
drawn from out of man and other bigger creatures

PREFACE

HAVING DISCOVERED as well all those things which are engendered between heaven and earth, as also their natures; there
remained nothing for me to discourse of, save only the minerals
digged out of the ground : but that this late treatise of mine, as
touching the medicinable properties of herbs, trees, and other
plants, draweth me quite aside from my purpose, and haleth
me back again, to consider the foresaid living creatures themselves (even the subject matter of physic) in regard of greater
means found out even in them, to advance physic and cure
diseases. For, to say a truth, since I have described and portrayed both herbs & flowers, since I have discovered many other
things, rare and difficult to be found out; should I conceal such
means for the health of man, as are to be found in man himself?
or should I suppress other kind of remedies which are to be had
from creatures living amongst us, as we do, if they may benefit
us? especially seeing that our very life is no better than torment
and misery, unless we be free from pain and sickness? No verily;
and far be it from me that I should do so. But on the contrary
side, I will do my best endeavour to perform and finish this task
also, how long and tedious soever it may seem to be : for my
full intent and resolution is, so I may benefit posterity and do
good to the common life of man, the less to respect the pleasing
of fine ears, or to expect thanks from any person. And to bring
this my purpose about, I mean to search into the customs of

foreign countries, yea and to lay abroad the rites and fashions of barbarous nations, referring the readers who shall make scruple to believe my words, unto those authors whom I allege for my warrant. And yet herein, this care I have ever had, to make choice in my reports of such things as have been held and in manner adjudged true, by a general consent and approbation of all writers; as coveting to stand more upon the choice substance, than the variety and plenty of matter.

REMEDIES IN THE HUMAN BODY

Begin then I will at man himself, to see what physic there may be found in him to help his neighbour. In which first entrance of mine, there presenteth itself unto mine eye, one object that troubleth and offendeth my mind exceeding much: For nowadays you shall see them that are subject to the falling evil, for to drink the very blood of fencers and sword-players as out of living cups: a thing, that when we behold within the same show-place, even the tigers, lions, and other wild beasts to do, we have it in horror as a most fearful and odious spectacle. And these monstrous minded persons are of opinion, that the said blood forsooth is most effectual for the cure of that disease, if they may suck it breathing warm out of the man himself; if they may set their mouth (I say) close to the vein, to draw thereby the very heart blood, life and all: how unnatural soever otherwise it be holden for a man to put his lips so much as to the wounds of wild beasts, for to drink their blood. Nay, there be others that lay for the marrow-bones, the very brain also of young infants, and never make strange to find some good meat and medicine therein. Ye shall find moreover among the Greek writers not a few, who have deciphered distinctly the several tastes as well of every inward part, as outward member of a man's body; and so near they have gone, that they left not out the paring of the very nails, but they could pick out of them some fine physic: as if health consisted in this, that a man should become as bloody as a savage beast; or that he counted a remedy, which indeed is cause of a mischief and malady. And well deserve such blood-suckers and cruel leeches to be frustrat of their cure, and thereby to work their own bane and destruction:

for if it be held unlawful and abominable to pry and look into the entrails and bowels of a man's body, what is it then to chew and eat them? But what monster was he, who first broached this gear, and devised such accursed drugs! Ah wicked wretch, the inventor and artificer of these monstrosities; thou that hast overthrown all law of humanity; for with thee will I have to do, against thee will I whet my tongue and turn the edge of my style, who first didst bring up this brutish leechcraft, for no other purpose but to be spoken of another day, and that the world might never forget thy wicked inventions. What direction had he who thus began to devour man's body limb by limb? nay, what conjecture or guess moved him so to do? what might the original and foundation be, whereupon this devilish physic was grounded? what should he be that bare man in hand, and would persuade the world, that the thing which is used as a poison in witchcraft and sorcery, should avail more to the health of man, than other known and approved remedies? Set case that some barbarous people used so to do: say that strange nations and far removed from all civility, had these manners among them, must the Greeks take up those fashions also, yea & credit them so much as to reduce them into a method, among other their goodly arts? And yet see what *Democritus* one of them hath done: there be extant at this day books of his inditing and penning, wherein you shall read, that the skull of a wicked malefactor, is in some cases better than that of an honest person; and in other, that of a friend and guest, preferred before a stranger. As for *Apollonius*, another of that brood, he hath written, that if the gums be scarified with the tooth of a man violently slain, it is a most effectual and present remedy for the toothache. *Artemon* had no better receipt for the falling sickness, than to draw up water out of a fountain in the night season, and to give the same unto the patient to drink in the brain-pan of a man who died some violent death, so he were not burnt. And *Antheus* took the skull of one that had been hanged, and made pills thereof, which he ministered unto those who were bitten by a mad dog, for a sovereign remedy. Moreover, these writers not content to use these sorceries about men, employed the medicines also of the parts of man to the cure of four-footed beasts; and namely, if kine or oxen were dew-blown or otherwise puffed up.

they were wont to bore holes through their horns, and so to inlay or interlard them (as it were) with men's bones: finally, when swine were diseased, they took the fine white wheat siligo, being permitted to lie one whole night in the very place where some men were killed or burnt, and gave it them to eat. As for me, and all us that are Latin writers, God forbid we should defile our papers with such filthiness: Our intention is to put down in writing, those good and wholesome medicines which man may afford unto man, and not to set abroad any such detestable and heinous sorceries: As for example, to show what medicinable virtue there may be in breast-milk of women newly delivered; what healthful operation there is in our (fasting) spittel; or what the touching of a man or woman's body may avail in the cure of any malady; and many other semblable things arising from natural causes. For mine own part verily, I am of this mind, that we ought not so much to make of our health or life, as to maintain and preserve the same by any indirect course and unlawful means: And thou, whosoever thou be, that doeth addict thyself to such villianies whiles thou livest, shall die in the end a death answerable to thy beastly and execrable life. To conclude therefore, let every man for to comfort his heart, and to cure the maladies of his mind, set this principle before his eyes, that of all those good gifts which nature hath bestowed upon man, there is none better than to die in a fit and seasonable time: And in so doing, this is simply the best, that in his power it is, and the means he hath, to choose what death he list.

THE POWER OF WORDS

The first point, concerning the remedies medicinable drawn from out of man, which moveth the greatest question, and the same as yet not decided and resolved, is this, whether bare words, charms, and enchantments, be of any power or no? If it be granted yea, then no doubt ought we to ascribe that virtue unto man. But the wisest philosophers and greatest doctors, take them one by one, doubt thereof, and give no credit at all thereto. And yet go by the common voice of the whole world, you shall find it a general belief, and a blind opinion always received, whereof there is no reason or certain experience to ground upon. For first

and foremost we see, that if any beast be killed for sacrifice
without a set form of prayer, it is to no purpose, and held unlawful: semblably, if these invocations be omitted, when as men
seek to any oracles, and would be directed in the will of gods by
beasts' bowels or otherwise, all booteth not, but the gods seem
displeased thereby. Moreover, the words used in craving, to
obtain anything at their hands, run in one form; and the
exorcisms in diverting their ire, and turning away some imminent
plagues, are framed after another sort: also there be proper
terms serving for meditation only and contemplation. Nay, we
have seen and observed, how men have come to make suit and
tender petitions to the sovereign and highest magistrates, with a
preamble of certain set prayers. Certes, so strict and precise men
are in this point about divine service, that for fear lest some
words should be either left out, or pronounced out of order,
there is one appointed of purpose as a prompter to read the
same before the priest, out of a written book, that he miss not in
a tittle; another also set near at his elbow, as a keeper to observe
and mark, that he fail not in any ceremony or circumstance; and
a third ordained to go before and make silence, saying thus to
the whole assembly and congregation, *Favete linguis* (i.e. spare
your tongues and be silent:) and then the flutes and haut-boys
begin to sound and play, to the end that no other thing be heard
for to trouble his mind or interrupt him the while. And verily,
there have been memorable examples known of strange accidents
ensuing both ways, namely, as often as either the unlucky fowls
by their untoward noise have disturbed and done hurt, or if
at any time there have been error committed in the prescript
prayer & exorcism: for by this means it falleth out oftentimes,
that all on a sudden as the beast standeth there in place to be
sacrificed, the master vein in the liver, named the head thereof,
is found missing among other entrails, and the heart likewise
wanting: or contrariwise, both these to be double and appear
twain for one. And even at this day there remaineth a most
notable precedent and example to all posterity, in that prescript
form of exorcism, whereby the two *Decii*, both the father and
son, betook themselves to all the hellish furies and fiends infernal: Moreover, the imprecation of the vestal Nun *Tuccia*
when she was put to prove her virginity, continueth extant upon

record; by virtue of which charm she carried water in a sieve without shedding one drop: which happened in the year after the foundation of Rome city 609. And verily, no longer ago than of late time in our own age, we saw two Grecians, to wit a man and a woman, yea, and some of other nations, with whom in those days we maintained wars, buried quick within the beast market in Rome: in which manner of sacrifice, whosever readeth the prayer or exorcism that is used, and which the Warden or principal of the College of the Quindecemvirs is wont to read & pronounce to the exorcist; he would no doubt confess, that such charms and execrations be of great importance: and namely, seeing they have been all approved and found effectual by the experience and events observed for the space of eight hundred and thirty years. As for our vestal virgins in these our days, we are certainly persuaded and believe, that by the virtue of certain spells and charms which they have, they be able to arrest and stay any fugitive slaves for running one foot farther, provided always, that they be not gone already without the pourprise and precinct of the city walls. Now if this be received once as an undoubted and confessed truth, and if we admit that the gods do hear some prayers, or be moved by any words; then surely we may resolve at once of these conjectures, and conclude affirmatively of the main question.

*   *   *   *   *

I assure you many folk there be of this belief, that by certain spells and words, in manner of charms, all the pots and vessels of earth baking in a furnace, may be cracked and broken, without touching them at all. And there are not a few who are persuaded for certain, that even the very serpents as they may be burst by enchantment, so they can unwitch themselves: and that as brutish otherwise and earthly as they be, yet in this one thing they have a quick sense and understanding, insomuch, as at the charms of the Marsians they will shrink from them and draw in their bodies round into a knot, though it were in the night season when they lie asleep. Some there be also that when a scarefire hath taken an house, write certain words upon the walls, and thereby limit and confine the fire, that it shall go no farther. Certes, I am not able to say, whether strange, foreign, and ineffable words hard to be pronounced, are more available to the effecting of these incredible things, or our Latin words, coming out at a venture unlooked for and spoken at random : which must needs seem ridiculous in our judgement, seeing that the spirit and mind of man, expecteth always some great and mighty matter in these conjurations and exorcisms, which may carry a majesty therewith to incline and move the gods to mercy and favour, or rather indeed to command their heavenly power perforce. But to proceed, *Homer* the poet hath written, that prince *Vlyxes* being wounded in the thigh, staunched the blood with a charm. And *Theophrastus* testifieth, that there be proper spells to cure the sciatica. *Cato* hath left in writing, that there is a special charm for dislocations, whereby any bone put out of joint may be set again. And *M. Varro* reporteth the like virtue of certain good words for the gout. As for *Caesar* the Dictator, it is commonly said of him, that having been once endangered with the fall or overthrow of his coach wherein he rode, would never afterwards ride in coach again, unless so soon as ever he had taken his place, and before that he set forward upon his way, he had pronounced a certain charm that he had in store : and persuaded he was, that if he said it over three times together, he should come by no mischance in his journey, but travel in security. A thing that I know many nowadays to practise ordinarily as well as he.

*   *   *   *   *

What moveth us to wish health and say, God help, or bless, when one sneezeth? for even *Tiberius Caesar*, who otherwise was known for a grim sir, and the most unsociable and melancholy man in the world, required in that manner to be salved and wished well unto, whenever he sneezed, though he were mounted in his chariot. And some there be who in this case ceremoniously do salute the party by name, and think there is a great point of religion lies in that. Moreover, is not this an opinion generally received, that when our ears do glow and tingle, some there be that in our absence do talk of us? *Attalus* avoucheth for a certainty, that if a man chance to espy a scorpion, and do no more but say this one word Duo, the serpent will be still and quiet, and never shoot forth his sting.

SUPERSTITIONS AT MEALS

Servius Sulpitius a principal person of our city, hath written a treatise of this argument, where he giveth a reason why we should not leave or shift our trenchers at every course or change of dishes; for in those days there were no more allowed than there sat guests at the tables, and those were served but once for all. If one chance to sneeze after repast, the order is to call for a dish of meat and a trencher again to be set upon the board : and in case he taste not of somewhat afterward, it is thought a most fearful and cursed presage on his behalf : like as to sit at the table and eat nothing at all. See how ceremonious those men were, and what precise ordinances they instituted, who were of belief, that in all our affairs and actions, and at all times, the divine power of God was present : and that by these means they left them pacified for all our sins and vices. Neither is there an end here : for over and besides it hath been marked, that many times all the table is hushed, and there is not a word heard from one end to the other : but this is noted never to happen but when the guests make a just even number. But what does this silence presage? Surely, everyone of them shall be in danger to lose or impair his credit, good name, and reputation. Moreover, if a piece of meat chanced to fall out of the hand down to the floor, it was taken up and delivered upon the board again, where it passed from one to another, and went through the table : but in anywise they were forbidden to blow thereupon, for a cleanse it from the dust or filth that it caught.

SNAKE-REPELLERS

In my former treatise as touching strange and wonderful nations, I spake of certain races of men which were of a monstrous nature, and carried a venomous regard and look in their very eyes : besides many other properties of beasts, which here to repeat were needless. Howbeit, in this place I think it not amiss to note, that some people there be whose bodies be from top to toe all medicinable and wholesome unto others. As for example, the men of those families which do terrify serpents, and drive them away with their very presence : who also are of this nature, that they be able to cure and ease such as are stung already either by touching only, or else by a medicinable sucking of the place : Of which kind are the Psylli and Marsi : those also in the island Cyprus, whom they call Ophugenes : and of this race and house there came an ambassador out of the said island, whose name was *Exagon*, who by the commandment of the Consuls was put into a great tun or pipe wherein were many serpents, for to make an experiment and trial of the truth : And in very deed the said serpents licked his body in all parts gently with their tongues, as if they had been little dogs, to the great wonder of them who beheld the manner of it. A man shall know those of this family (if any of them remain at this day) by this sign, that they breathe a strong and stinking scent from them, especially in the spring season. Now, these people beforenamed had not only a gift to cure folk with their spittle, but their very sweat also had a medicinable virtue against the sting of serpents. For as touching those men who are born and bred in Tentyrus (an island lying within the river Nilus) so terrible they be unto the crocodiles, that they will not abide so much as their voice, but fly from them so soon as they hear it. Moreover, it is known for certain, that all the sort of these people, who have their bodies thus privileged by that secret antipathy in nature between them & serpents, are able to ease those who are stung, if they do but come in place where they be : like as a wound will be more angry and sore, if they come near who at any time before have been hurt by sting of serpent or tooth of mad dog : such also carry about with them in their bodies so venomous a quality, that their only presence is enough to mar the eggs that a brood-hen sits upon, and make them all addle, yea, and to drive ewes and other cattle to cast their young before the time : such a virulent property remaineth still behind in their bodies which have been once stung and bitten, that notwithstanding they be cured thereof, yet venomous they are now and hurtful to others, who beforetime were poisoned themselves. But the only way to remedy this inconvenience, is to cause them to wash their hands before they enter into the room where the patients lie, and with the same water to besprinkle and wash them who are to be cured. Again, this is to be observed, that whosoever at any time have been pricked with a scorpion, shall never afterwards be stung by hornets, wasps, or bees. A strange thing this is no doubt, howbeit, no great wonder to them who know, that a garment or cloth which had been used at funerals, will never be afterwards moth-eaten : and how that serpents hardly can be plucked out of their holes, unless it be by the left hand.

FORTUNE-TELLING AND MAGIC

The inventions of *Pithagoras* as touching numbers, bear a great stroke in these matters, and lightly miss not : but principally in this, that the said philosopher would give judgement by the vowels contained in the proper name of any person, concerning their fortunes : For in case the vowels were in number odd, he pronounced, that if the party ever proved lame of a limb, lost an eye, or met with any such like accidents, the same should happen upon the right side of the body : but contrariwise, if the number of vowels were even, then these infirmities should befall the left side. Furthermore, it is commonly said, that if one take a stone, dart, or instrument of shot, wherewith a man hath killed these three living creatures, a man, a wild boar, and a bear, one after another, and that with one single stroke to every one of them; and fling the same clean over an house where there is a woman in hard travail of childbirth, so as it light on the other side without touching any part thereof, the woman shall presently be delivered. More reason there is that a light javelin or pertuisane should do this feat, which had been drawn forth of a man's body, so as it never touched the ground after : for do but bring this murdering javelin into the place where a woman is in labour, it willl forthwith procure her deliverance. *Orpheus* and *Archelaus* do write much after the same manner of arrows pulled out of men's bodies, namely, that if care be had that they touch not the earth, and then be laid under the bed where man or woman lieth, they will cause the parties to be enamoured upon them that bestowed the said arrows there. And these authors report moreover, that the venison of any wild beast killed with the same weapon which was the death of a man before, is singular for to cure the falling sickness.

THE POWER OF SALIVA

As touching the fasting spittle especially of man or woman, I have shewed already how it is a sovereign preservative against the poison of serpents. But that is not all: for in many other cases it is found by daily experience to be of great operation, and to work effectually. For first and foremost, if we see any surprised with the falling sickness, we spit upon them, and by that means we are persuaded, that we ourselves avoid the contagion of the said disease. *Item,* an ordinary thing it is with us to put by the danger of witchcraft, by spitting in the eyes of a witch: so do we also, when we meet with one that limpeth and is lame of the right leg. Likewise when we crave pardon of the gods for some audacious and presumptuous prayers that we make, we used to spit even into our own bosoms. Semblably, for to fortify the operation of any medicines, the manner is to pronounce withal a charm or exorcism three times over, and to spit upon the ground as often; and so we doubt not but it will do the cure and not fail. Also when we perceive a felon or such like uncom sore a-breeding, the first thing that we do, is to mark it three times with our fasting spittle. I will tell you of a strange effect, and whereof it is no hard matter ywis to make the trial. If one man hurt another, either by reaching him a blow near at hand, or by letting fly somewhat at him farther off, and repent him when he hath so done; let him presently spit just in the middle of the palm of that hand which gave the stroke, the party immediately that was smitten, shall be eased from pain, and take no harm thereby. And verily we find this to be so, by experiments often-times made upon the bodies of four-footed beasts: for let them be swayed in the back, or hipped by some stripe given them with a stone or cudgel, do no more than but spit into that hand which did the deed, and straightways they will go upright again upon all four. Contrariwise, some there be, who before they either strike or discharge anything from them against another, after the same manner first spit into the ball of their hands, & so they make account to do a great displeasure, and to hurt more dangerously. But this we may assure ourselves, that there is not a better thing in the world for to kill tettars, ringworms, and the foul leprosy, than to rub and wet them continually with our own fasting spittle : likewise to anoint therewith every morning our eyes, keepeth them from being bleared. Also cancerous sores are cured with the root of sowbread, which we call the earth apple, if the same be wrought into a salve with our fasting spittle. Moreover, if a man have a crick and ache in the nape of his neck, let him take the spittle of a man that is fasting, some in his right hand, and therewith anoint the ham of his right leg; and the rest with his left, and do the like to the left leg; and thereupon he shall find ease. If an earwig or such like vermin be gotten into the ear, make no more ado but spit upon the same, and it will come forth anon. Among countercharms and preservatives against sorcery, these be reckoned; namely, that a man spit upon his own urine as soon as he hath delivered it out of his body : likewise to spit into the shoe that serveth his right foot, before he put it on in a morning : also whensoever he goeth over or pass by a place where sometime he was in danger, to remember that he spit upon it. *Marcion* of Smyrna, who wrote a treatise of the virtues and effects of simples, reporteth, that the scolopendras of the sea will burst in sunder if one spit upon them : and so will hedge toads and other venomous frogs. *Ophilius* writeth, that spittle will do the like by serpents, if one spit into their mouths as they gape. As for the learned *Salpe*, she saith, that if one perceive any member or part of the body be asleep and benumbed, there is not a better thing to recover the sense thereof, than to spit into the bosom, or to touch the upper eyelids with fasting spittle. Now if we believe these things to be true, we may as well give credit to all that which followeth.

VARIOUS MEDICINES DERIVED FROM THE HUMAN BODY

Over and besides, the tooth of a man, especially when he is mad, is reckoned to be as dangerous and pernicious a biting as any other. The excrement found in a man's ears, called ear-wax, is thought in this case to be sovereign : and let no man marvel thereof, considering how it will heal the sting of scorpions and serpents also, if it be applied to the place presently : but it is better and more effectual, if it be taken out of the patient's own ears, who is thus wounded : and in that sort it healeth also the whitlows and impostumations that breed about the nail roots.

Moreover, take a man's or woman's tooth, and stamp it into powder, it is thought good for the sting of serpents. The hair of young boy-children which is first clipped off, is held to be a singular remedy for to assuage the painful fits of the gout, if the same be tied fast about the foot that is grieved: and generally their hair, so long as they be under fourteen years of age, easeth the said anguish, if it be applied unto the place. Likewise, the hair of a man's head cureth the biting of a mad dog, if it be laid to the place with vinegar: it healeth also the wounds in the head, applied with oil or wine. But if it were plucked from his head whiles he hangeth upon the gallows, then it is sovereign for the quartan ague: but we may choose whether we believe it or no. Certainly the hair of the head burnt to ashes, is known to be very good for a cancerous ulcer. If a woman take the first tooth that a young child cast, set it in a bracelet, and so wear it continually about her wrist, it will preserve her from the pains and grievances of her matrice & natural parts. Tie the great toe and that which is next unto it together, you shall see how it will allay any risings and tumours in the share. Bind gently the two middle fingers of the right hand, with a linen thread, mark of what force this remedy is to repress the rheum falling into the eyes, and how it will keep them from being bleared. If all be true that is commonly said, the stone that one hath voided and thrust out of the body, easeth all others that be pained with the stone, if the same be kept tied fast to the share: also it doth mitigate the grief of the liver; and procureth speedy deliverance to women in travail with child. *Franius* affirmeth moreover, that in all these cases it would do the better, if one were cut for it, and that it were taken forth of the bladder by way of incision. If a woman be near her time and looks every day to fall to labour and cry out, let the man come by whom she is with child, and after he hath ungirt himself, gird her about the middle with his own girdle, and unloose the same again, saying withal this charm, *I tied the knot, and I will undo it again,* and therewith go his ways, she shall soon after fall to her business and have more speedy deliverance.

*   *   *   *   *

Many maladies there be, that go away the first time that either a man hath carnal knowledge of a woman, or that a maiden seeth her monthly sickness: but if they end not at such a time, commonly they prove chronic diseases and continue a long time, and especially the falling sickness. It is said, moreover, that the company of a woman easeth them very much who are stung with a scorpion: but women in the same case catch harm by that means. Some say also, that if the eyes be dipped three times in that water wherein a man or woman hath washed their feet, they shall be troubled neither with blearedness nor any other infirmity.

* * * * *

As for the toothache, it is a common speech, that if one bite off a piece of some tree that hath been blasted, or smitten with lightning, provided always that he hold his hands behind him at his back in so doing, the said morsel or piece of wood will take away the toothache if it be laid unto the tooth. Some there be who give direction to take the perfume of a man's tooth burning in the fire, for to ease the toothache of a man; and sembably of a woman's tooth to help women in the same case. Others you shall have, that prescribe to draw one of the eye-teeth, called in Latin canini, out of the head of man or woman lying dead and not yet interred, and to wear the same against the toothache. It is a common speech, that the earth found in or about a man or woman's skull, is a singular depilatory, and fetcheth away the hair of the eyebrows. As for the grass or weed that groweth therein (if any such may be found) it causeth the teeth to fall out of the head with chewing only.

FICTION AND FACT

But for the quartan ague, they get me a broken fragment of a wooden pin which held the sides and cross-piece of a pair of gallows together, wrap it within a lock of wool, and so hang it about the patient: or else they take a piece of the halter or rope from the gallows, and use it in like manner for the foresaid purpose: but wot ye what? when the patient is by this means rid of the fever, the said parcel of wood or cord they use to bury or bestow close in some hole within the ground, where the sun may never shine on it, and then the access will return no more.

See the toys and vanities of these magicians! and yet these be not all: for they run on still and say, that if one take a whetstone which hath served a long time to whet knives and other edge tools on, and lay the same under the bolster or pillow where one lieth that is ready to faint and give up the ghost upon some indirect means, by sorcery, withcraft, or poisoning, (but this must be done without the knowledge of the said party) you shall from the very mouth of the patient hear, what poison was given, in what place, and at what time; but who it was that gave it, he or she shall not be able to name. Moreover, this is known for a truth, that if one be stricken speechless with lightning, and then the body be bent and turned toward the wounded place, the party shall recover presently and speak again.

FOR WARTS, CORNS, HEADACHES, ETC.

For to be rid of warts, some choose a time to pluck them up by the roots, when the moon is twenty days old at least, and then lay themselves along upon their backs in some ordinary highway, looking full upon the moon, and stretching their arms backward as far as they can beyond their heads, and look what they can catch hold of with their hands, therewith they rub the place. If one cut and pare an agnel or corn in any part of the body, observing a time when a star seemeth to shoot or fall, they say, it will quickly wear away and be healed for ever. They would bear us in hand, that if a man pour vinegar upon the hooks and hinges of doors, and make a liniment with the dirt that cometh of the rust thereof, and therewith anoint the forehead, it will assuage the headache. They promise also to do as much with a withy or halter that a man is hanged withal upon a gibbet, in case it be done about the temples of the head in manner of a frontal. Moreover, if any fish-bone stick in the throat and will not remove, it shall incontinently go down, if the party ready thus to be choked withal, make no more ado, but take some other little spills of the said bone and lay them upon the head, you shall see it pass away and do no harm. If a piece of bread have gone wrong or lie in the way ready to stop the breath, take the crumbs of the same loaf & put them into both the ears, you shall see it will be soon gone and do no farther harm.

S

SNEEZING AND HICCUPS

Sneezing dischargeth the heaviness of the head, and easeth the pose or rheum that stuffeth the nose : and it is common said, that if one lay his mouth to the nostrils of a mouse or rat and touch the same, it will do as much. To sneeze also, is a ready way to be rid of the yex or hiccough. And *Varro* giveth counsel, to scrape a branch of a date tree with one hand after another by turns, for to stay the said hiccough. But most physicians give direction in this case, to shift a ring from the left hand to the longest finger of the right; or to plunge both hands into very hot water.

SEXUAL INTERCOURSE

As touching carnal knowledge of man and woman, *Democritus* utterly condemned it : and who so? Because (quoth he) in that act, one man goeth out of another. And to say a truth, the less one useth it, the better it is for body and mind both : and yet our professed wrestlers, runners, and such gamesters at feats of activity, when they feel themselves ˈeavy or dull, revive and recover their lively spirits again by keeping company with women. Also this exercise cleanseth the breast and helpeth the voice, which being sometime before clear and neat, was now become hoarse and rusty. Moreover, the temperate sports of *Venus*, ease the pains of the reins and loins, mundify and quicken the eye-sight, and be singular good for such as be troubled in mind and given overmuch to melancholy.

VARIOUS REMEDIES

When a mote or anything else is fallen into one eye, it is good to shut the other hard. If there be water gotten into the right ear, the manner is to jump and hop with the left leg, bending and inclining the head toward the right shoulder : sembably, if the like happen to the left ear, to do the contrary. If one be fallen into a fit of coughing, the way to stay it is to let his next fellow spit upon his forehead. If the uvula be fallen, it will up again, if the patient suffer another to bite the hair in the crown of his head, and so to pull him up plumb from the ground. Hath the neck a crick or a pain lying behind, what better remedy than to rub the hams? Be the hams pained? do the like by the nape of the neck. Say the cramp take either feet or legs plucking and stretching the sinews when one is in bed, the next way to be used, is to set the feet upon the floor or the ground where the bed standeth: or put case the cramp take the left side, then be sure with the right hand to catch hold of the great toe of the left foot and contrariwise, if the cramp come to the right leg, do the likewise by the right foot. If the body fall a shaking and quivering for cold, or if one bleed excessively at the nostrils, it is passing good to bind straight and hard the extreme parts, to wit, hands and legs, yea and the ears also. It falleth out oftentimes, that one cannot lie dry nor hold his water, but it cometh from him ever and anon; what is then to be done? marry tie the foreskin of his yard with a linen thread or paper rush, & withal, bind his thighs about in the middle. If the mouth of the stomach be ready to turn, and will neither receive nor hold anything, it is good to press hard and strain the feet together, or else to thrust both hands into hot water.

HUMAN URINE

As for the urine of mankind, divers authors have treated of it; who as I find, have not only set down their reasons in nature as touching the virtue thereof, but also have been very ceremonious and superstitious in handling that argument; yea and they have written distinctly of the several kinds of urine digested into certain principal heads. And among other things, that they set down the urine of men that are unable for generation, to be singular good by way of injection, to make women fruitful. But to speak of such remedies as we may be bold to name with honesty: the urine of young children who be not yet under-grown nor fourteen years of age, is good against the venomous humour of those aspides or adders which the Greeks name ptyades, for that they spit their poison upon the eyes and faces of men and women. Also, the same is held to be singular for the pearl, the cataract, the films, the pin and web in the eyes; like as for the eye-lids also, and the accidents happening unto them.

Being incorporat with the flower of ervile, it is good for sun-burnings: sodden also with boiled leeks to the consumption of the one half in a new earthenware pot which was never occupied, it is excellent to mundify the ears that run with matter, or that have any worms or vermin within them: and verily a stouph made with the vapour of this decoction, bringeth down the desired sickness of women. Dame *Salpe* ordaineth to foment the eyes with the said decoction, for to fortify the sight, and to strengthen them that they fall not out of the head: she appointeth to make a liniment with it and the white of an egg, but principally if it be of an ostrich, and therewith to anoint the skin that hath been tanned and burnt in the sun, for the space of two hours together: with it a man may wash away any blots or blurs of ink. Man's urine is much commended for the gout in the feet, as we may see by fullers, who never be gouty, because ordinarily their feet are in men's urine. Stale chamber lie or urine long kept & incorporat together with the ashes of oyster shells, cureth the red gombe in young infants, and gener-ally all running ulcers: The same so prepared, serveth in a lini-ment for eating cankers, burns, and scalds, the swelling piles, the chaps and rifts in the seat and feet, also for the sting of serpents. The most expert and skilful midwives have pronounced all with one resolution, that for to kill an itch in any part of the body, to heal a scald head, to scout away dandruff and scurf in head or beard, and to cure the corroding ulcers in any place, but in the privy members especially, there is not a liquor more effectual than urine, with a little sal-nitre put thereto. But surely, every man's own water (if I may for reverence of manhood so say) is simply best; and namely, if the patient that is bitten with a dog do straightways bath the place therewith: or in case there may be any prick of urchin, hedgehog, or suchlike spill sticking in the flesh, to apply the same thereto in sponges or wool, and so let it lie on. But say it was a mad dog that bit the patient, or that he be stung with a serpent, it is good to temper it with ashes and lay it unto the sore. For as touching the virtue thereof against scolopendras, it is wonderful what is reported, namely, that whosoever be hurt by them, if they do wet the crown of their heads but with one drop of their own urine, it will presently cure the same, so as they shall feel no more pain nor harm thereby. Over and besides, by the speculation of our urine, we are able to give judgement and pronounce of health and sickness; for if the first water made in a morning be white and clear, and the next after it highly coloured and inclining to a deep yellow, the former sheweth that concoction was then begun, and the second is a sign that digestion is now perfect. A red urine is naught, but the black is worst of all: likewise if it be full of bubbles and froth aloft; and be withal of a gross and thick subsistence, the same is but a bad water. If the hypostasis or sediment which settleth heavy to the bottom, be white, it signifieth that there is some pain or grievance like to ensue about the joints or principal parts within the body. Doth an urine look greenish? it betokeneth some obstruction or disease already in the noble bowels and inwards: Is it of a pale hue? it saith that choler aboundeth in that body: If it look red, the blood be sure is predominant and distempered. The urine is not to be liked but presageth danger, wherein there appear certain contents like brans and blackish clouds. Also a white, thin, and waterish urine is never good; but in case it be thick and of a stinking smell withal, it is a deadly sign, and there is no way but one with the patient. As for children, if their water be thin and waterish, it is but ordinary and natural.

The magicians expressly forbid in making water, to lay bare the nakedness of that part against sun and moon, or to piss upon the shadow of any person. And therefore *Hesiodus* giveth a precept, to make water against a wall, or something standing full before us, for fear lest our nakedness being discovered, might offend some God or Angel. To conclude, *Hosthanes* doth upon his warrant assure us, that whosoever droppeth some of his own urine every morning upon his feet, he shall be secured against all charms, sorceries, and deadly poisons whatsoever.

WOMEN

And thus much in some good sort as touching the medicines proceeding from women. As for the rest that are written and reported, they exceed all reason, and there is no end of them.

For first and foremost it is said, that if a woman whiles her monthly sickness is upon her, be set into the wind abroad with her belly naked, she will scare away hailstorms, whirlwinds, and lightnings; yea, and avert any violence of the weather whatsoever. And at sea verily, any woman standing openly against the weather bare, although she have not her fleurs, is enough to secure the sailors and passengers from all tempests. As for the monthly flux itself of women, (a thing in other respects and at all times, as I have shewed before, of a monstrous nature) there be writers who tell and presage wonders thereof, such as be horrible, abominable, and indeed not to be spoken : and yet some of those things I hold it no shame to deliver in writing, namely, if it fall out just in the eclipse of sun or moon, that a woman hath her sickness come down, the same is of a pestilent quality, and apt to breed diseases incurable. Likewise, if haply the time of the change, when the moon is in conjunction with the sun, and those things occur together, the man who meddleth with her during that time, shall not avoid his bane, but it will bring upon him some pestilent malady, remediless. Moreover, the venom thereof is so strong at that time especially more than at any other, that the presence or breath only of a woman then, will infect and stain any purple cloth. And yet bad enough it is at all times : for whensoever they are in their fleurs, it skills not in what quarter of the moon, if they go about any field of corn with their nakedness uncovered, ye shall see the cankerworms, caterpillars, beetles, and all such worms and hurtful vermin, to fall from the corn as they pass along. This invention by the saying of *Scepsius* and *Metrodorus*, came from the Cappadocians, who being infested with a number of those green flies called cantharides, decised this means to be rid of them : for they caused their women at the time of their monthly terms (saving the reverence of womanhood be it spoken) to go through the standing corn, with their clothes tucked up around above their waist, and all bare beneath. In other countries yet they are more mannerly, and in a better respect to the honour of women, put them only to go barefoot for this purpose, with their hair hanging loose about their ears, ungirt, unlaced, and unbraced. Howbeit, great heed must be taken, that they walk not thus at the sun-rising, for then surely all the crops upon the ground will wither and dry away to nothing.

ABORTION AND CONTRACEPTION

As for the famous courtesans, *Lais* and *Elephantis*, who have written so contrary one unto the other of this argument, and namely, as touching abortions, and of what efficacy the coal of colewort, myrtle, or tamarisk root is, after it hath quenched in the said blood; as also how she-asses will not conceive for so many years as they chance to eat barley corns infected therewith; besides other strange devices that they have set abroach: I think them incredible, and I would not have any credit at all given unto their writings, considering the monstrosities and contrarieties which they have put down; whiles the one prescribeth medicines for to make fruitful, and the other ordaineth the very same, to hinder conception and cause them to be barren.

THE FOLLY OF MAGICIANS

Furthermore, this also is resolved clearly among all writers, that there is no charm or enchantment whatsoever, of any validity to do harm to that house where the side-posts or door-cheeks are striked lightly over with menstruous blood: an argument I assure you, that convinceth notably the folly of these magicians, the vainest people under heaven, and overthroweth all their art: and a point that pleaseth me very well, and which for mine own part I am right willing to believe. And since I am light thus upon them, I care not much, if to defect their vanities, I set down one of the most modest receipts that they have given their word for, and which may seem to carry some show of truth or probability. For thus they prescribe with great warrantize, to take all the nail parings of toes and fingers of man or woman lying sick of an intermittent fever, and to mix or incorporate them with wax, so as the party in the doing thereof do say these words, *I am about a remedy for the Tertian, Quotidian, or Quartan ague* (according as the patient is troubled with the one or other of these fevers) which done and said, to stick up the said wax upon the door of another man or woman's house that is not sick at all, and that before the sun is risen: which no doubt (as they say) will cure the sick person, and set the ague upon another that was well before. Now would I gladly know what greater vanity and folly there can be, if this medicine miss and does not the feat? Or what more villainy and mischief, than thus to transfer and remove diseases from those that be sick already, unto such as be sound and think no harm? To conclude, some of these magicians are so far gone, that after all the foresaid nails of fingers and toes be pared, they ordain them to be thrown into ant holes, and to observe that emmet that first begins to draw one of them into her nest, to catch her up quickly, and hang her about the neck of anyone that is sick of an ague, and so the patient *pro certo*, shall shake off the disease and be quite rid of it.

THE REST IS SILENCE

These be the remedies which the bodies of men and women do afford: as many I mean as I may with some honesty relate: and yet ywis many of them be such as are not to be read out and uttered, but with leave and patience first craved, for the reverence that we owe to chaste ears. I know full well there is a great deal more behind that I have not touched, but such stuff I assure you is detestable and not fit to be spoken or committed to writing, which makes me rather to make haste and leave the discourse of man and woman, and so to proceed to the singular virtues and operations of brute beasts.

A DIFFICULT PRESCRIPTION TO DISPENSE

The grease or fat of a lion tempered with oil of roses into an unguent, preserveth the skin of the face from all ill-favoured spots, and keepeth it white and smooth. The same ointment healeth the skin that is scorched and pilled with cold, by travelling over mountains charged with snow; yea, and abateth the tumours and nodosities upon the joints. Now, if we list to believe the fooleries of magicians, they would bear us in hand, that whosoever be anointed all over with the said grease, shall be gracious with princes and kings, yea, and win much favour among the people, and any state or nation where they shall converse: but principally it must be the fat in the forehead between the eyebrows (where indeed it is impossible to find any at all).

THE CAMEL

As touching the camel, his brain (by report) is excellent good against the epilepsy or falling sickness, if it be dried and drunk with vinegar: so doth the gall likewise taken in drink with honey: which also is a good medicine for the squinancie. It is said, that a camel's tail dried, causeth looseness of the belly: like as the dung reduced into ashes and incorporat with oil, doth curl and frizzle the hair of the head.

THE HYENA

But of all the fooleries that they have broached as touching the hyena, this passeth and may go for the chief, that the hindmost end of the gut in this beast is of virtue, that no captain, prince, or potentate, shall be able to wrong or oppress those who have but the same about them: but contrariwise assureth them of good speed in all their petitions, and of happy issue in all suits of law and trials of judgement. The concavity or wrinkle thereof, if a man do wear fast tied about his left arm, is so forcible to charm a woman, that if he do but set his eye upon her, she will leave all and follow him presently. The ashes of the hair growing thereabout made into a liniment with oil, and applied accordingly, causeth those men who before were given to lewd wantonness and lived in bad name, not only to became chaste and continent, but also to put on gravity and grow staid in their behaviour. Thus much of hyena.

THE CHAMELEON

Democritus telleth us a tale, that if one burn the head and throat of the chameleon in a fire made of oaken wood, there will immediately arise tempests of rainy storms and thunder together: and the liver will do as much (saith he) if it burn upon the tiles of an house. As for all the other virtues which the said author ascribeth to the chameleon, because they smell of witchcraft, and I hold them mere lies, I will overpass them all, unless they be some few, for which he deserveth well to be laughed at, and would indeed be reproved by no other means better: namely, that the right eye of this beast if it be pulled out of the head whiles it is alive, taketh away the pearl, pin and web in man or woman's eyes, so it be applied thereto with goats' milk. The tongue likewise plucked forth quick, secureth a woman from the danger of childbirth, if she have it bound to her body whiles she is in travail. If there be found by chance a chameleon in the house where a woman is in labour, she shall be soon delivered in safety: but if such an one be brought thither of purpose, the woman is sure to die. Also, the chameleon's tongue pulled out of the head whiles the chameleon is quick, promiseth good success in judicial trials. The heart bound within black wool of the first shearing, is a most sovereign remedy against quartan agues. The right forefoot hanged fast to the left arm within the skin of a hyena, is singular against the perils and dangers by thieves and robbers; as also to scare away hobgoblins and night-spirits. In like manner, whosoever carry about them the right pap of this beast, may be assured against all fright and fear. But the left foot they use to torrify in an oven with the herbs called also chameleon, and with some convenient ointment or liquor to make in certain trosches, whereof if a man do carry any in a box of wood about him, he shall go invisible, as saith *Democritus*, if we were so wise as to believe him.

*   *   *   *   *

As for those who be troubled in mind & given to melancholy, they find remedy, if out of this beast's skin they drink the juice of the herb chameleon. Furthermore, the guts, and the dung therein contained (and that is worthy to be noted, considering this beast liveth upon no meat at all) being striked upon the door of an enemy's house, together with the urine of apes, cause him to be hated of all the world. The like wonders they report of the chameleon's tail, how it will stay any violent stream of river; stop the course and inundations of waters: and withal, bring asleep & mortify serpents. The same being aromatized or spiced with cedar and myrrh, and tied fast to a branch of the date tree growing double or forked, will divide the waters that be smitten therewith, so as a man may see whatsoever is in the bottom. And would God *Democritus* himself had met with one crop of this branch, to have made him hold in so many lies as he hath told, considering that he hath reported this quality of it among other, namely, to repress intemperate speech and inordinate walking of the tongue. But evident it is, that the only reason why *Democritus* faulted that way, (being otherwise a man of a singular wit and wholly addicted to the good of mankind) was an excessive and extraordinary zeal that he had to profit and benefit the whole world.

A SORROW SHARED

Furthermore, if a man round an ass in the ear, and say closely, that he is wounded by a scorpion, the pain and grievance thereof will immediately pass away.

REMEDIES FOR HAIR AND SCALP

But now will I return to the remedies appropriate to diseases respective to the particular members of the body. And first to begin at the head: Bear's grease mixed with ladanum, and that kind of maidenhair which is called adiantum, retaineth the hair of the head which is given to fall off: also the places that be already bare, it replenisheth again with new hair. The same being incorporat with the fungus excrescence growing about the candle snuff, as also with the soot found sticking to the sockets of lamps and candlesticks, causeth the hair of the eyelids to come thick. Mixed with wine, it is good against the scurf and dandruff among the hairs: for which purpose serveth the ashes of hart's horn burnt and applied with wine: the same also preserveth the hair from breeding lice and nits. Likewise, goat's gall mixed with fuller's earth and vinegar, if the head be washed withal, so as the hairs may dry again by little and little. Semblably, the gall of buck-goats tempered with bulls' stale, killeth lice. Now if the said gall be old, add thereto brimstone, and it scoureth besides the dandruff. It is thought, that the ashes of an ass pizzle will make the hair to grow thick, and preserve them from being grey, if the place be first shaven and well rubbed therewith, or anointed with the liniment made of it and oil, punned together in a leaden mortar. Likewise, the urine of a young ass foal is supposed to thicken the hair: but there would be mixed some spikenard with this washing lie, to rectify the strong scent of the said urine.

FOR A HEADACHE

And if we may believe it, the genital member of a he-fox, worn about the head in manner of a wreath, cureth the headache.

THE BRASSEN MARE

The sperm that passeth from the mature of a mare after she hath been covered by a stallion, if the wick of a candle or lamp be therewith besmeared and set a-burning, doth represent a most strange and monstrous sight of horse heads, as *Anaxilaus* hath reported: even so will that also of the she-ass, make a show and apparition of ass-heads. As for hippomanes beforenamed, it is so strong and forcible a venom, especially to incite and stir unto lust, that being upon a time poured into the brassen metal that was cast into the form and similitude of a mare at Olympia, the stone-horses which came near unto the said image, were set into such a heat and so far enraged, that they could not by any means be held back but they would needs cover the said brassen mare.

AN EXCELLENT DENTIFRICE

Finally, the ashes of the ankle-bones of a female goat whiles they be fresh and new, are counted an excellent dentifrice to whiten the teeth: so are the said bones of all other four-footed beasts, reared and nourished about a farm-house, if they be in like manner calcined: which I note but once for all, because I would not repeat one thing so often.

THE CARE OF THE SKIN

It is thought generally, that the skin of the face may be made smooth and without wrinkles, tender and delicate, yea and be kept fair and white, with asses' milk; for well known it is, that some dainty dames (forsooth) there be, that keep and maintain daily in ordinary to the number just of five hundred she-asses for this purpose: according to the first example of the Empress *Poppaea*, wife to *Nero* the Emperor; for she used commonly to bath in the asses' milk, and devised whole bains to swim therewith: and ever as she rode in progress, or removed from place to place, she had her cuirie of she-asses in her train attending upon her for no other intent, but only to wash and bath her body in their milk. As for the pimple and weals that break out in the face, if they be anointed with butter, they will wear away and be gone; and the sooner, if ceruse or Spanish white be tempered therewith; but pure butter alone without anything else mingled with it, killeth any fretting humours in the face that be corrosive, if so be that presently after the inunction, barley meal be cast upon the place. The gleane of a cow having newly calved, taken whiles it is moist and so applied, is good for any ulcers of the visage. There is another receipt making for this purpose, which may seem but a fantastical and foolish thing; howbeit, for to satisfy and please in some sort, our fine dames that are desirous of such devices, I am content to set it down: They say (forsooth) that the pastern bones of a young white bulkin or steer, sodden for the space of forty days and nights together, until such time as they be resolved into the liquor, if the face be wet with a fine linen cloth dipped in the said decoction, it causeth the skin to look clear and white, and without any rivels or wrinkles; but the said liniment must be kept all night to the face in manner of a mask. Moreover, they say, that bulls' sherne is an excellent complexion forsooth, to set a fresh rosat or vermilion colour in the ball of the cheek: and the liniment crocolilea, made of crocodiles' ordure, doth it no better: but then they give order, that the face be washed with cold water both before and after this dressing. The dung of a calf tempered and wrought in one's hand with oil and gum, is singular good to take away sun-burning, or anything whatsoever whereby the colour is decayed and lost.

* * * * *

The urine of an ass taken about the rising of the Dog star, cleanseth the face from all spots: so doth the gall as well of an ass as a bull, used alone by itself, after it hath been well broken and tempered in water, and the old skin of the face taken off; but then the patient must forbear to go abroad either into the sun or wind.

FOR A BONE STUCK IN THE THROAT

If a thorn, fish bone, or any other such thing stick in the throat, take the dung of a cat, rub and anoint the place well without-forth, the same (by report) will thereupon come up again, or pass downward.

GOATS

But before I proceed any farther, it is to be noted, that magicians also have meddled with this part of physic, and have devised strange medicines, drawn from the parts and members of beasts. And first of all they would make us believe, that be a buck-goat never so much enraged, do but stroke him by the beard, he will come into good order and be quiet again: cut and lop the same off with a pair of shears, he will not stray away nor depart to another flock. But to return to the grief of the reins: the magicians add to the foresaid medicine, goats' dung, which being put into a linen cloth, and the same well greased, they give direction to hold in the hollow ball of the hand, as hot as may be endured; with this regard, that if the pain be in the left side, this medicine be made in the right hand, and so contrariwise. Moreover, the dung or treddles which must serve this turn, they give order, that it be gathered and taken up with the point of a brassen needle or bodkin. Now the foresaid medicine must be held in the hand so long, until the patient perceive that the vapour thereof do pierce as far as the loins: which done, they appoint afterwards to anoint the head with the juice of leeks stamped: to rub the loins also with the said dung tempered with honey: giving counsel, to eat the stones also of an hare, for to appease the same pain.

FOR THE SPLEEN

And if all be true that these magicians say, the milt of the calf is singular good for the malady of the spleen; but then it must be bought at the same price that the butcher setteth first upon it, without hucking and beating it lower for to have anything abated; because in their opinion (so ceremonious they be) therein lieth a great matter. Now when it is thus bought, it would be slit through the length in two parts, and both pieces attached to the shirt of the patient; with this charge, that when he is about to put on his other clothes and make himself ready, he suffer the said pieces to drop down to his feet, and then take them up again, and so dry them in the shadow : for in thus doing, the diseased spleen of the sick party will likewise fall and settle down, so as the patient shall sensibly perceive himself to be delivered of that infirmity.

FOR BED-WETTING

The magicians have a device by themselves, and they affirm, that for to hold one's urine, it is passing good to drink the ashes of a boar's pizzle in sweet wine : but they instruct the patient withal, to make water in a dog's kennel; and in so doing, to say these words, *I do this, because I would not piss my bed as the dog doth his couch.* This much for the incontinency of urine. Now if one be pent and would gladly void urine, let him take the bladder of a swine, so that it never touched the ground, and apply the same to the share, for it will provoke the water to pass.

A SOVEREIGN REMEDY

For the biles and impostumes rising in any place thereabout, there is not a better medicine to scatter and dissolve them, than bears' blood or bulls' blood, dried first and so beaten to powder. But the sovereign remedy of all others, is the stone which a wild ass is said to void with his urine, at what time as he is killed in chase : which urine as it cometh first forth of his body, seemeth very liquid and thin, but being shed once upon the ground it groweth thick and hard of itself. This stone tied to the twist or inner part of the thigh, is said to dispatch all collection of humours that might engender biles and botches; or at leastwise to resolve them, that they shall never impostumate and come to suppuration. This stone is very rare and hard to be found, for it is not in every wild ass: but surely famous it is and much spoken of by reason of this medicinable property that it hath.

QUARTAN FEVER

But against the quartan ague, the magicians give order to wear about the neck or hanging to the arm cats' dung, together with the claw or toe of a screech-owl, but so as they may not fall off nor be removed before seven fits be passed. Now tell me (I pray you) what was he that could find out this secret first? Gladly would I learn what reason there is in this mixture, and why an owls' claw or toe was chosen above all other for this purpose? Certes, there be some of them, yet more modest than their fellows: and they have given out, that the liver of a cat killed in the wane of the moon, laid up in powder with salt, is to be given in a draught of wine a little before the access or fit of a quartan. And these magicians have yet another pretty receipt against such agues: For they take the ashes of a cow or ox muck, and sprinkle it well with the urine of a young boy; wherewith they anoint the toe of the patient: but to his hands or arms they bind the heart of an hare; which done, they ordain also to give him before the fit, the hare's rennet in a draught of drink.

A SECRET MYSTERY

Furthermore, the ashes of hart's dung, and namely of that deer which is called the spitter: as also of neats' dung, such I mean as go abroad and feed with the herd, (and that they call by a peculiar name bolbiton) is a sovereign remedy for the dropsy. Marry, if the patient be a woman, there must be choice made of cow dung; but if a man, the dung of the other sex is to be taken: and this I may tell you is such a secret mystery, that the magicians would not have to be revealed & made known.

SPRAINS, DISLOCATIONS AND BRUISES

It is thought, that for the pain of the sinews, goats' dung boiled in wine with honey is sovereign, yea though a nerve began to putrify : convulsions, cramps, and sprains of nerves upon some violent stroke, are cured with boars' dung gathered in the spring & so dried. After the same manner, such as be overstrained and plucked with the draught of any chariot, or wounded with the wheels going over them, and generally, howsoever the blood be settled black under the skin by contusion or bruise, if the places be anointed with the said dung, though it were green and fresh, much ease and help ensueth thereupon : howbeit, some think that it were better to seethe the dung first in vinegar : and others reduce the same being dry into powder, & promise them that be either bursten, wounded and bruised inwardly, or have been overthrown and fallen from on high, if they drink it in vinegar, that they shall have help thereby. But the better and those that love not to make the greatest boast of their medicines, use the ashes thereof with water. And verily it is said, that the Emperor *Nero* was wont in this kind of drink to take great pleasure, and with it to refresh himself, when his purpose was by that means to win a name and approve himself a doughty wight, in running with coaches in the great cirque or show-place.

HARES

Many are of opinion, that if a woman eat with her meat the matrice of an hare, she shall thereupon conceive a man-child if she company with her husband. And some say, that the genetoirs of the male hare, yea & the rendles, are good for that purpose. And it is thought, that if a woman who hath given over bearing children, do eat the young leveret taken forth of the dam's belly when she is newly bagd, she will find the way again to conceive and breed freshly as before. But the magicians do prescribe the husband also to drink the blood of an hare, for so (say they) he shall sooner get his wife with child. And they affirm moreover, that if a maiden be desirous that her breasts or paps should not grow any more, but stand always at one stay knit up round and small, she is to drink nine treddles or grains of hares' dung : and for the same intent, they advise a virgin to rub her bosom with the hares' rennet and honey together : also to anoint the place with hares' blood where the hair is plucked off, if they be desirous that it should not grow again.

T

AN ANTIDOTE FOR DESIRE

Osthanes saith, that if the loins or small of a woman's back, be anointed with the blood of a tick taken from a black bull or cow that is of a wild kin, it will put her out of all fancies of venereous sports. He affirmeth moreover, that if she drink the urine of a male goat, with some spikenard among to take away the loathsome taste thereof, she will forget all love that she bare to any man before.

"THERE SURELY MUST SOME REASON BE"

Cato is of opinion, that whosoever use to eat hares' flesh, shall sleep well. And the common sort of people are persuaded, that the meat of this kind of venison, causeth them that feed upon it to look fair, lovely, & gracious, for a week together afterwards: For mine own part, I think verily it is but a toy and mere mockery; howbeit there must needs be some cause and reason for this settled opinion which hath thus generally carried the world away to think so.

SOME MORE APHRODISIACS

A liniment made of boar's gall, provoketh unto carnal lust: the same effect there is of that virulent slime, which *Virgil* the poet describeth to drop from a mare's shap, against the time that she is to be covered: also the stones of an horse so dried that they may be reduced into powder, for to be put in drink: moreover, the right genetoir of an ass drunk in wine as need requireth, or tied in a bracelet fast to the arm, inciteth to venery: furthermore, the frothy sperm that as ass sheddeth after he hath covered the female, gathered up in a piece of red cloth, and enclosed within silver and so carried about one, is of great power in this case, as *Osthanes* mine author saith. But *Salpe* (a famous courtesan) giveth direction to plunge the genital member of this beast seven times together in hot oil, and with the said oil to anoint the share and parts thereabout. *Bialcon* adviseth to drink the ashes of the said member, or the stale of a bull presently after he hath done his kind to a cow, and with the earth that is moistened & made mire with the said stale, to anoint the privy parts. Contrariwise, there is not a thing that cooleth the lust of a man more, than to anoint the said parts with the dung of mice and rats. To conclude, for to avoid drunkenness, take the lungs of an hog, be it boar or sow it matters not; in like manner of a kid, and roast it; whosever eateth thereof fasting, shall not be drunk that day, how liberally soever he take his drink.

THE HORSE

There be other admirable properties and virtues reported of the same beasts, over and besides those before rehearsed; so it is said, that whosever do find and take up an horse shoe taken from the hoof (an ordinary thing that happeneth upon the way when a horse casteth his shoe) and lay the same up, they shall find a remedy for the yox, if they do but call to mind and think upon the place where they bestowed the same.

THE DILIGENCE OF OUR ANCESTORS

But see how diligent & curious our ancestors have been in searching out the secrets of everything; insomuch as we find observed by them, that a deaf hare will sooner feed and grow fat, than another that heareth.

THE NINE AND TWENTIETH BOOK

treateth of the first authors and inventors of physic,
also of medicines taken from other creatures

PREFACE

THE ADMIRABLE nature of a number of medicines, as well those which I have already shewed, as those which remain as yet to be handled, forceth me to write yet more of physic, and to sound to the very depth and bottom : albeit I know full well, that there is not a Latin writer who hath travailed hitherto in this argument; and am not ignorant how ticklish and dangerous a point it is at first to set abroach any new matters, especially such, whereby a man is sure to reap but small thanks, and in delivery whereof, is to make account of a world of difficulties. But for as much as it is very like that those who are well acquainted with this study, will muse how it is come about, that the remedies drawn from simples, so easy to be found and so accommodat to maladies, are cast behind and grown out of use in the practice of physic; it cannot be, but withal they must marvel much, and think it a great indignity, that no science and profession in the world hath had less solidity in it and been more inconstant, yea, and how it daily changeth still, notwithstanding there is not any other more profitable and gainful than it.

WHEN DOCTORS DISAGREE

While this *Crinas*, with such others as himself, seemed with their astrology to command the course of the destinies, and to have men's lives at their own disposition, all on a sudden one *M*.

Charmis, a Marsilian likewise, put himself forward and entered the city of Rome, who not only condemned the former proceedings of the ancient physicians, but also put down the bains and hot houses : he brought in the bathing in cold water, and persuaded folk to use the same even in the midst of winter : nay, he feared not to give direction unto his sick patients for to sit in tubs of cold water. And I assure you, myself have seen ancient Senators, such as had been Consuls of Rome, all chilling and quaking, yea and stark again for cold, in these kind of baths : and yet they would seem to endure the same to show how hardy they were. And verily, there is a treatise extant of *Annaeus Seneca*, wherein he approveth highly of this course. Neither is it to be doubted, but such physicians as these, who having won credit and estimation once by such novelties and strange devices, shoot at no other mark but to make merchandise and enrich themselves even with the hazard of our lives. And hereupon come these lamentable and woeful consultations of theirs about their patients, wherein you shall see them ordinarily to argue and disagree in opinion, whiles one cannot abide that another man's judgement should take place, and seem to carry away the credit of the cure. From hence also arose that epitaph of his (whosoever he was) that caused these words to be engraven upon his unhappy tomb, *Turba medicorum perii*, i.e. The variance of a sort of physicians about me, were the cause of my death. Thus you see how often this art from time to time hath been altered, and how daily still it is turned like a garment new dressed and translated; insomuch, as we are carried away with the vain humour of the Greeks, and make sail as it were with the puffs of their proud spirit : For ever as any of these newcomers can venditate and vaunt his own cunning with brave words, straightways we put ourselves into his hands, and give him power to dispose of our life and death at his pleasure; and without further regard, are as obedient to him as a soldier to his captain and general of the field. A strange matter that we should do so, considering how many thousands of nations there be that live in health well enough without these physicians, and yet I cannot say altogether without physic.

THE FIRST ROMAN DOCTOR

And to begin withal, *Cassius Haemina*, an ancient historiographer doth report, that the first physician that ever came to Rome, was one *Archagathus*, the son of *Lysanias*, from out of Peloponnesus, which was when *L. Aemylius* and *M. Livius* were Consuls, and in the year after the foundation of the city of Rome 535. And this mine author saith, that he was enfranchized free denizen of Rome, and had a shop provided for him, standing in the carrefour of *Acilius*, bought at the charges of the city for to entertain his patients, and therein to exercise his cunning. Called he was (by report) the vulnerary physician or chirurgian : wonderful much seeking and running there was after him, and none more wealthy than he at his first coming. But soon after, when he was known once to carry a cruel hand over his poor patients, in cutting, lancing, dismembering, and cauterizing their bodies, they quickly began to alter his name, and to term him the bloody butcher or slaughterman.

DOCTORS

And here by the way, one word will I speak to the honour of our Romans for their singular wisdom and providence, namely, that howsoever they are grown to good proof and be accomplished in all other arts and professions of the Greeks, yet their gravity hitherto hath been such, as they would not give themselves to the practice of this only science. And notwithstanding the exceeding wealth that accrueth by physic, yet very few or none of our natural Roman citizens have meddled therewith. And those also that have betaken themselves unto it, presently have forsaken their native language and gone to the Greek tongue. For this opinion verily there is of this art, that if the professors thereof handle it in their vulgar and mother tongue, or otherwise in any other than Greek, all the authority, grace, and credit thereof is lost, even with those that be altogether unlearned and know not so much as the Greek alphabet. See the nature and foolish property of our countrymen, to have less confidence and trust in those things which concern their life and health, if they be intelligible and delivered to their capacity; than in others, which they understand never a whit! And hereupon verily it is come to pass, that the art of physic hath this peculiar gift and privilege alone, that whosoever professeth himself a physician, is straightways believed, say what he will: and yet to speak a truth, there are no lies dearer sold or more dangerous than those which proceed out of a physician's mouth. Howbeit, we never once regard and look to that, so blind we are in our deep persuasion of them, and feed ourselves each one in a sweet hope and plausible conceit of our health by them. Moreover, this mischief there is besides, that there is no law or statute to punish the ignorance of blind physicians, though a man lost his life by them: neither was there ever any man known, who had revenge or recompense for the evil intreating or misusage under their hands. They learn their skill by endangering our lives: and to make proof and experiments of their medicines, they care not to kill us. In a word, the physician only is dispensed withal, if he murder a man: so clear he goeth away with impunity, that none so hardy as once to twit or challenge him for it. But say that one be so bold as to charge them with any untoward dealing; out they cry presently upon the poor patients, at them they rail with open mouth, they are found fault with for their unruliness, distemperature, wilfulness, and I know not what: and thus the silly souls that be dead and gone, are shent and bear away the blame. The decuries or bands at Rome of those knights which are deputed and called judges, are not chosen by an ordinary trial and examination of their estate, quality, and person; and the same by the principal of that order and degree, both taken and approved: straight inquisition there is made of their demeanour from house to house; of their parentage also, yea and true information given to the electors before they can be chosen. Mint masters, such as are to give their judgement of money, and the touch of coin, be not taken hand over head: but if any be more skilful than others therein, they are sent for (rather than to fail) as far as from Calis and the straits of Gibraltar. And for to pronounce sentence as touching the banishment of a Roman citizen, the five deputed or elected delegates (named Quinqueviri) had no warrant or decree passed before 40 days were expired. But for these physicians, who are the judges themselves to determine of our lives, & who many times are not long about it, but give us a quick dispatch and send us to heaven or hell; what regard is there had, what enquiry and examination is made of their quality and worthiness? But surely, well enough are we served, and we may thank none but ourselves, if we come by a shrewd turn, so long as there is not one of us hath any care or desire to know that which is good for his life and health.

*   *   *   *   *

For to say a truth, is there any trade or occupation goeth beyond it for poisoning? that is the cause of more gaping and laying wait after wills and testaments, than this? What adulteries have been committed under the colour hereof, even in princes' and emperors' palaces? As for example, *Eudemus* and *Livia* the princess, and wife to *Drusus Caesar*; *Valens* likewise with the queen or empress above-named, *Messalina*. But say that these crimes and odious offences are not to be imputed unto the art itself, but rather to be charged upon the persons, I mean the corrupt and lewd professors thereof: yet surely I am of this belief, that in regard of these enormities, *Cato* was as much afraid of the entrance of physic, as of some queen into the city of Rome. For mine own part, I mean not to say aught of their extreme avarice; of the merchandise, spoil, and havoc that they make when they see their patients in danger of death, and drawing to their end; nor how high they hold (as it were in open market) the easement and release of the sick man's pains, whiles he is under their hands, ne yet what pawns and pledges they take as earnest of the bargain, to dispatch the poor patient out of the way at once; and lastly, of their hidden secrets and paradoxes, which forsooth they will not divulge abroad, but for some round sum of money. As for example, that a cataract or pearl in the eye is to be couched rather and driven down by the needle, than quite to be plucked forth. Whereby it is come to pass, that is is a very good turn & the best for us (as the case standeth) that we have so great a number of such murderers & thieves in the Commonwealth: for I assure you it is not long of any shame and honesty (whereof there is none in them) but their malicious emulation, being so many as they are, that the market is well fallen, and the prices come down of their workmanship.

*   *   *   *   *

For I myself have seen these that go for physicians, put commonly into their medicines and receipts *quid pro quo,* and namely, instead of the Lidian cinnabaris, minium; which is no better than a very poison, as I will prove and shew hereafter in my treatise of painters' colours: which error proceedeth only from this, that they are not well seen in grammar, nor in the proper signification of words. But these and such like errors touch and concern the health of every one in particular. As for those abuses in the art of physic, which *Cato* feared, foresaw, and would have prevented, they be such as are nothing so hurtful and dangerous as the rest, and indeed small matters in the opinion of man: and such as the principal professors and masters of this art do avow and confess among themselves. Howbeit, even those devices, as harmless as they seem to be, have been the overthrow of all virtue and good manners in our Roman state, I mean those things which we do and suffer in our health: our exercise of wrestling, our greasing and anointing with oil for that purpose, brought in forsooth and ordained by these physicians for to preserve our health. And what should I speak of their dry stoves, hot houses, and ardent bains, which they would bear men in hand to be so good for digestion of meat in their stomachs? Yet could I never see any, when he came forth of them upon his own feet, but he was more heavy & found himself feebler than before he went in: and as for those who have been more observant of their rules than the rest, and wholly governed by them, I have known many such carried out for dead, or else extreme sick. To say nothing moreover of the potions and drinks ordained by them, to be taken in a morning fasting, for to vomit and scour the stomach thereby; and all to make way for to quaff and carouse again upon it more lustily. I forbear also to write of their rosins and pitch-plasters devised by them for to pluck away and fetch off the hair where nature hath ordained it to grow, whereby they would seem to effeminate our men. I bash also to speak how even our women have prostituted their nakedness and privities unto them, by occasion of these their wanton devices. In sum, conclude we may, that considering these enormities and corruptions which have crept into our life, by nothing more than by the means of physic, *Cato* was a true prophet indeed, and his oracle is verified and fulfilled every day, when he said, that it was sufficient to look cursorily into the writings and witty devices of the Greeks, without farther studying thereupon and learning them thoroughly. This much I thought good to speak, in justification of that senate and people of Rome, who not without great reason continued 600 years without the entertainment of physicians; and against that art which of all others is most dangerous and full of deceit : in regard whereof, it hath bleared the eyes of good men, and they be those who have given credit and authority thereunto.

THE IMPORTANCE OF HUMBLE CREATURES

And withal, this much may suffice to meet with the fond opinion and foolish persuasion of those, who are ravished and carried away with a conceit, esteeming nothing good for the health of man, but that which is costly and precious. For certes I doubt not, but some there be who will loathe these receipts taken from divers beasts, whereof I shall have occasion to speak hereafter. But I comfort myself again herein, that *Virgil* disdained not to name the very pismires and the weevils; blind beetles also delighting in darkness, and their nests wherein they keep; of which he wrote, notwithstanding he was not urged thereto upon necessity. Neither did *Homer* think it improper, to mingle the description of a shrewd and unhappy fly, even with the heroic battles of the gods : ne yet dame Nature, who hath brought forth and made man, thought it any disparagement to her majesty for to engender also these silly and small creatures. And therefore let every man consider their virtues, properties, and effects, and not regard so much themselves. To come then unto those things that are most common and known, begin I will at sheep's wool, and birds' eggs, to the end that by means due honour may be yielded to the chief and principal of all others, as it doth appertain. Howbeit, I must of necessity speak of some other things by the way as occasion shall be offered, notwithstanding the place be not so proper and fit for them. Neither wanted I means sufficient to furnish this work of mine with many gallant matters and pleasant discourses, if my delight and mind had been to look after anything else but a plain and true narration, according to my first design and intention : For well I wot, that I might have inserted here and there, the rare receipts which are reported to be made of the ashes of the bird phoenix, and her nest; but that I know all to be mere fabulous, howsoever they carry a pretence of truth. Besides, I count it a very mockery and no better, to deliver unto the world those medicines which are not to be made but once in the revolution of a thousand years.

FOR TEETH AND GUMS

As touching the filthy excrements hanging to sheep's tails, and baltered together into round pills or balls, if they be dried and so beaten to powder, are singular for the teeth, yea, though they shook in the head, if they be rubbed therewith; also for the gums, though there were gotten into them a cancerous sore.

THE STRENGTH OF AN EGG-SHELL

And here I cannot choose but note unto you by the way, the strange property and wonderful nature that egg-shells have : for so hard compact and strong they be, that if you hold or set an egg endlong, no force nor weight whatsoever is able to break and crush it, so long as it standeth straight and plumb upright, until such time as the head incline to a side and bend one way more than another.

HOW TO SUCCEED AT COURT

The priests of France called Druidae, are of opinion, and so they deliver it, that these serpents when they have thus engendered this egg, do cast it up on high into the air, by the force of their hissing; which being observed, there must be one ready to latch and receive it in the fall again (before it touch the ground) within the lappet of a coat of arms or soldier's cassock. They affirm also, that the party who carrieth this egg away, had need to be well mounted upon a good horse and to ride away upon the spur, for that the foresaid serpents will pursue him still, and never give over until they meet with some great river between him and them, that may cut off and intercept their chase. They add moreover and say, that the only mark to know this egg whether it be right or no, is this, that it will swim aloft above the water even against the stream, yea though it were bound and enchased with a plate of gold. Over and besides, these Druidae (as all the sort of these magicians be passing cautelous and cunning to hide and cover their deceitful fallacies) do affirm, that there must be a certain special time of the moon's age espied, when this business is to be gone about, as if (forsooth) it were in the power and disposition of man to cause the moon and the serpents to accord together in this operation of engendering the egg aforesaid by their froth and salivation. I myself verily have seen one of these eggs, and to my remembrance, as big it was as an ordinary round apple : the shell thereof was of a certain gristly and cartilaginous substance, and the same clasped all about (as it were) with many acetables or concavities, representing those of the fish called a pourcuttle, which she hath about her legs. And it is the ensign or badge that the Druidae do carry for their arms. And they hold it a sovereign thing, for to procure ready access unto any princes, and to win their grace and favour; as also to obtain the upper hand over an adversary in any suit and process of law, if one do but carry it about him. But see how this vanity and foolish persuasion hath possessed the minds of men ! for I am able upon mine own knowledge to avouch, that the Emperor *Claudius Caesar* commanded a man of arms and gentleman of Rome, descended from the Vocantians, to be killed for no other reason in the whole world, but because he carried one of these eggs in his bosom, at what time as he pleaded his cause before him in the court.

BUGS AND LICE

Other vile creatures there are besides, which for their baseness I bash to name and relate in this place; howbeit, because so many authors with one consent have so constantly commended their medicinable properties, I make it a matter of conscience to pass over them in silence : considering that all our medicines proceed from that convenience and repugnance which is in the nature of all things, whereof we have so much spoken. As we may see for examples in these punies or wall-lice (the most ill-favoured and filthy vermin of all other, and which we loathe and abhor at the very naming of them) for naturally they are said to be a counterpoison against any venomous thing whatsoever: and folk ground their reason hereupon, because look what day the hens do eat a wall-louse, the same day there shall no aspis have power to kill them. And it is said moreover, that the very flesh of such hens as have eaten such punies, is singular good for those that be stung already by the said serpents. Other receipts there be set down by our great masters in physic, as touching this foul vermin: but those which carry most modesty with them and have greatest respect unto mankind and humanity, are these, namely, to rub or anoint the place which is stung, with the said wall-lice and the blood of a tortoise together: also to chase away serpents, with the smoke or perfume of them: likewise, if any beast which hath swallowed down horse-leeches, do take them to drink, they will either kill them or drive them out, yea, and in what part soever they are settled and stick fast, they will remove them and make them to fall off. And yet some there be who use this nasty and stinking creatures in eye-salves, for they incorporate them in salt and woman's milk, and therewith anoint their eyes: yea, and drop them into the ears with honey and oil rosat mingled together. Others there be who use to burn these punaises or wall-lice, such especially as be of a wild kind, and breed upon mallows, and incorporate their ashes in oil of roses, and instill them into the ears. Touching other medicinable properties which they attribute unto them, namely, for impostumes & botches that are broken and run, for the quartan ague and many more maladies; although they give direction to swallow them down in an egg, or else enclosed within wax or a bean, I hold them for lies, and therefore not worthy to be related in sadness. Marry I will not say but there is some probability and appearance of reason why they should put them in those medicines which are ordained for the lethargy: for surely they are known to be very proper against that drownsiness, which is occasioned by the venom of the aspis: to which effect seven of them be ordinarily given in a cyath of water, or but four, if the patient be a child. In case of strangury also, when a man pisseth dropmeal, they use to put wall-lice into a syringe, and so convey them into the passage of the yard.

See the goodness and industry of dame Nature, the mother of all, how she hath produced nothing in the world but to good purpose and with great reason. And yet here is not all that they report of these lice called punaises: For they say, that whosoever carry two of them in a bracelet about his left arm, within a lock of wool (but the same forsooth must be stolen from some shepherd) he shall be secured against those agues that come ordinarily in the night season: but say their fits use to return by day time, then the said punices ought to be lapped in a reddish clout of a carnation colour.

LOUD LIES

But above all other receipts, one composition there is which bewrayeth the impudent and lying humour of these magicians, who promise undoubted and infallible victory, unto those that have it about them, and this it is: Take (say they) the tail and head both of a dragon, the hair growing upon the forehead of a lion, with a little also of his marrow, the froth moreover that an horse foameth at the mouth, who has won the victory and prize in running a race, and the nails besides of a dog's feet: bind all these together with a piece of leather made of a red deer-skin, with the sinews partly of a stag and partly of a fallow deer, one with another in alternative course; carry this about you, and it will work wonders. Impostures all, and loud lies. And verily, it is as gracious a deed to discover and lay abroad these impudencies of theirs, as to show the remedies for the sting of serpents, considering how these devices be no better than mere mischiefs and sorceries, which hurt and bewitch poor patients, and such as trust in them. True it is, that all venomous beasts fly from those that be anointed with dragon's grease.

A CURE FOR INFIDELITY

Now for the spotted lizards, called stellions, a scorpion stamped is singular good against their poison. For this you must think, that of them there is made a venomous drink: for let him be strangled or drowned in wine, whosoever drink thereof shall find themselves empoisoned, insomuch as their faces will break forth into certain spots and pimples and foul morphew. And this is the reason that our jealous dames when they would avert the affection and love of their husbands from those concubines, upon whom they suspect them to be enamoured, will if they can possible, stifle a stellion in the complexion or ointment wherewith such harlots use to paint their visage; by means whereof they become disfigured, and grow both foul and ill-favoured. But what is the remedy to cleanse the skin from such deformities? The yolk of an egg incorporat with honey and salnitre, doth the feat. The gall of these lizards or stellions punned and dissolved in water, is said to have an attractive faculty to draw all the weasels about the place to resort thither in companies.

THE SALAMANDER

Of all venomous beasts, there are not any so hurtful and dangerous as is the salamander. As for the other serpents, they can hurt but one at once, neither kill they many together: to say nothing, how when they have stung or bitten a man, they die for very grief and sorrow that they have done such a mischief, as if they had some prick and remorse of conscience afterwards; and never enter they again into earth, as unworthy to be received there: but the salamander is able to destroy whole nations at one time, if they take not heed and provide to prevent them: For if he get once to a tree, and either clasp about it or creep upon it, all the fruit that it bears is infected with his venom; and sure they are to die, whosoever eat of that fruit, and that by the means of an extreme cold quality that his poison hath, which doth mortify no less than if they had taken the Libard-bane called Aconitum. Moreover, say that she do but touch any piece of wood, billet, or hedge stake, wherewith either a loaf is baked, or a shive of bread toasted, as many as eat thereof, shall catch their bane by it: and if one of them chance to fall into a well or pit of water, look whosoever drink thereof, shall be sure to die upon it: and that which is more, if there happen never so little of the spittle or moisture which she yieldeth, to light upon any part of the body, though it touched no more but the sole of the foot, it is enough to cause all the hair of the body to fall off.

MORE MONSTROUS LIES

But to return again to our receipts and medicines against serpents: the flesh of young pigeons newly hatched, as also of swallows, is very good: so are the feet of a screech-owl burnt together with the herb plumbago. But before I write farther of this bird, I cannot overpass the vanity of magicians which herein appeareth most evidently: For over and besides many other monstrous lies which they have devised, they give it out, that if one do lay the heart of a screech-owl upon the left pap of a woman as she lieth asleep, she will disclose and utter all the secrets of her heart: also whosoever carry about them the same heart when they go to fight, shall be more hardy, and perform their devoir the better against their enemies. They tell us moreover, I wot not what tales of their eggs, and namely, that they cure the accidents and defects befalling to the hair of the head. But I would fain know of them what man ever found a screech-owl's nest and met with any of their eggs, considering that it is holden for an uncouth and strange prodigy to have seen the bird itself? And what might he be that tried such conclusions and experiments, especially in the hair of his head? Furthermore, they affirm assuredly, that the blood of their young birds will curl and frizzle the same hair? Much like to these toys are their reports also of the bat: for (say they) if a man go round about an house three times, carrying a live bat with him, and then nail it upon the window with the head downward, it is a sovereign countercharm against all sorceries and witchcrafts: and more particularly, if a bat be borne thrice round about a sheep-cote, and then hanged upon the lintel of the door, with the heels upward, it will serve for a singular preservative to defend the sheep for all such harms.

A CONTRACEPTIVE

A second sort there is of these venomous spiders phalangia, which the Greeks distinguish from others by the name of lupus. Those that be of a third kind, and yet named phalangia are the spiders which be covered all over with a certain down, and of all the rest have the biggest heads. Cut one of them and rip the

U

belly, you shall find within two little worms or grubs, which (if it be true that *Caecilius* hath left in writing) hinder women for conception, in case they be knit within a piece of leather of a red deer skin, and tied to their arms or other parts of their body before the sunrising: but this virtue continueth not above one year. Thus have I shewed one receipt only, of all those that keep women from conceiving; which I may be allowed to do in regard of some wives, who being too fruitful and overcharged with child-bearing, have some reason to play them a while and rest from teeming: and therefore may be pardoned, if they use some means therefore.

FOR HYDROPHOBIA

For the biting of a mad dog, take the ashes of a dog's head burnt, and apply it to the sore, it will save the patient from that symptom of being afraid of water; which is incident unto such as be so bitten. (And now by occasion of speech, know thus much once for all, that all things which are to be calcined, require one and the same name of burning; to wit, within a new earthen pot never occupied before, well luted all over with strong clay, and so set into an oven or furnace until such time as the contents be calcined.) The said ashes made of a dog's head, is singular good likewise to be drunk in the same case: and therefore some there be who have given counsel, to eat also a dog's head. Others seek after the worms that breed in the carcass of a dead dog, and hang the same fast about the neck or arm of a party that is bitten: or else they lap within a cloth some of the menstrual blood of a woman, and put it under the cup or pot's bottom, out of which the patient drinketh. And there be some again, who burn the hairs of the same mad dog's tail, and convey their ashes handsomely in some tent of lint into the wound. Moreover, it is commonly said, that as many as have a dog's head about them, no other dogs will come near to do them any harm. In like manner, if a man carry a dog's tongue in his shoe under his great toe, there will no dogs bay or bark at him: or if he have about him a weasel's tail, which hath been let go again after it was cut away.

A STONE OF CONTENTION

These may seem to some men strange things and monstrous;
but less will they wonder hereat, when they shall hear and
consider, that a stone which a dog hath taken up with his mouth
and bitten, will cause debate and dissension in the company
where it is, and yet this is held for a certain truth, insomuch
as it is grown into a common proverb and by-word, when we
perceive those that dwell in one house together to be evermore
jarring and at variance one with another, to say, You have a
dog-bitten stone here among you. Again, whosoever maketh
water in the same place where a dog hath newly pissed, so as
both urines be mingled together, shall immediately find a coldness and astonishment in his loins, as folk say.

FOR BALDNESS

The naked places in head or beard, are replenished again
with hair by a liniment of the ashes of sheep's dung incorporat
in cyprin oil & honey : also with the ashes of mules or mullets'
hoofs, applied with oil of myrtles. Our countryman and Latin
writer *Varro* affirmeth moreover, that the dung of mice (which
he by a proper name calleth Muscerda) is a convenient medicine
for the said infirmity and defect : he attributeth also the same
operation to the heads of flies applied fresh to the bald place, if
so be the same were before rubbed hard, and in some sort fretted
with a figtree leaf. Some use in this case the blood of flies : others
mingle their ashes with the ashes of paper used in old time,
or else of nuts; with this proportion, that there be a third
part only of the ashes of flies to the rest, and herewith
for ten days together rub the bare places where the hair is
gone.

AN UNFAILING REMEDY

Many do say, that the little hard bone in the head of snails
(such especially as are found between two cart-tracks) if it be
put through the ear, and hanged thereto within a little box of
ivory, or otherwise tied fast and carried about one within a piece

of dog's skin, is a remedy for the headache that never faileth, and may serve to do many good.

FOR BLEARED EYES

Others get a green lizard and put out her eyes, and bestow her in a glass with a bed of earth under her in the bottom thereof, and withal, enclose within the said glass certain rings, either of solid iron or massy gold : and so soon as they perceive through the glass, that the lizard hath recovered her sight again, they let her forth : but the said rings they keep with great care and regard, as a special means for to help any bleared eyes.

FOR RUNNING EYES

The cobweb which the common spider maketh, that useth to catch flies; but especially that which she hath woven for her nest or hole wherein she lieth herself, is sovereign good for the flux of humours into the eyes, if the same be applied all over the forehead, so as it meet with the temples on both sides : But wot you what, none must have the doing hereof, either to get the said cobwebs, or to lay it unto the place, but a young lad not as yet undergrown, nor fourteen years of age : neither must he be seen of the party whom he cureth, in three days after : ne yet during the space of those three days must either he or his patient touch the ground with their bare feet : Which circumstances and ceremonies being duly observed, it is wonderful to see what a cure will follow thereupon.

THE CRICKET

Nigidius attributeth many properties to this poor creature, and esteemeth it not a little : but the magicians much more a fair deal : and why so? Forsooth because it goeth as it were reculing backward, it pierceth and boreth an hole into the ground, and never ceaseth all night long to creak very shrill. The manner of hunting and catching them is this, they take a fly and tie it about the midst at the end of a long hair of one's head, and so put the said fly into the mouth of the cricket's hole : but first they blow the dust away with their mouth, for fear lest the fly should hide herself therein : the cricket spies the silly fly, seizeth upon her presently and claspeth her round, and so they are both drawn forth together by the said hair.

THE THIRTIETH BOOK

*speaketh of Magic, and certain medicines appropriate
to the parts and members of man's body*

MAGIC

THE FOLLY and vanity of art magic I have oftentimes already taxed and confuted sufficiently in my former books, when and wheresoever just occasion and fit opportunity was offered: and still my purpose and intention is to discover and lay open the abuse thereof in some few points behind. And yet I must needs say, the argument is such as deserveth a large and ample discourse, if there were no more but this only to induce me, that notwithstanding it be of all arts fullest of fraud, deceit, and cousenage, yet never was there any throughout the whole world either with like credit professed, or so long time upheld and maintained. Now, if a man consider the thing well, no marvel it is that it hath continued thus in so great request and authority; for it is the only science which seemeth to comprise in itself three professions besides, which have the command and rule of man's mind above any other whatsoever. For to begin withal, no man doubteth but that magic took root first, and proceeded from physic, under the pretence of maintaining health, curing, and preventing diseases: things plausible to the world, crept and insinuated farther into the heart of man, with a deep conceit of some high and divine matter therein more than ordinary, and in comparison whereof, all other physic was but basely accounted. And having thus made way and entrance, the better to fortify itself, and to give a goodly colour and lustre to those fair and flattering promises of things, which our nature is most given to hearken after, on goeth the habit also and cloak of religion : a point, I may tell you, that even in these days holdeth captive the spirit of man, and draweth away with it a greater part of the world, and nothing so much. But not content with this success and good proceeding, to gather more strength and win a greater name, she intermingled with medicinable receipts and religious ceremonies, the skill of astrology and arts mathematical, presuming upon this, that all men by nature are very curious and desirous to know their future fortunes, and what shall betide them hereafter, persuading themselves, that all such foreknowledge dependeth upon the course and influence of the stars, which give the truest and most certain light of things to come. Being thus wholly possessed of men, and having their senses and understanding by this means fast enough bound with three sure chains, no marvel if this art grew in process of time to such an head, that it was and is at this day reputed by most nations of the earth for the paragon and chief of all sciences : insomuch as the mighty kings and monarchs of the Levant, are altogether ruled and governed thereby.

MAGIC IN HOMER

But the greatest wonder of all is this, that *Homer* the poet, in his Ilias (a poem composed purposedly of the Trojan war) hath not so much as one word of magic : and yet in his Odyssaea, where he discourseth of the adventures, travels, and fortunes of prince *Vlysses*, such ado and stir there is with it, as though the whole work consisted of nothing else but magic. For what it meant by the variable transformations of *Proteus*, or by the songs of the Mermaids, whereof he writeth so much; but that the one was a great sorcerer, the other famous witches or enchantresses? As for that which he relateth of lady *Circe* how she wrought her feats by conjuration only and raising up infernal spirits; surely it savoureth of art magic and nothing else.

MAGIC IN BRITAIN

But what should I discourse any longer in this wise, of that art which hath passed over the wide ocean also, and gone as far as any land is to be seen, even to the utmost bounds of the earth; and beyond which, there is nothing to be discovered but a vast prospect of air and water. And verily in Britain at this day it is highly honoured, where the people are so wholly devoted unto it, with all reverence and religious observation of ceremonies, that a man would think, the Persians first learned all their magic from them. See how this art and the practice thereof is spread over the face of the whole earth! and how those nations were conformable enough to the rest of the world in giving entertainment thereto, who in all other respects are far different and divided from them, yea and in manner altogether unknown unto them. In which regard, the benefit is inestimable that the world hath received by the great providence of our Romans, who have abolished these monstrous and abominable arts, which under the show of religion, murdered men for sacrifices to please the gods; and under the colour of physic, prescribed the flesh to be eaten as most wholesome meat.

NERO

Magic may be practised after divers sorts, according as *Osthanes* hath set down in writing: for it worketh by the means of water, globes or balls, air, stars, fire-lights basins, and axes: yea and many other means there be, that promise the foreknowledge of things to come: besides the raising up & conjuring of ghosts departed, the conference also with familiars and spirits infernal. And all these were found out in our days, to be no better than vanities and false illusions, and that by the Emperor *Nero*. And yet was he never more addicted to play upon the cithern, nor took greater pleasure to hear and sing tragical songs, than to study art magic: and no marvel if he were given to such strange courses, having wealth and world at will; and his fortunes besides attended upon and accompanied with many deep corruptions of the mind. But amid those manifold vices whereunto he had betaken and sold himself, a principal desire he had, to have the gods (forsooth) and familiar spirits at his command; thinking that if he could have attained once to that, he had then climbed up to the highest point and pitch of magnanimity. Never was there man that studied harder, and followed any art more earnestly, than he did magic. Riches he had enough under his hands, and power he wanted not to execute what he would; his wit was quick and pregnant, to apprehend and learn anything; over and besides other means that he practised for to bring about this design of his, which were so intolerable, that the world could not endure them : and yet he gave it over in the end without effect : an undoubted & peremptory argument to convince the vanity of this art, when such an one as *Nero* rejected it. But would to God he had conferred with familiars and spirits, yea and taken counsel of all the devils in hell, for to be resolved of those suspicions which were gotten into his head, rather than give commission as he did in the professed bawds and common harlots in stinking stews and brothel-houses, for to make inquisition from house to house after those whom he had in jealousy. Certes, no bloody and detestable sacrifices (how inhuman and barbarous soever) he could have performed, but they had been far more easy and tolerable, than those cruel imaginations which he conceived, and whereupon he murdered most piteously so many good citizens, and filled Rome with their restless ghosts. But to return again to art-magic, which *Nero* would so fain have learned : what might be the reason that he could not reach unto it? Surely these magicians are not without their shifts and means of evasion to save the credit of their art, if haply they miss and come short at any times of their purpose : For otherwhiles they bear us in hand, that ghosts and spirits will not appear, nor yield any service to those persons who are freckled and full of pimples : and haply *Nero* the Emperor was such an one.

AN ABOMINABLE ART

And therefore we may be fully assured and boldly conclude, that it is a detestable & abominable art, grounded upon no certain rules; full of lies and vanities, howsoever it carry some show or shadow rather of verity : and to say a truth, that certitude which it hath in effecting anything, proceedeth rather from the devilish cast of poisoning practised therewith, than from the art itself of magic. But what needs any man to seek and hearken after the lies which the magicians in old time have let fly and sent abroad? When I myself in my youth have seen and heard *Apion* (that great and famous grammarian) tell strange tales of the herb cynocephalia, which the Egyptians call osyrites, and namely, that it hath a divine and heavenly virtue, and was a singular preservative against all poison, charms, and enchantments; but whosoever plucked or drew it out of the ground (saith he) could not escape present death. The same *Apion* reported in my hearing, that he hath conjured and raised up spirits, to enquire and learn of *Homer*, what countryman born he was? and from what parents descended? marry he durst not report what answer was made again, either unto him or them.

FOR CATARRH

If the rheum cause the mur, the pose, or heaviness in head, I find a pretty medicine to rid it away, by kissing only the little hairy muzzle of a mouse.

A DEPILATORY AND DEODORANT

To keep young boys from having any hair growing on their face, that they seem always young, it is good to anoint their cheeks and chin with ant's eggs. Also the merchants or hucksters that buy young slaves to sell them again for gain, use to hinder the growth of hair as well of the visage, as in the armholes and upon the share, that they may be taken for young youth still, by anointing those parts with the blood that cometh from lambs when they be libbed: which ointment doth good also to the armpits, for to take away the rank and rammish smell thereof: but first the hair there growing out to be pulled up by the roots.

A USE FOR LAP-DOGS

Now that I am come to speak of the precordial region of the body, know this, that by this one word *Praecordia*, I mean the inwards or entrails in man or woman, called in Latin *Exta*. Whensoever then there shall be pain felt in those parts or any of them, apply thereto a young sucking whelp, and keep it hard huggled to the place, doubtless the said grief will pass away from the part to the puppy itself, as men say : and this hath been found true by experience in one of those whelps ripped and opened alive, and the said bowels taken forth : for look what part in man or woman was grieved, the very same was seen infected thereupon, in the puppy. And such whelps thus used for the curing and taking upon them our maladies, were wont to be interred with great reverence and ceremonial devotion. As touching the pretty little dogs that our dainty dames make so much of, called Melitaei in Latin, if they be ever and anon kept close unto the stomach, they ease the pain thereof. And in very truth a man shall perceive such little ones to be sick, yea, and many times to die thereupon; whereby it is evident, that our maladies pass from us to them.

SCIATICA

To conclude with the sciatica, the magicians give order to put an earthworm in a treen or wooden dish, which having been cleft, was stitched up again with iron wire, or bound with a plate or hoop of iron : then to lade up some water therewith, & in it to wash and rinse the said worm very well, and then to inter or bury the same again in the very place from whence it was digged forth; which done, to give the said water anon to the patient for to drink out of the said wooden dish : and this they hold to be a wonderful medicine.

STOMACH-TROUBLE

There are other secret and hidden diseases incident to the guts, whereof there be wonders told : and namely, that in these cases, if young whelps before they can see be applied for three days together unto the stomach especially, and the breast : so that they suck milk from out of the patient's mouth the while : the said disease shall pass into the body of the poor whelps, whereof in the end they shall die. Let the same be ripped & opened, then it will appear evidently what the cause was of the foresaid secret malady of the patient : But such whelps ought when they are dead to be interred and buried. As for the magicians, they avouch, that if the belly be anointed lightly with the blood of a bat, the party thus dressed, shall not need to fear any pain of that part for one whole year after: or if it chance that one be pained in the belly, let him (say they) endure to drink the water that runneth down from his feet when his legs be washed, and he shall find help anon.

CALCULUS AND STRANGURY

For them that are troubled with the stone, it is good to anoint the region of the belly with mouse dung. It is said, that the flesh of an urchin or hedgehog is very good meat and pleasant in taste, if so be he were killed outright in the head at one blow, before that he had time to shed his own urine upon himself: and look whosoever eat this flesh, shall never be subject to the disease of the strangury. The flesh of an urchin killed in this sort, helpeth the bladder, in case the urine pass by dropmeal from it. But contrariwise, if the urchin chance to wet and drench himself with his own urine, as many as eat of the flesh shall fall into the infirmity of the strangury or pissing dropmeal.

DOGS AND TICKS

First and foremost, the magicians say, that the gall of a black dog (a dog I say and not a bitch) is a singular countercharm and preservative against all sorceries, enchantments, and poisons, which may endanger a whole house, in case there be a perfume made therewith to purify the air thereof; yea and to hallow and bless it against all such dangers. The like effect (say they) we are to look for, if the walls of the said house be sprinkled or striked with the blood of the said black dog; with this charge, to burn under the threshold or door-sell at the entry of the said house the genital member of the same dog. Men may marvel well enough at these fooleries and absurdities of theirs: but surely wonder less will they thereat, who know what store they set by ill-favoured ticks, the foulest and nastiest creatures that be: and why do they thus magnify so filthy a vermin? because (forsooth) this creature only of all others hath no passage at all for the voidance of excrements, suck it never so much: and no way there is but death with them when they are thus full, but so long as they continue hungry and fasting: and yet they say, that they will endure so a long time, even a whole seven-night together with abstinence and sparie feeding: marry let them feed still to the full, they will not hold out so long, but burst again in fewer days' space. Well, this tick, so filthy as it is, and of so admirable and strange a nature in their conceit, they hold to be of exceeding virtue to appease all pains and torments of the body whatsoever, in case a man take one of them, with the left ear of a dog, and carry them hanging to some part about him. And more than that; these magicians take marks by it, and presage of the life or death of their patients; for they hold it for a certain and assured sign of life, if one having a tick about him, stand at the bed's feet where the sick man lieth, and when he ask him how he doth, and where he is amiss etc. if the patient make answer readily unto him; but in case he make no answer at all, then surely he shall die, there is no remedy. But take this withal: this tick must be plucked likewise from the left ear of a dog, and the same dog ought to be coal-black without any speck or other colour.

THE AMPHISBAENA

Nicander writeth, that whosoever carry about them the serpent amphisbaena dead, or no more but the very skin thereof hanging fast to any part of their bodies, they shall find it to be a most sovereign remedy for any through-cold or chilling fit that hath surprised them. Nay he stayeth not there, but added moreover and saith, that if the said serpent be bound unto any part of a tree that is to be felled and laid along, the workmen that hew at the but thereof, shall feel no cold all the while; and the tree by that means shall the sooner and more easily be cut down and overthrown. No marvel therefore, if this serpent aforesaid dare leave his nest, and commit himself to the cold weather; for he ventureth first to come abroad, and is to be seen above ground before the cuckoo begins to sing. But since I have made mention of the cuckoo, there comes into my mind a strange and miraculous matter that the said magicians report of this bird; namely, that if a man the first time that he heareth her to sing, presently stay his right foot in the very place where it was when he heard her, and withal mark out the print and just proportion of the said foot upon the ground as it stood, and then dig up the earth under it within the said compass, look what chamber or room of the house is strewed with the said mould, there will be no fleas breed there.

THE LIZARD

Some physicians are so venturous and bold, that they have given unto those who be subject to the falling sickness, the very stellion itself, after it is rid and cleansed from the garbage or guts, and so kept dried; appointing their patients to drink the powder thereof is some convenient liquor, through a pipe of a cane: others appoint it to be roasted upon a wooden broch or spit, and so to be eaten for meat. And seeing I have occasion thus to write of this stellion, and the skin thereof, it were very convenient and necessary in this place to shew the manner how the said slough (which is grown over him in winter) may be gotten from him when he hath turned himself out of it, considering that he useth commonly to devour and eat it himself, because it should not do any man good; for there is not a beast again more spiteful to mankind, and envious of our commodity: insomuch as this word stellio is grown to be a reproachful term among us. Well, to meet with this skin of his (as crafty as he is to beguile men of it) they use to observe in hot summer days, his nestling hole into which he is wont to retire himself; and ordinarily they find it to be in some hollow crannies about doors & windows, or else under vaults and sepulchres: when they have espied where it is, they wait for the prime of the spring, they set just against his hole certain little cages or leaps made of cloven and slived reeds, and the same wrought and woven good and thick: and in very truth, he delighteth to get between the straits and narrow passages of the staves and windings, whereof the said cages are made, for by means thereof he may the better slip himself out of that coat which cloggeth his body and maketh him unwieldly: and thus in getting through the said lattices, he leaveth the same behind him: but after he hath thus done, hard bested he is, for back he cannot the same way again for to eat the said slough.

FOR JAUNDICE

A bird there is called in Greek icterus, of the yellow colour which the feathers carry, which if one that hath the jaundice do but look upon, he or she shall presently be cured thereof; but the poor bird is sure to die for it.

NOT ALTOGETHER NONSENSE

As for the phrensie, it seemeth that the lights of a mutton, applied hot round about the head and so kept fast, is sovereign to bring their heads again into temper, who are besides themselves. Say that true it were, that not only the brains of mice given in water to drink, or the ashes of a weasel, but also the flesh of an urchin kept in salt or dried, are very good for such as are bereft of their right wits; who will venture to give them these medicines, be they never so certain and assured? For as touching the ashes verily of screech-owls eyes calcined, (which these magicians so highly commend for the phrensie) I take it to be one amongst many others of their illusions, whereby they mock and abuse the world. But above all, the course that they take in the cure of fevers, savoureth nothing at all of physic, which indeed is opposite to all their rules and proceedings: for they have divided and digested the same into all the twelve signs in the Zodiac, according as the sun or moon passeth through any of them: All which, is nothing else but a mere mockery to be rejected and utterly condemned, as I will plainly prove and shew to the view of the eye by some few examples and instances gathered out of many. For in the first place they ordain, that when the sun is in Gemini, the combs, the ears, the nails, and claws of cocks should be burned, and the ashes thereof tempered with oil, wherewith the sick persons are to be anointed all over: but if the moon do pass through the said sigh, the same cure (say they) is to be done with the ashes that come of their barbs and spurs: whiles either sun or moon be in Virgo, the cure doth alter, and is to be wrought with barley corns in the same manner used. But how if either of these two planets be in Sagittarius? then the wings of a bat must serve the turn. In case the moon be entered into Leo, they employ the leaves and branches of the tamarisk; marry it must be the tame and garden tamarisk in any case. Lastly, if she be in Aquarius, they prescribe the coals made of box-wood, punned and pulverized. Certes, I purpose not to run through all their receipts : such only as are found and approved good, or a: leastways carried some show and probability thereof, I am content to set down : as namely, when they give order for strong odours and perfumes to be applied unto patients lying in a lethargy, for to awaken and raise them out of their dead sleep : among which peradventure, the stones of a weasel dried and long kept, or their liver burnt, may do some good. And whereas they think it convenient to apply hot unto their heads all about, the lungs of a mutton, they speak not altogether besides sense and reason.

THE PHRYGANIUM

Chrysippus the philosopher was of opinion, and so he hath put down in writing, that to carry one phryganium tied to some part of the body, is excellent for the quartan. But what living creature he should mean by that same phryganium, neither hath he himself described, nor ever could I meet with any man that knew it : howbeit, I thought it good to set down this remedy, being thus delivered by so grave an author as *Chrysippus* was, to stir up the diligence of others, if haply there be any so industrious as will take pains to search further into the thing, and learn what it might be.

ANTS AND RATS

It is said, that ants' eggs stamped and incorporate with flies likewise punned together, will give a lovely black colour to the hairs of the eyebrows : also, if a woman be desirous that her infant should be born with black eyes, let her eat a rat while she goes with child.

LIZARDS AND MICE

Some thing there remain as touching this argument, which hardly methinks I should not handle seriously and deliver in

X

good earnest: howbeit, since there be divers writers who have put them down in writing, I must not pass them over in silence. They are of opinion and do give order, to cure the rupture and descent of the guts in little children, with a lizard: how how? first, it ought to be of the male kind, which is taken for this purpose: and that may soon be known, if under the tail it have one hole and no more: then there must be used all means possible that the same lizard do bite the tumour of the rupture through a piece of cloth of gold, cloth of silver, or purple: which done, the said lizard must be tied fast within a new cup or goblet that never was occupied, and so set in some smoky place where it may die. If little infants piss their beds, a ready way to make them contain their water, is to give them sodden mice to eat.

TO PREVENT DRUNKENNESS

Moreover, if you would know a remedy against drunkenness, mark this experiment; give for three days together unto great drunkards the eggs of an owl continually in their wine, they will take a loathing thereto and forbear drinking. Whosoever taketh the lights of a mutton roasted, and eateth the same before he sit down to drinking, shall not be overtaken or drunken, how freely soever he poureth down the wine. The ashes of swallows' bills incorporat with myrrh, will secure any man from drunkenness, and cause him to bear his drink well, in case the wine that he drinketh be spiced therewith: And *Horus* king of the Assyrians, devised first this receipt against drunkenness.

ARISTOTLE ASSISTS IN A MURDER

Last of all, I cannot overpass one notable and memorable example as touching the hoof of a mule; when *Antipater* should send the venomous water of the fountain Styx for to poison king *Alexander* the Great, he could meet with no matter that would hold this poison, without piercing and running through it, but only the hoof of a mule: and to the knowledge hereof he came, by the direction of *Aristotle* the philosopher, who devised a cup to be made thereof. A foul stain and blot of *Aristotle's* name, for being privy to such villainy, and setting it forward as he did.

THE ONE AND THIRTIETH BOOK

containeth the medicinable virtues of fishes and water creatures

---

WATER

Now FOLLOWETH the discourse of water-beasts, and how beneficial they be unto us in regard of physic: wherein verily dame Nature (the mother and work-mistress of all things) sheweth how little idle she is, not ceasing even there also by her continual operations to make known her wonderful power, among the waves and surging billows, amid the reciprocal tides of the sea, ebbing and flowing in their alternative turns; yea and in the swift course and streams of great rivers. And verily, to say a truth and speak as it is, there is no part of the world wherein the might and majesty of Nature more appeareth, than in the waters: for this one element seemeth to rule and command all the rest. Waters devour and swallow up the earth: waters quench and kill the flames of fire: they mount up aloft into the air, and seem to challenge a seigniory and domination in the heavens also; whiles by a thick ceiling and floor as it were of clouds, caused by the dim vapours arising from them, that vital spirit which giveth life unto all things, it is debarred, stopped, and choked. And what might the reason be of thunders and lightnings flashing and breaking forth in that violence, and causing such troubles and broils, as if the world were at war within itself? And can there be anything more wonderful and miraculous, than to see the waters congealed above in the air, and so to continue pendant in the sky? And yet as if they were not contented to have risen thus to that exceeding height, they catch and snatch up with them into the upper region of the air, a world of little fishes: otherwhiles also they take up stones, and charge themselves with that ponderous and weighty matter which is more proper to another element. The same waters falling down again in rain, are the very cause of all those things here below which the earth produceth and bringeth forth. And therefore considering the wonderful nature thereof, and namely, how the corn groweth upon the ground, how trees and plants do live, prosper, and fructify by means of waters, which first ascending up into the sky, are furnished from thence with a lively breath, and bestowing the same upon the herbs, cause them to spring and multiply; we cannot choose but confess, that for all the strength and virtue which the Earth also hath, she is beholden to the Waters, and hath received all from them.

LAKES, SPRINGS AND RIVERS

The lake or mere Alphion is medicinable, and cureth the foul morphew. *Varro* mine author maketh mention of one *Titius*, a man of good worth, and sometimes lord Praetor, who was so berayed and painted all over his face with spots of morphew, that he looked like an image made of spotted marble . . .

Eudicus reporteth, that in the territory of Hestiaea, a city of Thessaly, there be two springs, the one named Ceron, of which, as many sheep as drink, prove black: the other Melas, the water whereof, maketh black sheep turn white: let them drink of both waters mingled together, they will prove flecked and of diver colours. *Theophrastus* writeth, that the river Crathis in the Thurians' country, causeth both kine and sheep as many as drink thereof, to look white: whereas the water of Sybaris giveth them a black hue. And by his saying, this difference in operation is seen also upon the people that use to drink of them: for as many as take to the river Sybaris, become blacker, harder, and withal of a more curled hair than others: contrariwise the drinking of Crathis causeth them to look white, to be more soft skinned, & their bush of hair to grow at length . . .

In Boeotia likewise, near unto the temple of the god *Trophonius* & hard by the river, Orchomenas, there be two fountains; the one helpeth memory, the other causeth oblivion, whereupon they took their names. In Cilicia, hard at the town Crescum, there runs a river called Nus : and by the saying of *M. Varro*, whosoever drink thereof, shall find their wits more quick, and themselves of better conceit than before. But in the isle Chios there is a spring, which causeth as many as use the water to be dull and heavy of spirit. At Zamae in Africa, the water of a certain fountain, maketh a clear and shrill voice. Let a man drink of the lake Clitorius, he shall take a misliking and loathing of wine, saith *M. Varro*. And yet *Eudoxus* and *Theopompus* report, that the water of the fountains beforesaid make them drunk that use it. *Mutianus* affirmeth, that out of the fountain under the temple of father *Bacchus*, within the isle Andros, at certain times of the year for seven days together, there runneth nothing but wine; insomuch as they call it the wine of god Bacchus : howbeit, remove the said water out of the prospect and view (as it were) of the said temple, the taste will turn to be waterish again . . .

At Cyzicum there is a fountain of Cupid, and whosoever drink of the water thereof, shall lay aside and forget all affection of love, as *Mutianus* doth report and believe. At Cranon there is a hot spring, and yet not so boiling as many others be : the water thereof, if it be put into a bottle or flagon of wine, will maintain the heat thereof, for three days together, that it shall drink hot . . .

Now if any man suppose some of these strange reports to be incredible, let him learn & know, that in no part of the world Nature hath shewed more admirable works than in this element of Water. And albeit in the beginning of this mine history I have written in ample manner of many a wonder observed in the waters, yet somewhat remaineth still to be related. For *Cretsias* saith, that the Indians have a lake or pool, wherein nothing will swim, but all sinks to the bottom. And *Caelius* also our countryman avoucheth, that the leaves which fall into the lake Avernus will settle downward and not float above. And *Varro* avoucheth moreover, that what birds soever fly over it, or approach the air and breath thereof, they will die presently . . .

There is a river in Bithynia called Olachas, running close unto Briazus (which is the name both of a temple, and also of the god therein honoured) the water whereof will discover and detect a perjured person: for if he that drinketh thereof, feel (as it were) a burning fire within his body, take him for a false forsworn villain. Furthermore, in Cantabria or Biscay the fountains of the river Tamaricus, are endued with a secret virtue to presage and foretell future events . . .

In Iurie there is a river which every Sabbath day is dry.

THE BEST WATER

Much question there is & controversy among physicians, what kind of water is best? and yet with one general consent they condemn, and that justly, all dead and standing waters; supposing those that run to be better: for it standeth with good reason, that the very agitation and beating upon the banks as they bear stream in their current, maketh them more subtle, pure and clear, and by that means they get their goodness. Which considered, I marvel very much at those who make most account of the water gathered and kept in cisterns: But they ground their opinion upon this reason, because rain water is of all others lightest, as consisting of that substance which was able to rise and mount up aloft, and there to hang above in the air. Which is the cause also, that they prefer snow water before that which cometh down in showers: and the water of ice dissolved, before the other of melted snow; as if the water were by ice driven together and reduced to the utmost point of fineness. They collect hereby, that these waters, to wit, rain, snow, and ice, be all of them lighter than those that spring out of the earth: and ice among the rest far lighter than any water, in proportion. But this opinion of theirs is to be reputed as erroneous, and for the common good and profit of mankind to be refuted: For first and foremost, that Levity whereof they speak, can hardly or unneath be found and known by any other means than by the sense and feeling of the stomach: for if you go to the weighing of waters, you shall perceive little or no difference at all in their poise. Neither is it a sufficient argument to prove rainwater to be light, because it ascendeth on high into the air, for we may see stones likewise drawn up into the clouds: and besides, as the rain falleth down again, it cannot choose but be infected with the gross vapours of the earth. Whereby it cometh to pass, that we find rain water ordinarily to be most charged and corrupted with ordure and filthiness : and by reason thereof it heateth most quickly, and corrupteth soonest. As for snow and ice, that they should be thought to be composed of the most subtle parts of this element, and yield the finest water, I wonder much, considering the near affinity which is between them and hail, which might induce us also to think the same of it : but all men confess and hold, that the same is most pestilent and pernicious for to be drunk. Moreover, there are amongst them not a few, who contrary unto the opinion of other physicians their fellows, affirm flatly and confidently the water of snow and ice to be the unwholesomest drink that is, for that all the purity and fineness thereof hath been drawn and sucked out. And in very truth, we find it by experience, that any liquour whatsoever doth diminish and consume greatly by being frozen or congealed into an ice. We see besides, that over-gross and foggy dews breed a kind of scurf or scab in plants : white frost burn and singe them : and both of these, the hoar frost as well as the dew, proceed from the same causes in a manner that snows do. Certes, all philosophers agree in this one point, that rain water putrifieth soonest of any other, and leastwhile continueth good in a ship, as sailor know full well . . .

Moreover, when you see or perceive any river to gather abundance of mud and filth, wot well, that ordinarily the water thereof is not good nor wholesome : and yet if the same river or running stream be given to breed great store of yeeles, the water is counted thereby wholesome and good enough. And as this is a token of the goodness, so the worms called tineae, engendered about the head or spring of any river, is as great a sign of coldness. Bitter waters of all others be most condemned : like as those also which soon follow the spade in digging, and by reason that they lie so ebb, quickly fill the pit. And such be the waters commonly about Troezen. As for the nitrous, brackish, and salt waters, found among the deserts : such as travel through those parts towards the Red Sea, have a device to make them sweet and potable within two hours, by putting parched barley meal into them; and as they drink the water, so when they have done, they feed upon the said barley groats, as a good and wholesome gruel. Those spring waters are principally condemned which gather much mud and settle gross in the bottom: those also which cause them to have an ill colour who use to drink thereof. It skilleth also very much to mark if a water stain any vessels with a kind of green rust; if it be long before pulse will be sodden therein; if being poured upon the ground, it be not quickly sucked in and drunk up; and lastly, if it fur those vessels with a thick crust wherein it useth to be boiled: for all these be signs of bad water. Over and besides, it is a fault in water, not only to stink, but also to have any smack or taste at all, yea, though the same be pleasant and sweet enough, and inclining much to the relish of milk, as many times it doth in divers places. In one word, would you know a good and wholesome water indeed? Choose that which in all points resembleth the air as near as is possible. At Cabura in Mesopotamia there is a fountain of water, which hath a sweet and redolent smell: setting it aside, I know not any one of that quality in the whole world again: But here there belongs a tale, namely, that this spring was privileged with this extraordinary gift, because queen *Iuno* (forsooth) sometimes bathed & washed herself therein. For otherwise, good and wholesome water ought to have neither taste nor odour at all. Some there be who judge of their wholesomeness by the balance, and they keep a weighing and poising of waters one against another: But for all their curiosity, they miss of their purpose in the end: for seldom or never can they find one water lighter than another. Yet this device is better and more certain, namely, to take two waters that be of equal measure and weight: for look whether of them heateth and cooleth sooner, the same is always the better. And for to make a trial thereof, lade up some seething water in a pail or such like vessel, and set the same down upon the ground out of your hand, to ease your arm of holding it hanging long in the air; and if it be good water, they say it will immediately of scalding hot become warm only and no more. Well, what waters then according to their sundry kins in generality, shall we take by all likelihood to be best? If we go by the inhabitants of cities and great towns, surely, well water or pit water (I see) in simply the wholesomest. But then such wells or pits must be much frequented, that by the continual agitation, and often drawing thereof, the water may be more purified, and the terrene substance pass away the better by that means. And thus much may suffice for the goodness of water, respectively to the health of man's body.

HOW TO FIND WATER

But to come now unto particulars. Look where you see growing rushes, reeds, or the herb whereof I made relation before, be sure you shall find water underneath. *Item*, Wheresoever you find frogs lying in any place upon their breasts, make account of good store of water there. As for the wild and wandering sallow, the alder tree, agnus castus, or ivy, they come up many times of their own accord, in some low grounds where there is a settling or stay of rain water fallen from higher places: insomuch, as they that go by these signs to find some spring, may be soon deceived. A surer aim yet by far, is a mist or exhalation, which a man may discover afar off, a little before the run-rising. And for to spy it the better, some there be who get up into an high place, and lay themselves grovelong, with their chins touching the ground, and by that means discern where any such smoke or vapour ariseth. There is another special means besides to find out waters, but known it is to those only who be skilful and expert in this feat: For they that are guided by this direction to water, go forth in the hottest season of the year, and about the noontide of the day to mark the reverberation of the sunbeams in any place; for if this repercussion and rebounding appear moist, and namely, when the face of the earth looketh dry and thirsty, they make no doubt to find water there. But they had need to look so intentive and wistly, that oftentimes their eyes ache and be pained withal. For avoiding which trouble and inconvenience, some betake themselves to other experiments; and namely, they dig a trench or ditch five foot deep within the ground; the mouth whereof they cover all over with earthen vessels of potter's work unbaked, or else with a barber's brassen basin, well enhuiled: and withal a lamp burning: over all which, they make a little arch-work of leaves and boughs, and mould thereupon. Now if they come within a while after to this place, and either see the earthen pots broken or wet, or perceive a dew or sweat standing upon the brass, or find the lamp aforesaid gone out and yet no want of oil to maintain light, or if they feel a lock of wool which they hung within the trench to be moist, they assure themselves they shall find water if they sink the pit deeper. Some there be, who for better assurance hereof, make a fire in the place, and burn it thoroughly; for then the vessels aforesaid, if they prove to be wet, give a more infallible hope of a spring. Moreover, the very leire itself of the soil, if it be spotted with white specks, or be altogether of a reddish bright colour, promiseth spring water to be underneath : for if the ground look black, lightly the water will soon fail, if there be any spring there found. If you chance to light upon a vein of potter's clay or chalk, make account you shall meet with no spring there, sink as deep as you will : and therefore workmen when they come to it, give over presently : for a great regard they have to observe the change of every coat (as I may so say) of the earth as they dig, to wit, from the black delfe, until they meet by degrees with the veins aforesaid . . .

Moreover, in digging or sinking pits, mark this for an assured and infallible sign that you approach unto water; namely, if the earth appear and show moist more and more still as you go lower and lower : also if the spade enter more willingly, and go down with ease and facility. When pioneers have wrought deep under the ground, and then chance to meet with a vein of brimstone or alum, the damp will stop their breath and kill them presently, if they take not the better heed : and therefore to foresee and prevent this danger, they use to let down into the pit, a candle or lamp burning; for if it go out, they may be sure it hath met with the damp. Therefore if pits be subject to the rising of such vapour, cunning and expert workmen make on either side of such pits, both on the right hand and the left, certain out-casts, tunnels, or venting-holes, to receive those hurtful and dangerous vapours, whereby they may evaporate and breathe forth another way. Otherwhiles it falleth out, that the air which they meet with in digging very low, doth offend the pioneers, albeit there be no brimstone or alum near; but the ready means to amend the same and avoid the danger, is to make wind and fresh air, with continual agitation of some linen clothes. Now when the pit is sunk and digged as far as to the water, the bottom must be laid, and the lowest sides of the wall reared of stone simply without any mortar made of (lime and) sand, for fear least the veins of the source be stopped.

Some waters there are, which in the very prime and beginning of the Spring, are of this nature, that they grow to be exceeding cold; namely, such as have their source or spring lying but ebb: for they are maintained only of winter rain. Others again, begin to be cold at the rising of the Dog-star. And verily we may see the experience both of the one and the other about Pella, the capital city of Macedonia: for the water of the mere or marrish there before the town, in the beginning of summer is cold; and afterwards, when the weather is at the hottest, the spring water in the higher parts of the city is so extreme cold, that it is ready to be frozen. The semblable happeneth in Chios, where there is the same reason of the haven and the town itself. At Athens, the great and famous fountain named Enneacrunos, in a rainy and stormy summer, is colder than the pit-water or well in *Iupiter's* garden, within that city; and yet the said well-water, if it be a dry season, will stand with an ice at midsummer.

WATER-PIPES

If a man convey water from any head of a spring, the best way is to use pipes of earth made by potter's art; and the same ought to be two fingers thick, and one jointed within another, so as the end of the upper pipes enter into the nether, as a tenon into a mortise, or as a box into the lid: the same ought to be united and laid even, with quicklime quenched and dissolved in oil. The least level for to carry and command water up hill from the receipt, is one hundred foot; but if it be conveyed up by one canal and no more, it may be forced to mount the space of two actus, i.e. 240 foot. As touching the pipes by means whereof the water is to rise aloft, they ought to be of lead. Furthermore, this is to be observed, that the water ascend always of itself at the delivery, to the height of the head from whence it gave receipt: if it be fetched a long way, the work must rise and fall often in the carriage thereof, that the level may be maintained still. As for the pipes, ten foot long apiece they would be, if you do well. Now if the said pipes of lead be but five fingers in compass, ordinarily they should weigh sixty pounds: if they be of eight fingers' size, they must carry the weight of one hundred pound: but in case they bear a round of ten fingers, their poise would be at the least 120 pound; and so the rest more or less according to this proportion. Those pipes be called properly in Latin denariæ, the web of sheet whereof beareth ten fingers in breadth, before it be turned in and brought to the compass of a pipe: like as quinariæ, when the same is half so broad. Moreover, this is to be observed, that in every turning and twining of an hill, the pipe ought of necessity to be five fingers round and no more, for to repress and break the violence of the water in the current. Likewise the vaulted heads which receive and contain water from all the sources meeting together, must be of that capacity, as need requireth.

HOT SPRINGS

To come to the use of natural bains and hot waters: many men in a bravery sit long in a bath, and they take a pride in it, to endure the heat of the water many hours together; and yet is there nothing so hurtful for the body: for in truth, a man should continue little longer in them than in ordinary artificial bains or stouphs; and then afterwards when he goeth forth, he is to wash his body with fresh cold water, not without some oil among. Howbeit, our common people here, think this to be very strange, and will not be brought to it: which is the reason, that men's bodies in no place, are more subject to disease: for the strong vapours that stem from thence, stuff and fill their heads; and although they sweat in one part, yet they chill in another, notwithstanding the rest of their bodies stand deep within the water. Others there are besides, who upon the like erroneous conceit, take great joy in drinking a deal of this water, striving avie who can pour most of it down the throat. I have myself seen some of them so puffed up & swollen with drinking, that their very skin covered and hide the rings upon their fingers, namely, when they were not able to deliver again the great quantity of water that they had taken in. Therefore this drinking of much water is not good to be used, unless a man do estsoons eat salt with all. Great use there is and to good purpose, of the mud which these fountains do yield, but with this regard, that when the body is besmeared and bedaubed outwardly therewith, the same may dry upon it in the sun.

A USE FOR SEASICKNESS

Moreover, the sea affordeth other uses in divers and sundry respects, but principally the air thereof is wholesome for those who are in a phthisic or consumption (as I have before said) and cureth such as do reach or void blood upward: And verily, I remember of late days, that *Annaeus Gallio* after that he was Consul, took this course; namely, to sail upon the sea, for this infirmity. What is the cause think ye, that many make voyages into Egypt? surely it is not for the air of Egypt itself, but because they lie long at sea, and be sailing a great while before they come thither. Furthermore, the vomits also which are occasioned at sea by the continual rolling and rocking of the ships never standing still, are good for many maladies of head, eyes, and breast; and generally they do cure all those accidents, for which the drinking of hellebore serveth.

SEA-WATER

Sea water serveth well to wash the head, & to rid it of nits and filthy lice : yea and reduceth black and blue marks in the skin, to the fresh and lively colour again. In all these cures, after the use of salt water, it is passing good to foment the place affected, with vinegar hot. Over and besides, it is thought to be very handsome and good against the venomous stings of serpents, and namely of the spiders phalangia and scorpions. Semblably, it cureth those that be infected outwardly with the noisome salivation or spittle of the deadly aspis called ptyas : but in these cases it must be taken hot. Furthermore, a perfume made with sea water and vinegar, is singular for the headache. If it be clysterized hot, it allayeth the wrings and grindings of the belly; yea and stayeth the violent motions of choleric humours working upward and downward. Those that be once chaufed and set into an heat with sea water, shall not so easily feel the cold again. When women's paps are overgrown, and so exceeding great that they meet and kiss one another, there is not a better thing to take them down, than to bath in a tub of sea water : the same also may serve to amend the grief of the bowels and precordial parts, yea and to restore those that be exceeding lean and worn away. The fumes and vapours of this water boiling together with vinegar, are sovereign for those that be hard of hearing, or troubled with the headache. Sea water hath this especial property, that of all things it scoureth away rust of iron soonest. The scab that annoyeth sheep, it healeth, and maketh their wool more soft and delicate. But what mean I to say thus much of sea water, knowing as I do full well, that for those who dwell far up into the main, and inhabit the inland parts, all this may seem needless and superfluous? And yet there hath been means devised to make artificial sea water, wherewith every man may serve his own turn when he will. In which invention, one wonderful thing is to be seen; namely, if a man put more than one sextar of salt to four of water, the nature of the water will be so far overcome, that salt shall not dissolve nor melt therein : but if you mingle one sextar of salt just with four sextars of water, you shall have a brine as strong as the saltest water that is in the sea : but to have a kind and most mild brine, it is thought sufficient to temper the foresaid measure of water with eight cyaths of salt : and this water thus proportioned, is very proper for to heat the sinews, without any fretting of the skin at all.

SALT

At Carrhæ, a city of Arabia, all the walls thereof, as also the houses of the inhabitants, be reared and built of salt stones : and the same be laid by masons' work, and the joints closed and soudered by no other mortar but plain water.

*   *   *   *   *

A strange and wonderful nature it hath if it be right : for so long as it lieth under ground within the mine, it is passing light in hand, and may be easily wielded; take it forth once, and lay it abroad above ground, a man would not believe or imagine how exceeding heavy it is. But surely the reason thereof is evident : for the moist vapours contained within those mines where it lieth, bear up the said pieces of salt, and are a great ease to those that deal therewith, much like as the water helpeth much to the stirring and managing of anything within it, be it never so weighty.

*   *   *   *   *

And not only we men are solicited and moved by salt more than by anything else to our meat; but muttons, boeufes, and horses also have benefit thereby in that respect: they feed the better, give more store of milk, and the cheese made thereof hath a more dainty and commendable taste by that means. And to conclude all in one word, the life of mankind could not stand without salt, so necessary an element (if I may say so) it is for the maintenance of our life, that the very delights and pleasures of the mind also are expressed by no better term than salt: for such gifts and conceits of the spirit as yield most grace and contentment, we use in Latin to call salis. All the mirth of the heart, the greatest cheerfulness of a lightsome mind, and the whole repose and contentment that a man findeth in his soul, by no other word can be better showed.

SPONGES

That sponges have life, yea and a sensible life, I have proved heretofore, for there is found of their blood settled within them. Some writers report, that they have the sense of hearing, which directeth them to draw in their bodies at any sound or noise made, and therewith to squeeze out plenty of water which they contained within: neither can they easily be pulled from their rocks, and therefore must be cut away; whereby they are seen to shed a deal of blood, or that which resembleth blood very near.

*   *   *   *   *

Furthermore, sponges, in friction and rubbing or crazy bodies, may well stand instead of currying combs, and coarse linen cloths: besides, they serve right handsomely and fitly, to cover and defend the head against the extreme heat of the sun. Moreover, the ignorance of our physicians, is the cause that all sponges be reduced to two only kinds, to wit, under the name of African, which be of a more tough and firm substance; and the Rhodiack, which are softer, and therefore meet for fomentations. At this day, the tenderest and most delicate sponges are found about the walls of the city Antiphellus. And yet *Trogus* writeth, that about Lycia, the softest sponges called penicilli, do grow in the deep sea, and namely in those places, from when other sponges beforetime had been plucked and taken away. Finally, *Polybius* doth report, that if sponges be hung about the tester or ceiling of a bed over sick persons, they shall take the better rest and repose all night for it.

THE TWO AND THIRTIETH BOOK

sheweth other properties of fishes, &.

PREFACE

HAVING so far proceeded in the discourse of Nature's history that I am now arrived at the very height of her forces, and come into a world of examples, I cannot choose but in the first place consider the power of her operations, and the infiniteness of her secrets, which offer themselves before our eyes in the sea: for in no part else of this universal frame, is it possible to observe the like majesty of Nature: insomuch as we need not seek any farther, nay we ought not to make more search into her divinity, considering there cannot be found anything equal or like unto this one element, wherein she hath surmounted and gone beyond her own self in a wonderful number of respects. For first and foremost, is there anything more violent than the sea, and namely, when it is troubled with blustering winds, whirlpuffs, storms, and tempests? Or wherein hath the wit of man been more employed (seek out all parts of the whole world) than in seconding the waves and billows of the sea, by sail and oar? Finally, is there ought more admirable, than the inenarrable force of the reciprocal tides of the sea, ebbing and flowing as it doth, whereby it keepeth a current also, as it were the stream of some great river?

THE ECHENEIS

The current of the sea is great, the tide much, the winds vehement and forcible; and more than that, oars and sails withal to help forward the rest, are mighty and powerful: and yet there is one little silly fish, named echeneis, that checketh, scorneth, and arresteth them all: let the winds blow as much as they will, rage the storms and tempests what they can, yet this little fish commandeth their fury, restraineth their puissance, and maugre all their force as great as it is, compelleth ships to stand still: A thing, which no cables be they never so big and strong, no anchors, how massy and weighty soever they be, stick they also as fast and unmovable as they will, can perform. She brid-leth the violence, and tameth the greatest rage of this universal world, and that without any pain that she putteth herself unto, without any holding and putting back, or any other means, save only by cleaving and sticking fast to a vessel: in such sort, as this one small and poor fish, is sufficient to resist and withstand so great power both of sea and navy, yea and to stop the passage of a ship, do they all what they can possible to the contrary. What should our fleets and armadas at sea, make such turrets in their decks and forecastles? what should they fortify their ships in warlike manner, to fight from them upon the sea, as it were from mure and rampier on firm land? See the vanity of man! alas, how foolish are we to make all this ado? when one little fish, not above half a foot long, is able to arrest and stay perforce, yea and hold as prisoners our goodly tall and proud ships, so well armed in the beakhead with iron pikes and brassen tines; so offensive and dangerous to bouge and pierce any enemy ship which they do encounter. Certes, reported it is, that in the naval battle before Actium, wherein *Antonius* and *Cleopatra* the queen were defeated by *Augustus*, one of these fishes stayed the admiral ship wherein *M. Antonius* was, at what time as he made all the haste and means he could devise with help of oars, to encourage his people from ship to ship, and could not prevail, until he was forced to abandon the said admiral and go into another galley. Meanwhile the armada of *Augustus Caesar* seeing this disorder, charged with greater violence, and soon invested the fleet of *Antonie*. Of late days also, and within our remem-brance, the like happened to the royal ship of the Emperor *Caius Caligula*, at what time as he rode back and made sail from Astura to Antium; when and where, this little fish detained his ship, and (as it fell afterward) presaged an unfortunate event thereby : for this was the last time that ever this Emperor made his return to Rome : and no sooner was he arrived, but his own soldiers in a mutiny fell upon him, and stabbed him to death. And yet it was not long ere the cause of this wonderful stay of his ship was known : for so soon as ever the vessel (and a galliace it was, furnished with five banks of oars to a side) was perceived alone in the fleet to stand still, presently a number of tall fellows leapt out of their ships into the sea, to search about the said galley, what the reason might be that it stirred not? and found one of these fishes sticking fast to the very helm : which being reported unto *Caius Caligula,* he fumed and fared as an Emperor, taking great indignation that so small a thing as it, should hold him back perforce, and check the strength of all his mariners, notwithstanding there were no fewer than four hundred lusty men in his galley that laboured at the oar all that ever they could to the contrary. But this prince (as it is for certain known) was most astonied at this, namely, that the fish sticking only to the ship, should hold it fast; and the same being brought into the ship and there laid, not work the like effect.

THE TORPEDO

Well, however it be, considering that mighty puissance which this fish is well known to have in staying ships, who will ever make doubt hereafter of any power in Nature herself, or of the effectual operation in physic, which she hath given to many things that come up by themselves. But say we had no such evidence by the example of this echeneis; the cramp-fish torpedo, found and taken likewise in the same sea, were sufficient alone to prove the might of Nature in her works, if there were nothing else to shew the same : for able she is to benumb and mortify the arms of the lustiest and strongest fishers that be; yea and to bind their legs as it were, how swift and nimble soever they are otherwise in running : and how? even by touching only the end of a pole, or any part of an angle-rod, which they hold in their hands, although they stand aloft and a great way from her. Now if we cannot will nor choose, but must needs confess by the evident instance of this one fish, that there is something in Nature so penetrant and powerful, that the very smell only or breath and air proceeding from it, is able thus to affect, or infect rather the principal limbs and members of our body : what is it that we are not to hope for and expect from the virtue of all other creatures that Nature (through her bounty) hath endued with medicinable power for the remedy of diseases?

THE INTELLIGENCE OF FISH

Wonderful in my conceit is the wit and subtlety of some fishes, if all be true which *Ovid* the poet hath reported of them, in that book of his which he entitled Halieuticon : For first and foremost he saith, that the goldenie *scarus* perceiveth himself to be taken in a weire, or enclosed within a wicker-net or leap, never striveth to get out again with the head forward, or to thrust his muffle between the osiers, for fear he should be caught by the head : but turning his tail upon them, keepeth such a flapping therewith, that he maketh himself way by that means, and so breaketh forth of prison backward. Now, in case whiles he struggleth and laboureth thus to get out, another goldenie that is without happen to espy him thus a prisoner, the same will take hold with his mouth of his fellow's tail, and help to get him forth out of the said net, which he endeavoured to break through. Also that the sea pike lupus, when he seeth that he is compassed about with nets, maketh a furrow with his tail into the sands, wherein he coucheth and lieth close, that when the fishers draw their nets unto them, they may glide and pass over him. As for the lampreys, knowing what a smooth, round and flippery back they have, they make no more ado, but seeing themselves within the net, go between the very meshes, which with their much winding and wriggling they will wrest wider and wider still, until they be gotten through and escaped.

LAMPREYS

The lampreys devour the hooks, yea, they gobble in and swallow more than so, until they come to the very lines, which they set their sharp teeth unto, and never rest until they have fretted and gnawn them asunder. And *Pytheas* is mine author, who writeth thus of them besides, that if they find themselves to be once upon the hook, they turn their bodies and writhe with their backs, as knowing the same to be armed with trenchant and keen-edged fins like knives, and so with their very sharp chine and fins cut the lines atwo. *Licinius Macer* writeth of lampreys, that they be all of the female sex only, and do conceive by serpents engendering with them, as I have heretofore observed : which is the cause, that fishers lure them with hissing like unto serpents, and by that means call them forth to their holes and catch them. He saith moreover, that they will feed fat with milk : and if a man give them a good knock with a cudgel, they will not die thereupon : rap them only with a fennel stalk or some such wand, you shall see them dead forthwith. And verily it is held for certain, that their life lieth in the tail : which if it be smitten, they are very soon gone and bereft of vital breath : strike them upon the head, you shall hardly and with much ado kill them.

SWORD-FISH AND CUTTLE-FISH

The sword-fish, called in Greek xiphias, that is to say in Latin gladius, i.e. a sword, hath a beak or bill sharp-pointed, wherewith she will drive through the sides and planks of a ship, and bouge them so, that they shall sink withal. The experience whereof is seen in the ocean, near unto a place in Mauritania called Gotta, which is not far from the river Lixos. And the foresaid writer *Trebius Niger* reporteth, that the sea-cats or cuttle fishes, called loligines, will fly out of the sea, and settle upon ships in such multitudes, that they force them under water, and so drown them.

THE FISH OF VENUS

About Hierapolis, a city in Syria, the fish within the lake or pool of *Venus,* obey the voice of the wardens or sextons who have the keeping of her chapel there; and orderly they come at their call, garnished with their ornaments of gold about them : they will abide to be scratched and clawed, they will wag their tails like a dog in a fawning and flattering manner, nay, they will gape with their mouths wide open, and suffer them to thrust their hands or fingers into them.

BEAVERS

The power and majesty of Nature is very conspicuous and visible, even in those creatures also which live indifferently on land and in the water : and namely in the beavers, which commonly the physicians call Castores, like as their stones also Castorea. Some hold, that these beavers when they be near driven and pressed by hunters, and at the point to be taken, bite off their own stones. But *Sextius* who hath written most exactly in physic, denieth it flatly. He saith moreover, that these cods be small, knit short and trussed up, so as they stick close upto the shin bone, and cannot possibly be taken from the beast but the life goes away withal. By his saying also they are sophisticated; and the kidneys of the beaver which are big, be obtruded and foisted to us many times instead of their stones, which indeed are never found but very little and slender. Furthermore he affirmeth, that they be not the right stones of a beaver when they are seen without a twofold burse or skin, which no living creature hath besides. In these two bags there is found (saith he) a certain oleous liquor, which ordinarily is kept and preserved with salt : And therefore many other marks to know false and sophisticat castoreum iis this, if you see a pair of cods hanging (as it were) knit together by one string in one bag. And yet the best may be falsified by the fraud and cunning of such as put gum thereto with salt ammoniac, because the true beaver's stones ought to bear the colour of ammoniac; to be enclosed also within their several tunicles; and to lie in a certain liquor resembling cereous honey, standing much upon wax; to have a strong and rank smell, a bitter, hot and fierce taste; and withal, apt to crumble between the fingers. The best castoreum and most effectual, is brought out of Pontus and Galatia : next to it is that of Africa or Barbary. The virtue of castoreum is to provoke sneezing, if a man hold it to his nose and smell thereto.

TORTOISES

As touching those kind of tortoises that live and breed in mud and moory waters, which I reckoned to be the third kind : broad they be and flat in the back as well as upon the breast; neither doth their shell arise archwise in manner of a vault : These are illfavoured to see to, and yet as loveless as they be, they are not without some medicinable virtues and remedies : for take three of them and throw them into a fire made of vine twigs, or their cuttings; when their shells or covers begin to divide in sunder and part one from another, pull them hastily out of the fire, pluck the flesh out of their shells, seethe them in a gallon of water, with a little quantity of salt put thereto; thus let them boil until a third part of the liquor be consumed : This broth or decoction if it be drunken, is thought to be sovereign for those that be troubled either with the palsy, gout, or pain of joints.

FROGS

Moreover, *Democritus* saith, that if a man take out the tongue of a frog alive, so that no other part thereof stick thereto, and after he hath let the frog go again into the water, apply the said tongue unto the left pap of a woman whiles she is asleep, in the very place where the heart beateth, she shall answer truly and directly in her sleep, to any interrogatory or question that is put unto her. But the magicians tell more wonders than so of the frog; which if they be true, certes frogs were more commodious and profitable to a commonwealth, than all the positive written laws that we have : for they would make us believe, that if the husband take a frog and spit her (as it were) alength upon a reed, so as it go in at the skut or mature behind and come forth again at the mouth; and then prick the same reed or broch in the menstrual blood of his wife, she will never have mind afterwards to entertain any adulterers, but detest and loathe that naughty kind of life. Certain it is, that if frogs' flesh be put within a net, or that a hook be baited therewith, purple fishes above all others, will come flocking thither. Moreover, it is commonly said, that a frog hath a double liver, which ought to be laid before ants; and look which of the two lobes or flaps thereof they make unto and seem to gnaw, the same is a most singular antidote against all poisons whatsoever.

Some frogs there be that live only among bushes and in hedges, which thereupon we call in Latin by the name of rubetae, and the Greeks term them phrynos : the biggest they are of all other, with two knobs bearing out in their front like horns, and full of poison they be. They that write of these toads, strive a-vie who shall write most wonders of them : for some say, that if one of them be brought into a place of concourse where people are in great number assembled, they shall be all hushed, and not a word among them. They affirm also, that there is one little bone in their right side, which if it be thrown into a pan of seething water, the vessel will cool presently and boil no more, until it be taken forth again. Now this bone (say they) is found by this means : If a man take one of these venomous frogs or toads, and cast it into a nest of ants for to be eaten and devoured by them, and look when they have gnawed away the flesh to the very bones, each bone one after another is to be put into a kettle seething upon the fire, and so it will be soon known which is the bone, by the effect aforesaid. There is another such like bone (by their saying) in the left side; cast it into the water that hath done seething, it will seem to boil and waulme again presently : this bone (forsooth) is called apocynon : and why so? because ywis, that there is not a thing more powerful to appease and repress the violence and fury of cursed dogs, than it. They report moreover, that it inciteth unto wanton love; and yet natheless if a cup of drink be spiced therewith, it will breed debate and quarrels among those that drink thereof : also, whosoever carrieth it about him, shall be provoked to fleshly lust : and contrari- wise, if the bone in the right side be likewise used, it will cool as much, and take down the pride of flesh and heat of concupis- cence. Others there be who are of opinion, that if it be but worn about one, either hanging to the neck, or fastened upto any other part of the body, enfolded within a little piece of a new lamb's skin, it will cure a quartan ague, or any other fever besides. The same also represseth the affection of love. Moreover, they bear us in hand, that the milt of these toads is a counterpoison against their own venom : but the heart (say they) is much more effectual.

CRABS AND SNAKES

The sea-crabs are nothing so good of operation in all these causes, as the land-crabs or crayfishes aforesaid, according as

Thrasillus mine author doth report. Howbeit, he saith nevertheless, that there are no such enemies to serpents, as crabs: and he affirmeth moreover, that if swine be stung or hurt by serpents, they help and cure themselves by feeding upon sea-crabs only, and seek for no other help or remedy. He addeth furthermore and avoucheth, that serpents are ill at ease yea and much tormented with pain when the sun is in the sign of the Crab, called commonly Cancer.

OYSTERS

Now proceed I will to their medicinable virtues, and before I go any further, in this very place set down how far forth they serve in physic. First and foremost, they be the only meat to comfort and refresh a decayed stomach: they recover an appetite that was clean gone. But see the practice of our delicate wantons! to cool oysters forsooth, they must needs whelm and cover them all over with snow; which is as much as to bring the tops of mountains and bottom of the sea together, and make a confused medley of all. This good moreover do oysters, that they generally loose the belly, and make a body soluble: seethe the same with honeyed wine, they cure the tinesme, which is an inordinate and bootless desire to the stool without doing anything, especially if the tiwill (which is the place affected) be not exulcerat.

FOR THE HAIR

If by occasion of some infirmity the hair be fallen off or grow very thin, the ashes of the fish called the sea-horse, mingled with sal-nitre and swines' grease, or applied simply with vinegar, replenish the bare places with new hair, and cause it to come up thick again: and for to apply such medicines for this purpose, the powder of a cuttle-bone prepareth the skin well beforehand. Also the ashes of the sea-tortoise incorporat with oil: of a sea urchin likewise burnt and calcined flesh and all together: as also the gall of a scorpion, be appropriate medicines to recover hair that was lost. In like manner, take the ashes of three frogs burnt together alive in an earthen pot, meddle them with honey, it is a good medicine to cause the hair to grow : but the operation will be the better, in case the same be tempered with liquid pitch or tar. If one be disposed to colour the hair of the head black, let him take horse-leeches which have putrified and been resolved together in some gross red wine for the space of three score days, he shall find this to be an excellent medicine. Others there be who give order, to put as many horseleeches as a sextar will hold, in two sextars of vinegar, and let them putrify in a vessel of lead as many days together; and when they be reduced into the form of a liniment, to anoint the hair in the sunshine for the same purpose. And *Sornatius* attributeth so much power unto this composition, that unless they that have the anointing of the hair with it hold oil in their mouths all the while, their teeth also (by his saying) who have the doing of it, will turn black.

FOR THE TEETH

Furthermore, to make a collution to wash the teeth withal, & to hold the liquor in the mouth, some seethe frogs in vinegar, with this proportion, that to every frog they take one hemine of vinegar. But because many a man's stomach loathed and abhorred such a medicine, *Sallustius Dionysius* found the means to hang many of them by the hinder legs over a vessel or pan of seething vinegar, that out of their mouth there might fall the humour within their bodies into the said vinegar. But to those who had good stomachs and were of stronger complexions, he prescribed to eat the very frogs' broth and all wherein they were sodden.

A COUGH-CURE

Item, it is said, that frogs boiled in some broth between two platters after the manner of fishes, are good for a cough : and being hanged by the heels, after that their salivation and humidity is dropped from them into a pan or platter underneath, they are to be rid of their garbage, and when the same is flung away, they ought to be kept and preserved for the purpose aforesaid.

There is a little frog that useth to climb trees, & from thence crieth and croaketh : if a man spit into the mouth of one of them, and then let her go again, it is thought he shall be delivered by that means from the cough.

LEECHES

On the contrary side, the horseleeches which we call in Latin sanguisugas, (i.e. bloodsuckers) are used for to draw blood. And verily it is judged, that there is the same reason of them, as of ventoses and cupping-glasses used in physic, for to ease and discharge the body of blood, and to open the pores of the skin. But here is all the harm and discommodity of these horseleeches, that if they be once set to for to draw blood, the body will look for the same physic again every year after, about the same time, and be ill at ease for want thereof. Many physicians have thought it good to use them for the gout of the feet also. Well, set them to the haemorrhoids, and where you will, they fall off lightly when they are full and satisfied, even with the very weight of the blood which pulleth them down; or else by strewing some salt about the place where they stick to : and otherwhiles it falleth out, that they leave their heads behind them fast fixed in the place where they settled, and by that means make the wound incurable and mortal, which hath cost many a man his life : as it happened to *Messalinus* a nobleman of Rome, and who in his time had been a consul, whose fortune it was to die thereupon, having set them to his knee : whereby we may see, that oftentimes they bring a mischief for a remedy : and the red ones are they that in this respect ought to be feared. To prevent therefore this dangerous inconvenience, they use with a pair of scissors to clip them at the very mouth as they be sucking; and then shall you see the blood spring out, as it were at the cock of a conduit, and so by little and little as they die, they will gather in their heads, and the same will fall off, and not tarry behind to do hurt.

DEPILATORIES

But in using any depilatory whatsoever, this one point is generally to be observed, that the hairs be first pulled up by the roots, in any place, where you would not have them to grow.

FOR CHILDREN

To come now unto the gums of children, and their breeding of teeth : the ashes of dolphins' teeth mixed with honey, is a sovereign medicine : yea or if you do but touch their gums with a dolphin's tooth all whole as it is, the effect thereof is admirable : the same hanged about their necks, or tied to any part of the body, riddeth them of sudden frights, whereunto infants are much given.

DARKNESS VISIBLE

The black liquor resembling ink which is found in the cuttlefish, is of that force, that if it be put to the oil of a lamp burning (*Anaxilaus* saith) it will drown and put out the former clear light, and make all those in the room to look like blackamoors or Aethyopians.

THE CREATURES OF THE SEA

Having thus treated before sufficiently of the natures and properties of fishes, and such creatures as the water doth yield : it remaineth now for a final conclusion, to present under one view, all those fishes name by name, which are engendered and nourished not only in those mediterranean and inland arms of the sea, which for many a mile take up a great part of the continent and firm land, but also in that vast and wide ocean without the main, bounded as it were and limited only by the compass and circumference of the heaven : and those, namely as many as be known, may be reduced all into 176 kinds : a thing which cannot be done either in the beasts of the land or fowls of the air. For how is it possible to decipher and particularize the wild beasts and fowls of India and Aethyopia, of the deserts, and of Scythia, which we are not come to the knowledge of, seeing we have found so many different sorts in men, of whom we have some notice and intelligence ? To say nothing of Taprobane, and other islands lying within the ocean, whereof so many fabulous reports are delivered : certes, there is no man but he must needs confess and agree to this, that it was not possible in this history of Nature to comprise all sorts of creatures which the earth and air do yield. Howbeit, those that are bred in the ocean, as huge and vast as it is, may be comprehended under a certain number : a wonderful matter that we should be better acquainted with those, considering how Nature hath plunged and hidden them in the deep gulf of the main sea.

THE FISH HYAENA

As for the fish hyaena, I myself have seen one of them taken in the island Aenaria, which used to put forth and draw in his head at his pleasure.

THE THREE AND THIRTIETH BOOK

treateth of gold and silver mines.

PREFACE

Now IS it time to enter into the discourse of the metals and minerals, the very riches and precious treasure of the world, which men so curiously and carefully seek after, as that they stick not to search into the very bowels of the earth by all the means they can devise: for some you shall have (to enrich themselves) for to dig into the ground for mines of gold and silver, base metal electrum, copper and brass: others again, upon a desire of dainty delights and bravery, to lay for gems and precious stones, for such minerals (I say) which may serve partly to adorn their fingers, and partly to set out the walls of sumptuous buildings with clostly colours, rich marbles, and porphyries. Lastly, there be many, who to maintain rash quarrels and audacious attempts, spare for no labour to get iron and steel, and esteem it better than gold, for cruel wars and bloody murders. In sum, there is not a vein in the whole earth but we pry and search into it: we follow it also as far as it goeth. Thus having undermined the poor ground, we live and go aloft upon it, as over hollow vaults and arches under our feet: and yet we would seem to wonder, that otherwhiles she cleaveth asunder into wide and gaping chinks, or else trembleth and quaketh again: and we will not see how these be apparent signs of the wrath of this our blessed mother, which we wring and force from her, to express the indignation that she taketh for this wrong and misusage. We descend into her entrails: we go down as far as to the seat and habitation of the infernal spirits, & all to meet with rich treasure : as if the earth were not fruitful enough and beneficial unto us in the upper face thereof, while she permitteth us to walk and tread upon her. Howbeit, in all this pains that we take to ransack the mines thereof, the least matter of all other is to seek for anything that concerneth physic and the regiment of our health : For among so many masters as there be of mines, where is there one that would be at such expense of digging, in regard of any medicines? And yet I must needs say, that as the earth otherwise is no niggard, but boun- teous and liberal, ready also and easily entreated to bring forth all things good and profitable for us : so in this behalf she hath furnished us sufficiently with wholesome drugs and medicinable simples growing above and fit for our hand, without need of dig- ging deep for the matter. But the things that she hath hidden and plunged (as it were) into the bottom, those be they that press us down, those drive and send us to the devil in hell : even those dead creatures (I say) which have no life nor do grow at all. In such sort, as to consider the thing aright, and not to captivate our spirits to such base matters, how far think we, will covetous minded men pierce & enter into earth? or when will they make an end of these mines, hollowing the ground as they do in all ages from time to time, and making it void and empty? Oh how innocent a life, how happy and blessed, nay, how pleasant a life might we lead, if we coveted nothing else but that which is above the ground : and in one word, if we stood contented with that which is ready to hand and even about us. But now, not sufficed with the gold which we fetch out of the mines, we must seek for the green earth borras also, which lieth hard by, yea, and give it a name respective unto gold, whereby it might be though more dear and precious. For why? we thought not the invention and finding out of gold alone to be enough for to infect and corrupt our hearts, unless we made great account also of that vile and base mineral, which is the very ordure of gold, and no better. Men upon a covetous mind would needs seek for silver, and not satisfied therewith, thought good withal to find out mineral vermilion, devising means how to use that kind of red earth. Oh the monstrous inventions of man's wit! What a num- ber of ways have we found to enhance the price and value of everything! for painters of the one side with their artificial paint-

ing and enamelling: the gravers of the other side with their
curious cutting and chasing, have made both gold and silver the
dearer by their workmanship: such is the audacity of man,
that he hath learned to counterfeit Nature, yea, and is so bold
as to challenge her in her work.. And wherein is the art and
cunning of these artificers so much seen, as in the workmanship
of such portraitures upon their gold and silver plate, which
might incite and provoke men to all kind of vices: for in process
of time we took pleasure to have our drinking bowls and goblets
engraven all over with those works which represent lust and
wantonness: and our delight was to drink out of such beastly
cups which might put us in mind of sinful and filthy lechery:
but afterwards these cups also were cast aside and laid away,
men began to make but base account of them: gold and silver
was so plentiful and common, that we had too much thereof.
What did we then? Forsooth we digged into the same earth for
cassidony and crystal, and we loved to have our cups and other
vessels of such brittle minerals; and the more precious we held
them, as they were more subject to breaking: so as nowadays he
is thought to have his house most richly furnished, who hath his
cupboards best stored with this ticklish ware: and the most
glorious show that we can make of excess and superfluity, is this,
to have that which the least knock may break, and being once
broken, the pieces thereof might be worth nothing. Neither is
this all, for stay we cannot here, we are not yet at cost enough,
unless we may drink out of a deal of precious stones. Our cups
otherwise chased, engraved, and embossed in gold, must be set
out with emeralds besides: to maintain drunkenness, to make
a quarrel to carouse and quaff, we must hold in our hand and
set to our mouth the riches of India. So as, to conclude, our
golden plate comes behind precious stones and pearls, and we
count it but an accessory and dependant, which may be
spared.

RINGS

Well, a bad example and precedent gave he unto the world,
who first devised to wear rings upon the fingers: But who he
was that did this harm unto mankind, it appeareth not for cer-

z

tain upon any record. For as touching the reports that go of *Prometheus*, I hold them all but fabulous tales: and yet in all the ancient pictures and portraitures of him, he is to be seen by a general consent of antiquity, with a ring of iron: howbeit, I suppose that they represented thereby his bonds and imprisonment, rather than any custom that he had to wear a ring as an ornament upon his finger.

* * * * *

Certes, long it was first (as appeareth evidently by the chronicles) ere the very Senators of Rome had rings of gold. For plain it is, that the State allowed and gave rings only to certain especial lieutenants when they were to go in embassage to foreign nations: and in mine opinion, it was for their credit and countenance, for that the most honourable personages in strange countries were distinguished from others by that ornament. And verily, no person (of what degree soever) was wont to wear rings, but such as had received them first from the Commonwealth upon that occasion: and so it served them ordinarily in triumph, as a token and testimonial of their virtue and valour. For otherwise, he that triumphed in Rome, although there was a Tuscan coronet all decked with spangles of gold, born up behind and held over his head, had no better than a ring of iron upon his finger, no more than the slave at his back, who haply carried the said Tuscan chaplet. For certainly in that manner triumphed *C. Marius* over king *Iugurtha*: and as the chronicles do show, received not a golden ring, nor took upon him to wear it before his third Consulship. And even those also who from the State had golden rings given them, in regard of embassage aforesaid, never used them but when they came abroad into open place, for within doors they might wear none but of iron: which is the reason, that even at this day the wedding ring which the bridegroom sendeth as a token of espousal to his bride, is of iron simply without any stone set in it.

* * * * *

And verily in my conceit whosoever began first to wear these rings, did it covertly by little and little, putting them upon the fingers of the left hand, the better to hide them, as if they were ashamed to have them openly seen : whereas if they might have avowed the honouring of their fingers by that ornament, they should have shewed them at the first upon the right hand. Now if any man object and say, that the wearing them on the right hand might be of some impeachment to a soldier for using his offensive weapon which he beareth in that hand; I allege again, that the hindrance was more in the left hand, which serveth to hold and manage the target or buckler defensive.

*　　*　　*　　*　　*

And verily we hold in these days a seal to be the best assurance in contracts, that may be : but I wot not how long it is since that custom first came up. And yet if we consider the fashions and manners of strange nations, we may peradventure find how these signets came into such credit and authority : and namely by the history of *Polycrates* the tyrant or king of the isle Samos : who having cast into the sea a ring which he loved and esteemed above all other jewels, met with the same again by means of a fish which was taken, in the belly whereof the said ring was found. Now this king was put to death, about the two hundred and thirtieth year after the foundation of our city. Howbeit, the ordinary use of these signets (as I suppose by all reason and likelihood) began together with usury : for proof whereof, mark how still at this day, upon any stipulation and bargain parole made, off goes the ring presently to confirm and seal the same. The which custom no doubt came from old time, when there was no earnest nor godspenie more ready at hand than a signet. So we may conclude assuredly and affirm, that among us here at Rome, when the use of money and coin was taken up, soon after came the wearing of rings in place.

GOLD AND JEWELLERY

All the gold employed in sacrifice to the honour of gods, was in gilding the horns of such beasts as were to be killed, and those only of the greater sort. But in warfare among soldiers, the use of gold grew so excessive, that the field and camp shone again withal : insomuch as at the voyage of Macedonia, where the marshals of the field and colonels bare armour set out with

rich buckles and clasps of gold, *M. Brutus* was offended and
stormed mightily at it, as appeareth by his letter found in the
plains about Philippi. Well done of thee, O *M. Brutus*, to find
fault with such wasteful superfluity : but why saidst thou
nothing of the gold that the Roman dames in thy time wore in
their shoes? And verily this enormity and abuse, I must needs
impute unto him (whosoever he was) that first devised rings, and
by that means caused gold to be esteemed a metal of much
worth : which evil precedent brought in another mischief as bad
as it, which hath continued a long time; namely, that men also
should wear about their arms, bracelets of gold next to their bare
skins : which device and ornament of the arm is called Dar-
danium, because the invention came from the Dardanians : like
as the fine golden carcanets viriæ, we term Celticæ, and the
necklaces of gold viriolæ, Celtibericæ. Oh the monstrous disorders that are crept into the world! But say that women may
be allowed to wear as much gold as they will, in bracelets, in
rings on every finger, and joint, in carcanets about their necks,
in earrings pendant at their ears, in stays, wreaths, & chinbands;
let them have their chains of gold as large as they list under
their arms or cross over their sides, scarf-wise; be gentlewomen
and mistresses at their collars of gold, beset thick and garnished
with massy pearls pendant from their neck, beneath their waist;
that in their beds also when they should sleep they may remember
what a weight of pearls they carried about them : must they
therefore wear gold upon their feet, as it were to establish a
third estate of women answerable to the order of knights, between
the matrons or dames of honour in their side robes, and the
wives of mean commoners? Yet methinks, we men have more
reason and regard of decency, thus to adorn with brooches and
tablets of gold, our youths and young boys, and a fairer sight
it is to see great men attended upon to the bains by beautiful
pages thus richly decked and set out, that all men's eyes may
turn to behold them. But what mean I thus bitterly to inveigh
against poor women; are men not also grown to such outrageous
excess of this kind, that they begin to wear upon their fingers
either Harpocrates, or other images of the Egyptian gods engraven upon some fine stone?

MONEY

In sum, the very source and original of all avarice proceedeth from this money and coin, devised first by loan and usury, and continued still by such idle persons that put forth their moneys to work for them, whiles they sit still, and find the sweetness of the gain coming in so easily. But this greedy desire of having more still, is grown after an outrageous manner to be excessive, and no more to be named covetousness, but rather unsatiable hunger after gold: insomuch as *Septimuleius*, an inward and familiar friend of *C. Gracchus*, forgot all bonds of amity, and having cut off his friend's head, upon promise to have the weight of it in gold, brought the same unto *Opimius*; howbeit, he poured molten lead into the mouth thereof to make it more heavy, and so together with this particide and unnatural murder, cousened also and beguiled the Commonweal. But to speak no more of any particular citizen of Rome, the whole name of the Romans has been famous among foreign nations for avarice and corruption in this kind: as may appear by the conceit that king *Mithridates* had of them, who caused *Aquilius* (a general of theirs, whose hap was to fall into his hands) for to drink molten gold. See what covetousness brings home with it in the end.

AN INSULT TO NATURE

Messala the great Orator hath left in writing, that *M. Antonius* used to discharge all the ordure and filthy excrements of the body into vessels of gold, yea, and allowed *Cleopatra* likewise to do the same by her monthly superfluities, most shamefully. Noted it was among foreign nations for excessive licentiousness, & that in the highest degree, that king *Philip* of Macedonia was never wont to go to bed and sleep without a standing cup of gold under his pillow: also, that *Agnon Teius* (a great captain under *Alexander* the Great) was given to such wasteful prodigality, as to fasten his shoes and pantophles with buckles of gold. But *Antonie* abovenamed, to the contumely and contempt of Nature, abused gold, and employed it to the basest service that is: an act (as much as any other) deserving proscription and outlawing indeed.

DISPLAYS OF GOLD AND SILVER

Besides, there had reigned beforetime over the Colchians, *Salauces* and one *Esubopes*: who having newly broken up a piece of ground in the Samnians' country, is reported to have gotten out thereof great store of silver and gold, notwithstanding that the whole kingdom is renowned for the golden fleeces there. And verily this prince had the arched and embowed roofs of his palace made of silver and gold: the beams and pillars also sustaining the said building, yea, the jambs, posts, principals, and standards, all of the same metal, namely, after he had vanquished *Sesostres* king of Egypt, so proud a prince, that (as the chronicles make mention) he was wont every year to have one or other (as the lot fell out) of those kings who were his tributaries and did homage unto him, for to draw in his chariot like horses, when he was disposed to ride in triumph. These and suchlike things have been thought fabulous tales: but have not our Romans done semblable acts, which the age and posterity hereafter will think incredible? *Caesar* afterwards Dictator, was the first that in his Aedileship, when he exhibited a solemn memorial in the honour of his father departed, did furnish the whole cirque and show-place, with all things meet for such a solemnity, of clean silver; insomuch as the chasing staves and boarspears were of silver, wherewith the wild beasts were assaulted: a spectacle never seen before. And not long after *C. Antonius* set forth his plays (when he was Aedile) upon a stage or scaffold of silver: after whose example, divers free cities and towns of the Empire have done the like. Semblably, *L. Muraena* and *C. Caligula* the Emperor, erected a frame or pageant to go and rise up of itself with vices, supporting images and jewels in the place of public pastimes, which was thought to have in it 124,000 pound of silver. *Claudius Caesar* who succeeded Emperor after him, when he rode in triumph for the conquest of Britain, among other crowns of beaten gold, shewed twain that were principal, the one of seven pound weight, which high Spain had given unto him; the other weighing nine pounds, sent unto him as a present from that part of Gaul which is called Comata: as compared by the inscriptions and titles which they bare. *Nero* his successor, to show unto *Tyridates* king of Armenia

what abundance of treasure he had, kept the great Theatre of
Pompeius for one whole day covered all over with gold. But
what was that furniture in comparison of his golden house, which
took up a great part of the city, and seemed (as it were) to
compass it about.

WHY GOLD IS THOUGHT PRECIOUS

As for the estimation of this metal, that it should be chief as
it is, I suppose it proceedeth not from the colour, for silver hath
a brighter lustre, more like to the day, and in this respect more
agreeable to the ensigns of war than that of gold, because it
glittereth and shineth farther off: And hereby is their error
manifestly convinced, who commend the colour of gold, in this
regard, that it resembleth the stars: for well it is known that their
colour is not reputed richest, either in precious stones or in many
things besides. Neither is gold preferred before other metals,
because the matter is more weighty or pliable than the rest; for
lead surmounteth it, both in the one and the other. But I hold,
that the reputation which it hath, cometh from hence, that it
alone of all things in the world, loseth nothing in the fire: for
say that a house be burnt wherein gold is, yet it wasteth not:
and look what gold is committed to the funeral flames, it consumeth not with the dead body, but is found all again among the
ashes. Nay, the oftener that it hath been in the fire, the better
it is and the more refined: in such sort, that the best gold which
they call obryzum, is known by this, if it be of the same deep
red colour that the fire is wherein it is tried. And a principal
argument this is of fine gold, if it hardly be kindled and set on
fire red hot. Moreover, this is wonderful in the nature of gold,
that in a fire made of light straw or chaff, it will most quickly
become red hot and melt; put the same among the hottest burning coals that can be of wood, unneath or hardly will it yield to
the heat thereof and resolve: as also for the purifying thereof,
it ought to be melted with lead. A greater reason there is besides
that maketh gold so precious: for that with use or handling
there is little of it lost and wasted; whereas silver, brass, and lead,
if you draw any lines therewith, colour as they go and leave
somewhat behind: they soil their hands also who occupy the

same with the substance and matter that sheddeth from them. Over and besides, there is not a metal will be driven out broader with the hammer, or divide easily into more parcels than gold, insomuch as every ounce of it may be reduced into seven hundred & fifty leaves, or more, and each one of them four fingers large every way.

*   *   *   *   *

But this passeth all, that spun it may be as wool and silk, woven also in manner of yarn, choose whether you will work it twisted with (silk) thread, or single in wire by itself. *Verrius* the historiographer reporteth, that king *Tarquinius*, surnamed *Priscus*, rode in triumph in a robe of wrought gold. I myself have seen the Empress *Agrippina*, wife to *Claudius Caesar*, sitting by her husband the Emperor to behold the brave show of a naval skirmish upon the water which he exhibited, all gorgeously arrayed in a royal mantle, woven without any other matter save only pure gold.

MINING FOR GOLD

The third manner of searching for this metal, is so painful and toilsome, that it surpasseth the wonderful works of the Giants in old time : For necessary it is in this enterprise and business, to undermine a great way by candlelight, and to make hollow vaults under the mountains. In which labour the pioneers work by turns successively, after the manner of the relief in a set watch, keeping every man his hours in just measure : and in many a month space they never see the sun or daylight. This kind of work and mines thus made, they call arrugiae, wherein it falleth out many times, that the earth above head chinketh, and all at once without giving any warning, settleth and falleth, so as the poor pioneers are overwhelmed and buried quick : insomuch as considering these perils, it seemeth, that those who dive under the water into the bottom of the Levant seas for to get pearls, hazard themselves nothing so much as these pioneers. A strange thing, that by our rashness and folly we should make the earth so much more hurtful unto us than the water. Well then, to prevent as much as possibly may be, these mischiefs and dangerous accidents, they underprop the hills, and leave pillars and arches (as they go) set thick one by another to support the same. And yet, say they work safe enough and be not in jeopardy of their lives by the fall of the earth, yet there be other difficulties that impeach their work : for otherwhiles they meet with rocks of flint and rags, as well in undermining forward, as in sinking pits downright; which they are driven to pierce and cleave through with fire and vinegar. But for that the vapour and smoke that ariseth from thence, by the means, may stifle and choke them within those narrow pits and mines, they are forced to give over such fire work, & betake themselves oftentimes to great mattocks and pickaxes; yea, and to other engines of iron, weighing 150 pound apiece, wherewith they hew such rocks in pieces, and so sink deeper or make way before them. The earth and stones, which with so much ado they have thus loosed, they are fain to carry from under their feet in scuttles and baskets, upon their shoulders, which pass from hand to hand evermore to the next fellow. Thus they moil in the dark both day and night in these infernal dungeons, and none of them see the light of the day, but those that are last and next unto the pit's mouth or entry of the cave. If the flint or rock that they work into, seem to run in a long grain, it will cleave in length, and come away by the sides in broad flakes; and therefore the pioneers with ease make way, trenching and cutting round about it. Howbeit, be the rock as ragged as it will, they count not that their hardest work : For there is a certain earth resembling a kind of tough clay (which they call white loam) and the same intermingled with gritty sand, so hard baked together, that there is no dealing with it; it so scorneth and checketh all their ordinary tools and labour about it, that it seemeth inpenetrable. What do the poor labourers then? They set upon it lustily with iron wedges, they lay on load uncessantly with mighty beetils; and verily, they think that there is nothing in the world harder than this labour, unless it be this unsatiable hunger after gold, which surpasseth all the hardness & difficulty that is. Well, when the work is brought to an end within the ground, and that they have undermined & hollowed the hills as far as they think good, down they go with their arch-work abovesaid, which they builded as they went : They begin first at those props which are farthest

off, cutting the heads of the stanchions still as they return backward to the entrance of the work. Which done, the sentinel only,
who of purpose keepeth good watch without upon the top of the
same mountain that is thus undermined, perceives the earth
when it beginneth to sink and cleave, menacing by that token
a ruin thereof anon. Whereupon presently he giveth a sign either
by a loud cry or some great knock, that the pioneers underneath
may have warning thereby to get them speedily out of the mines,
and runneth himself apace down from the hill as fast as his legs
will give him leave. Then all at once on a sudden the mountain
cleaveth in sunder, & making a long chink, falleth down with
such a noise and crack, as is beyond the conceit of man's understanding, with so mighty a puff and blast of wind besides, as it
is incredible. Whereat these miners and poineers are nothing
troubled, but as if they had done some doughty deed, and
achieved a noble victory, they stand with joy to behold the ruin
of Nature's works, which they have thus forced. And when they
have all done, yet are they not sure of gold : neither knew they
all the whiles that they laboured and undermined, that there
was any at all within the hill : The hope (only) that they conceived of the thing which so greatly they desired, was a sufficient
motive to induce them to enterprise, and endure so great dangers,
yea and to get through withal and see an end. And yet I cannot
well say that here is all : for there is another labour behind as
painful every way as the other, and withal of greater cost and
charges than the rest, namely, to wash the breach of this mountain (that is thus cloven, rent, and laid open) with a current :
For which purpose they are driven many times to seek for water
a hundred miles off, from the crests of some other hills, and to
bring the same in a continued channel and stream all the way
along unto it. These riverets or furrows thus devised and conveyed, the Latins express by the name of corrugi : a word as I
take it derived *a corrivando*, i.e. of drawing many springs and
rills together into one head and channel. And herein consisteth
a new piece of work as laborious as any that belongeth to mines.
For the level of the ground must be so taken aforehand, that the
water may have the due descent and current when it is to run :
and therefore it ought to be drawn from the sources springing
out of the highest mountains : in which conveyance, regard

would be had as well of the valleys as the rising of the ground between, which requireth otherwhiles that the water be commanded by canals and pipes to ascend, that the carriage thereof be not interrupted, but one piece of the work answer to another. Otherwhiles it falleth out, that they meet with hard rocks and crags by the way, which do impeach the course of the water: and those are hewed through, and forced by strength of man's hand to make room for the hollow troughs of wood to lie in, that carry the foresaid water. But a strange sight it is to see the fellow that hath the cutting of these rocks, how he hangeth by cables and ropes between heaven and earth: a man that beheld him afar off, would say it were some flying spirit or winged devil of the air. These that thus hang, for the most part take the level forward, and set out by lines the way by which they would have the water to pass: for no treading out is there of the ground, nor so much as a place for a man's footing to rest upon. Thus you see what ado there is. And these good fellows whiles they be aloft, search with their hands and pluck forth the earth before them, to see whether it be firm and fast, able to bear the trunks or troughs for the water; or otherwise loose and brittle, which defect of the earth they call urium: for the avoiding thereof the fountainers fear neither rocks nor stones to make passage for their pipes or trunks aforesaid. Now, when they have brought the water thus to the edge & brow of the hills where these mines of gold should be, and from whence as from an head there is to be a fall thereof to serve their purpose; they dig certain square pools to receive the water, two hundred foot every way, and the same ten foot deep: in which they leave five several sluices or passages for the delivery of the water into the mines, and those commonly three foot square. When the said pools stand full, as high as their banks, they draw up the flood-gates: And no sooner are the stopples driven and shaken out, but the water gusheth forth amain with such a force, and carrieth so violent a stream therewith, that it rolleth down with it any stones be they never so big, lying in the way. And yet are we not come to an end of the toil, for there remaineth a new piece of work to do in the plain beneath. Certain hollow ditches are to be digged for to receive the fall of the water both from the pools above, and the mines also. These trenches the

Greeks term agogae, as a man would say conduits, and those are to be paved by degrees one under another. Besides, there is a kind of shrub or bush, named ulex, like unto rosemary, but that it is more rough and prickly, and the same is there planted because it is apt to catch and hold whatsoever pieces of gold do pass beside. The sides moreover of these canals and trenches, are kept in with planks and boards, and the same borne upon arches pendant through steep places, that by this means the canal may have passage and void away at length out of the land into the sea.

Lo what a work it is to search out and meet with gold!

SILVER-MINES

And verily, strange it is and wonderful, that the mines of silver in Spain which were so long ago begun by *Annibal*, should continue still as they do, and retain the name of those Carthaginians who first found, discovered, and brought them to light: of which, one named then Bebelo, & so called at this day, yielded unto *Annibal* daily 300 pound weight; which mine even at that time had gone under the ground and hollowed the mountain a good mile and a half: and all that way the Aquitans at this day standing in water, lade the same up, labouring night and day by the candle or lamp-light, every man in his turn, and during the burning of a certain measure of oil, in such wise as they divert the water from thence, and make a good big river thereof, to pass and run another way. A vein of silver which lieth but ebb within the ground, and is there discovered, the miners called crudana, as it were a raw vein. In old time those that digged for silver, if they met once with alum, were wont to give over their work and seek no farther: but of late days it happened, that under alum there was found a vein of white brass or laton, which fed men's hopes still, and cause them now to sink lower, and never rest so far as they can dig. And yet there is a damp or vapour breathing out of silver mines, hurtful to all living creatures, and to dogs especially.

QUICKSILVER

Furthermore, within these veins and mines aforesaid, there is a certain stone found, which yieldeth from it an humour continually, and the same continueth always liquid : men call it quick-silver (howbeit, being the bane and poison of all things whatsoever, it might be called death-silver well enough) so penetrant is this liquor, that there is no vessel in the world but it will eat and break through it, piercing and passing on still, consuming and wasting as it goeth : it supporteth anything that is cast into it, and will not suffer it to settle downward but swim aloft, unless it be gold only; that is the only thing which it loveth to draw unto it and embrace : very proper it is therefore to affine gold; for if gold and it be put together into earthen pots, and after shaking be poured out of one into another, it will mightily purify the gold and cast forth all the filthy excrements thereof; and when it hath rid away all the impurities and gross refuse, itself ought then to be separated from the gold : for which purpose, poured forth the one & the other ought to be, upon certain skins of leather well tewed and dressed until they be soft; through which the quick-silver may pass; and then shall you see it stand upon the other side in drops like unto sweat sent out by the pores of our skin, leaving the gold pure and fine behind it.

VERMILION

There is found also in silver mines a mineral called minium, i.e. vermilion, which is a colour at this day of great price and estimation, like as it was in old time : for the ancient Romans made exceeding great account of it, not only for pictures, but also for divers sacred and holy uses. And verily *Verrius* allegeth and rehearseth many authors, whose credit ought not to be disproved, who affirm, that the manner was in times past to paint the very face of *Iupiter's* image upon high and festival days, with vermilion : as also, that the valiant captains, who rode triumphant into Rome, had in former times their bodies coloured all over therewith : after which manner, noble *Camillus* (they say) entered the city in triumph. And even at this day, according to that ancient and religious custom, ordinary it is, to colour all the unguents that are used in the festival suppers at a solemn triumph, with vermilion. And no one thing do the Censors give charge & order for to be done, at their entrance into office, before the painting of *Iupiter's* visage with minium. The cause and motive that should induce our ancestors to this ceremony, I marvel much at, and cannot imagine what it should be.

*　　*　　*　　*　　*

Furthermore, this hath been observed, that the shining beams either of sun or moon, do much hurt to the lustre of vermilion, or anything painted therewith. But what means to prevent this inconvenience? Even to varnish the wall after the colour is dried upon it in this manner: Take white Punic wax, melt it with oil, and while it is hot, wash the said painting all over with pencils or fine brushes of bristles, wet in the said varnish. But when this varnish is laid on, it must be well chafed and heat again with red hot coals made of gall-nuts held close unto it, that the wall may sweat and fry again: which done, it ought afterwards to be rubbed over well with cerecloths, and last of all, with clean linen cloths, that it may shine again and be slick as statues of marble be.

Moreover, the workmen that are employed in their shops about the making of vermilion, do bind unto their faces in manner of masks, large bladders, that they may take and deliver their wind at liberty, and yet not be in danger of drawing in with their breath that pernicious and deadly powder, which is no better than poison: yet so, as they may see out of the said masks nevertheless.

To conclude, vermilion is used much in limning the titles and inscriptions of rolls and books, it setteth forth the letters also, and maketh them more fair and beautiful which are written in tables over sepulchres, be they enriched otherwise either with gold or marble stone.

HOW TO TELL GOOD SILVER

As touching silver, two degrees there be of it, different in goodness, which may be known and discerned in this manner: For lay a piece of silver ore upon a sclise, plate, or fire pan of iron red hot, if it continue white still, it is very good, if the same become reddish, go it may for good too in a lower degree;

but in case it look black, there is no goodness at all in it. Howbeit, there is some deceit also in this trial and experiment, which may cross a man in his judgement : for let the said sclise or plate lie a time in a man's urine, be the ore never so base that is laid thereupon when it is burning red hot, it will seem to take a white colour for the time, and deceive him that shall see it. To conclude, there is another pretty proof of silver fine, if it be bright and burnished, and that is by breathing upon it : for if the breath be seen thereupon presently as a sweat, and the same pass away incontinently as a cloud, it is a sign of perfect silver.

MIRRORS

An opinion it was sometime generally received and believed, that no plates might be driven by the hammer, nor mirrors made, but of the best and purest silver : And even this experiment is falsified and corrupted by deceit. But surely a wonderful thing in nature this is of those mirrors of silver, that they should represent so perfectly the image of anything that is before them, as they do : which must needs be (as all men confess) by the reverberation of the air from the solid body of the mirror, which being beaten back again from it, bringeth therewith the said image expressed therein. The same reverberation is the cause that such looking glasses as by much usage are polished and made subtile, do in that sort gently drive back the image represented within them, that it seemeth infinitely big in proportion of the body itself : such difference there is in them, and so material it is, whether they repercuss and reject the air, or receive and entertain it. Moreover, there be drinking cups so framed and fashioned with a number of mirrors within, that if there do but one look within them, he shall imagine that he saw a multitude of people, even as may images as there be mirrors. There are devised looking glasses also, which will represent monstrous shapes; and such be those mirrors that are dedicated in the temple at Smyrna : but this cometh by reason that the matter whereof they be made, is in that sort fashioned. For it skilleth much whether mirrors be hollow, either in manner of a drinking pot, or of a Threcidian buckler : whether the middle part lie low and inward, or rise

and bear out with a belly : whether they be set cross and over-
thwart, or stand bias : whether they hang with their heads bending backward, or bolt upright : For according as the matter
which receiveth the image, is disposed to this of that fashion, or
set one way or other, so it returneth the shadows back again :
for verily the said image represented in a mirror, is nothing else
but the brightness and clearness of the matter which receiveth
the same, returned and beaten back again. But to go through in
this place with all things concerning such looking glasses, the
best known in old time unto our ancestors, came from Brindis,
and those consisted of tin and brass tempered together. But when
silver mirrors came in place, those went down, and these were
preferred before them. The first that made them of silver, was
Praxiteles in the days of *Pompey* the great. Of late, men had this
opinion of silver mirrors, that they would represent an image
more lively and truly, in case their back part were laid over with
gold.

PAINTING ON SILVER

But to return again to silver, the Egyptians use a device to
paint it, to the end that they would drink more devoutly, seeing
their god *Anubis* painted within their pots. And in truth they rest
contented with painting their plate, and never grave or chase
any pieces. This devised fashion is grown into such credit by the
precedent received from thence, that the statues of silver carried
in a show at triumphs, be nought set by, unless they be also
enamelled and painted black : & wonderful it is how much
more precious they are thought to be when the native brightness
thereof is hidden, & the light thereof quite but out or
blindfolded.

FALSE COIN

To come now unto those that counterfeit money. *Antonius*
whiles he was one of the three usurping Triumvirs, mixed iron
with the Roman silver denier. He tempered it also with the
brassen coin, and so sent abroad false and counterfeit money.
Others there be that make money too light (namely, under the

lawful proportion) which is, to coin and stamp for every pound weight of silver fourscore and four deniers. This enormity grew to this pass, that *M. Gratidianus* published a law, by virtue whereof there was an act instituted and ordained for the proof and allowance of silver deniers, what touch & what poise they should have: by which act of his he so pleased the Commons of Rome, that there was not a street throughout all the city, but they erected a silver statue, portrayed all whole in a gown in the favour and honour of *Marcius Gratidianus*. But strange it is, and a man would not think it, that this art and cunning devised for the detecting of falsehood and forgery, is the only means to teach deceit and wickedness, for many a man will give too much for false money: yea, and many silver deniers for one counterfeit, well and cleanly made; to take forsooth a pattern thereby, and learn to deceive others.

THE FIRST PLUTOCRAT

In old time men knew no number above a hundred thousand: and therefore at this day also instead of a million we multiply the said number by ten, and say thus in Latin, *Decies centena millia*, i.e. a hundred thousand ten times told, and so forward repeating always a hundred thousand to the numeral adverb, as the sum doth amount. Usuries, interests, and coined money have been the cause of these multiplications; and by that occasion also came debts to be called even to this age, by the name of *aes alienum*. And thereof arose the proud name of *divites*, i.e. rich, for great monied men were so called. Yet take this withal, that the first man that ever was known by that surname *Dives*, brought a shilling to nine pence in the end, proved bankrupt, and defeated his creditors.

THE VANITY OF WEALTH

But what of all this? Set case these and suchlike men gathered together innumerable sums of money, and an infinite mass of goods, yet they shall come nothing near to the wealth of king *Ptolomaeus*, who according to the testimony of *M. Varro* (at what time as *Pompey* the Great warred about Jewry) maintained eight thousand horsemen in pay continually with his own private purse: kept an ordinary table within his court of a thousand persons, and those had every man his own cup of gold to drink out of, and at each course and change of meats that came in, new plate was served up still to the board. These guests of his fared so highly, that a man would have said they had been frank-fed. But how far short was this mighty and sumptuous prince think ye (for I will say no more now of kings) in comparison of one *Pythius* a Bithynian, who sent unto *Darius* the king a present of a plane-tree, all entire of beaten gold, and withal, that famous gold vine, so much renowned by all writers: feasted the whole army of that mighty monarch, & those were 788,000 men: promising over and above five months pay for them all, and corn for so long to serve the whole camp, if of five sons that he had of his own, the king would spare him but one to bear him company in his old age, and not prest him for to serve in the wars. Certes, a man that heareth thus much of this *Pythius*, might compare him with that rich *Croesus* king of Lydia. But what folly and madness in the devil's name is this, to hunger and thirst so much in this life after that, which either is common to base slaves and may fall unto them, or else whereof kings themselves can find no end? And thus much of gathering good and heaping riches together.

A SILVER DISH

No longer since, than in the days of *Claudius* the Emperor, *Drusillanus* a slave of his surnamed *Rotundus*, (the seneschal or treasurer under him in high Spain) had a silver charger of five hundred pound weight (for the working whereof, there was a forger framed beforehand of set purpose:) and the same was accompanied and attended with eight more of a smaller size, weighing fifty pound apiece. Now would I gladly know (if it might please you) how many of his fellows (such slaves I mean as himself) there must be to carry the said vessel and serve it up to the table? or what guests they might be who were to be served with such huge plate?

MODERN EXTRAVAGANCE IN THE USE OF SILVER

Moreover, it falleth out sometimes, that silver is used instead of gold also upon some urgent cause and just occasion : as we may see by our proud and sumptuous dames, that are but commoners' and artisans' wives, who are forced to make themselves carquans and such ornaments for their shoes, of silver, because the rigour of the statute provided in that case, will not permit them to wear the same of gold. And I myself, as I remember, have seen *Aurelius Fuscus* (a gentleman of Rome, who being put beside his place, and having lost the dignity of a man of arms, by reason of a notable calumniation framed against him, when as young gentleman's sons used to accompany him because he had the name of a brave soldier) wear his rings, of silver. But to what purpose do I collect these examples, seeing how our soldiers make no reckoning of ivory, but the hilts of their swords and the hafts of their daggers, be garnished with silver, damasked, and engraven; their scabbards and sheaths be set out with silver chapes, and their sword girdles, hangers, and baldrics, jingle again with thin plates of silver. And do we not see how our young boys are kept in and restrained with silver, during the time that they be under man's age? how our fine dames use to wash and bath in silver, disdaining and setting light by any other bathing-vessels in the bains? insomuch as the same metal and matter which we are served with at the table, is employed also in shameful and uncleanly uses. Oh that *Fabricius* were alive now again to behold these things! If he saw our women bathing together with men in one and the same bains, and those paved (as it were) under foot with silver so smooth and slippery that they cannot hold their feet : *Fabricus* I say, who forbade expressly, that any warriors and general captains should have in plate more than one drinking bowl or goblet, and a saltcellar : If he saw silver (which was wont to be given in presents and rewards to brave men and valiant captains) thus to be melted and broken to serve for these purposes, what would he say? but, what a world is this!

PRICES

To conclude with the prices of all those things named heretofore : howsoever hitherto I have set them down, yet I am not ignorant, how they vary according to the place; yea and alter in manner every year : And well I wot, that as shipping and navigation speed well or ill, as the merchant buyeth cheap or dear, the price may rise and fall. Again, it falleth out, that sometime one rich monger or other, buying up a commodity, and bringing it wholly into his own hands, for to have the monopoly of it, raiseth the market, and enhanceth the price : for I remember well, how in the days of *Nero* late Emperor, all the spicers, druggers, and apothecaries, preferred a bill of complaint unto the Consuls, against one *Demetrius* a regrater. Yet notwithstanding, I thought it necessary to put down the prices of things as they are ordinary valued at Rome one year with another, to shew in some sort (by a general estimate) the worth of such wares and commodities whereof I have written.

THE FOUR AND THIRTIETH BOOK

speaketh of copper and brass mines, also of lead, also of excellent brass-founders and workmen in copper

---

CORINTHIAN BRASS

BUT SETTING aside the glorious mascellin of old time, the Corinthian brass metal was most highly commended: And the same mixture happened even by mere chance and fortune, when the city Corinth was won, sacked and burnt to the ground: and wonderful it is how the minds of many great men was affected to this compound metal, and how they stood upon the having thereof, insomuch as (by report) there was no other cause in the world why *Verres,* whom *Cicero* had caused to be condemned, was together with him proscribed, outlawed, and banished by *Antonie,* but only this, for that he vaunted that he had as goodly vessels and pieces of Corinth metal as himself, and would not part with any of them to *Antonie.* Howbeit in my conceit, the most part of these men who delight thus in this Corinth mascellin, in a certain singularity by themselves, because they would seem to know more than their fellows, make semblance rather of a special insight and skill that they have therein, than know indeed anything by it of such exquisite stuff. And this will I shew and declare unto you in few words: The city of Corinth was won and destroyed in the 156 Olympias, and the third year thereof, which fell out to be in the 608 year by our computation at Rome: now long before this time, those great masters and imageurs, so famous for metal-founding and casting of images, were dead & gone; and yet all the pieces of their making, these men forsooth at this day will needs have to be of the Corinthian medley, and so they call them. And therefore to disprove this erroneous opinion of theirs, I purpose as I proceed in this my discourse, to range all the notable artificers that antiquity hath known in this kind, according to the several ages wherein they lived and flourished in the world. For easy it will be to calculate and collect the years from the foundation of our city, by the former comparison of them with the Olympiads. All the vessels then which our delicates have, those I mean that would seem to be more fine in their houses than their neighbours, are only of the Corinth metal and no better, which they cast partly into pots and pans and such like kitchen vessel for to seethe meat in : partly into candlesticks, chafers, chamber pots, and such-like homely and base vessels, without any regard of cleanness and neat service.

GEGANIA AND THE HUNCHBACK

In old time the island Aegina was in especial name for the workmanship only of the branches, sockets, and heads of candlesticks; like as Tarentum, for the shank, shaft, & body supporting the same : and therefore that candlestick was counted rich indeed, when both these places seemed to concur unto the making & workmanship thereof. For such a candlestick some have not been ashamed to give as much money as the salary and yearly pension of a Tribune military or Colonel, cometh unto : and yet you see, an implement or moveable it is, that hath but a vile and base name, for called it is in Latin candelabrum, of sticking a candle in it. But will you know who was so foolish as to bestow so much upon a candlestick, and what a tale belongeth thereunto, for to amend the hard bargain ? thus stood the case : It was a jolly dame in Rome, named *Gegania,* who made this wise match. And when she had so done, she must needs forsooth make a feast for to show this candlestick to her guests, which cost her fifty thousand sesterces. Now the founder or brazier that sold it her, was mis-shapen and bunch-backed. And order was taken by the commandment of *Clesippus,* a public crier of Rome, that he should in the midst of supper be brought into the place stark naked as ever he was born (and as foul and ill-favoured a fellow he was otherwise as a man should lightly see) under a colour to make sport and to set the company a laughing, but indeed to mock *Gegania* the mistress of the house. But what followed thereupon? The woman cast a fancy to him by and by, and in that heat of love, or lust rather, admitted him anon to her bed, and after set him in her will, and made him her heir. This crookbacked squire seeing himself exceedingly enriched by this double bargain, adored the said candlestick no less than a god, as the only cause of his rising and all the wealth he had: And thus by his occasion, one tale more goeth current abroad in the world, of Corinthian vessels. And yet afterwards (as it were to punish his mistress for that light behaviour of hers) he caused a stately and magnificent sepulchre to be made for her, whereby the infamy and shame of *Gegania* might be eternized and continue fresh in remembrance with all posterity.

STATUES

Certes, the manner was not in old time to express the lively similitude of men in brass, unless they were such worthy persons as by some notable and famous acts deserved to be immortalized, as namely, for winning the prizes at any of the four sacred and solemn games holden in Greece, & principally at those of Olympia, where it was an ordinary thing to see the statues of those erected and dedicated, who had achieved any victory there. But in any case any one were so happy as to obtain victory at those solemnities three several times, his statue in brass was so lively & perfectly cast, that it resembled his person full and whole, according to the proportion of every member, joint, and muscle of the body, yea even to the hair of head and beard. And such kind of complete images, the Greeks use to call iconicæ, i.e. personages. The manner of the Athenians was to honour men of singular virtue and valour, by representing their personages in brass: but I am not sure whether those Athenians were the first that brought up that manner, or no: true it is, that long ago they caused the statues of *Harmodius* and *Aristogiton*, to be made of brass at the charges of the state, and to be erected in public place, for that they had the courage and heart to kill *Pisistratus*, who tyrannized over them: and this fell out just in that very year wherein the kings also were deposed at Rome, and expelled the city for ever. And in process of time this manner was taken up in all parts of the world: so plausible unto the nature of man, is the ambitious desire to perpetuate their memory by such monuments, insomuch as there is not a good town within our provinces, but they have begun already to beautify their market places with many such ornaments of brassen statues and images; together with titles, honours, and dignities engraven at the bases or pied-stall thereof, for the better continuance of men's memorial, that the posterity might be informed by such inscriptions, as well as by their tombs and sepulchres. And at length the ambition of men proceeded so far, that as well their private houses within as the base-courts and porches without, were so beset with images, that a man would take them for some public places within a city: and all this arose from the devote courtesy of vassals, in token of homage and honour done to those their patrons and lords, whom they acknowledged to be the protectors and maintainers of their life and liberty.

COMPENSATION

As touching the statue of *L. Actius* a famous poet, I will report unto you what writers have recorded, namely, that being himself a very little man and low of stature, he caused his image to be made exceeding big and tall, and so to be set up within the temple of the Muses of Rome.

THE AMBASSADOR AND THE NUN

And here I cannot overpass one point noted in the annals, that the measure of these statues erected in the common place at Rome, was set down precisely to be three foot in height: whereby it may appear, that this proportion and scantling in those days was thought to be honourable. Neither will I conceal from you & omit the memorable example of *C. Octavius*, who for one word speaking, lost his life: This man being sent as Ambassador unto King *Antiochus,* and having delivered his message unto him according to his charge and commission, when he saw that the king made no haste to give him his dispatch presently, but said he would make him an answer another day; made no more ado, but with a wand or rod that he had in his hand, drew a circle about the king, and compelled him perforce to give him his answer before he stirred his foot without that compass. But this cost him his life : and for that he was killed thus in his embassage, the Senate of Rome ordained, that his statue should be erected in the most conspicuous place of the city, and that was in the public pulpit for pleas and orations, the rostra beforenamed. I read in the chronicles, that the Senate made a decree, that *Taracia Caia,* or, as some say, *Suffetia,* a votary or vestal nun, should have her image made of brass, with this special prerogative besides, that she might set it up in what place she would herself : which addition or branch of the decree implieth no less honour than the grant itself of a statue of a woman. What her desert might be, in consideration whereof she was thus honoured, I will set down word for word, as I find it written in the chronicles, namely, *For that she had conferred frankly upon the people of Rome, a piece of meadow ground lying under the river Tiber, which was her own free land.*

THREE HUNDRED AND SIXTY STATUES OF ONE MAN

Now, if a man be desirous to know the reason of these columns and pillars, which supported those statues aforesaid, it was to signify, that such persons were now advanced and lifted up above all other mortal men : which also is meant by the triumphant arches, a new invention, and devised but of late days : yet both it, and all other such honourable testimonies, began first with the Greeks. But among many and sundry statues which they granted and allowed unto such as they affected and liked of, I suppose, there was never man had more than *Phalerius Demetrius* at Athens : for the Athenians honoured him with three hundred and threescore : and yet soon after they brake them all to pieces, even before one full year went over their heads, that is to say, a few days more than there were images. Moreover, all the tribes or wards of Rome set up a statue in every street of the city (as I have said before) in the honour of *Marius Gratidianus,* and those they overthrew every one, against the coming in of *Sylla.*

STATUES OF AN INVADER

At length, there grew such disorder and confusion of these statues, that we had them pell mell at Rome without any choice or regard at all: insomuch, as at this day, there are no fewer than three statues of *Annibal* to be seen at Rome, in three several places of that city, within the walls whereof he was the only enemy ever known to have launched his javelin.

THE BRASS DOG

What good speed this art had, may appear by an example which I will set down, of an image, devised to express the likeness neither of god nor man: and a dog it was in brass, which many a man hath seen in our time in a chapel of *Iuno* within the Capitol temple, before it was burnt now last by the *Vitellians*: This dog was made licking his own wound; but how artificially it was wrought, and how lively it expressed the proportion and feature of a dog indeed, to the wonder of all those that beholding it could not discern the same from a living creature, is apparent not only by this, that it was thought worthy to stand in that place and to be dedicated to that goddess, but also by the strange manner of charge laid upon them that had the keeping and custody thereof: for no real caution of money was thought sufficient to be pledged and pawned for the warrantize, or to countervail the worth thereof: Order therefore was given by the state, and the same observed from time to time, that the sextons or wardens of the said chapel should perform the safety and forth-coming of it under pain of death.

THE COLOSSUS OF RHODES

But the coloss of the Sun which stood at Rhodes, and was wrought by *Chares* of Lyndus, apprentice to the above-named *Lysippus,* was above all others most admirable; for it carried seventy cubits in height: well, as mighty an image as it was, it stood not on end above threescore years and six; for in an earthquake that then happened, it was overthrown: but lying as it doth along, a wonderful and prodigious thing it is to view and behold : for first and foremost, the thumbs of the hand and great toes of the foot are so big, as few men are able to fadome one of them about : the fingers and toes are bigger than the most part of other whole statues and images : and look where any of the members or limbs were broken with the fall, a man that saw them would say they were broad holes and huge caves in the ground : for within these fractures and breaches, you shall see monstrous big stones, which the workmen at the first rearing and setting of it had couched artificially within, for to strengthen the coloss, that standing firm and upright so ballaised, it might check the violence of wind and weather. Twelve years (they say) *Chares* was in making of it before he could fully finish it, and the bare workmanship cost three hundred talents : This money was raised out of *K. Demetrius* his provision which he had set for that purpose, and paid from time to time by his officers, for that he would not himself endure to stay so long for the workmanship thereof. Other images there are besides of the nature of colosses in the same city of Rhodes to the number of one hundred, lesser indeed than the foresaid coloss of the Sun; yet there is not one of them, but for the bigness were sufficient to give a name to the place and ennoble it, wheresoever it should stand.

ANOTHER HUGE STATUE

Moreover, *Sp. Garvillius* long ago made the great image of *Iupiter* which standeth in the Capitol hill, after the Samnites were vanquished in that dangerous war, wherein they bound themselves by a sacred law and oath to fight it out to the last man, under pain of death to as many as seemed to turn back or once recule; to the making whereof, he took the brassen cuirasses, greaves, and morions of the enemies that lay dead and slain upon the ground : which is so exceeding big and large, that he may very plainly and evidently be discovered and seen from the other *Iupiter* in Latium, called therefore *Latiarus*. The powder and dust which the file made in the workmanship and polishing of this coloss, *Carvilius* himself cast again and thereof made his own image and portraiture, and the same standeth (as you may see) at the foot of the other.

THE COLOSSUS OF NERO

But to speak indeed of a great image, and that which surpasseth in bigness all the rest of that kind, look but upon the huge and prodigious coloss of *Mercury,* which *Zenodorus* in our age and within our remembrance, made in France at Auvergne : ten years he was about it, and the workmanship came to four hundred thousand sesterces. Now when he had made sufficient proof of his art there, *Nero* the Emperor sent for him to come to Rome, where he cast indeed and finished a coloss a hundred and ten foot long, to the similitude and likeness of the said Emperor, according as it was first appointed and as he began it : but the said prince being dead and his head laid, dedicated it was to the honour and worship of the Sun, in detestation of that most wicked monster, whose ungracious acts the city condemned and abhorred.

STATUETTES

The images and wrought pieces of brass, commonly called Corinthian works, many men take such pleasure and delight in, that they love to carry the same with them whithersoever they go; as *Hortensius* the famous orator, who would never be without the counterfeit of *Sphinx,* which he had from *Verres* his client, at what time as he was in trouble and called into question, for his extortions and oppressions in Sicily : in which trial of *Verres,* wherein *Cicero* was his adversary and accuser, upon occasion that *Hortensius* who pleaded at the bar against him in the behalf of *Verres,* among other cross words that passed between, happened to say, that he understood no parables and riddles, and therefore willed him to speak more plainly; *Cicero* made answer readily again, that by good reason he should be well acquainted with riddles, seeing he had a *Sphinx* at home in his house. Likewise, *Nero* the Emperor had a great fancy to a piece or counterfeit of an Amazon, (whereof I mean to write more hereafter) which by his good will he would never be without.

POLYCLETUS

As for *Polycletus* the Sicyonian, who learned his cunning under

Agelades, he it was that made in brass, *Diadumenus,* an effeminate young man looking wantonly, with a diadem of wreath about
his head; a piece of work of great account and much spoken of,
for that it cost a hundred talents : and of his making was *Dory-
phorus,* a young boy with a manly countenance, bearing a spear
in his hand. Moreover, he made that which workmen do call
Canon, that is to say, one absolute piece of work, from whence
artificers do fetch their draughts, symmetries, and proportions,
as from a perfect pattern or rule which guideth and directeth
them in their work : so as we may well and truly judge, that
Polycletus alone reduced the skill of foundry and imagery into an
art and method, as may appear both by that Canon, and by
other works which passed his hands. Of his workmanship was the
brassen image, representing one scraping and rubbing himself in
the bath or hothouse : as also another all naked, and challenging
to the dice : *Item,* two boys both naked playing at dice, which
thereupon be called Astragalizontes. And these remained to be
seen in the court or portal belonging to the house of *Titus* the
Emperor, which is such an exquisite piece of work, that many do
judge, there cannot be set another to it more absolute or perfect :
also, he it was that wrought the image of *Mercury* which is at
Lysimachia; of *Hercules* at Rome, and namely, how he heaved
and held up *Anteus* from the ground between heaven and earth :
and the counterfeit of *Artemon,* that effeminate and wanton person, who because he was ordinarily carried in a litter, men called
Periphoretos. This *Polycletus* was judged to have brought this art
of imagery to a consummate perfection : the feat also of engraving and embossing, he was thought to practise and promote; like
as *Phidias* before him opened the way to it, and gave instruc-
tions. This proper and special gift he had besides above all
other, to devise how images might stand upon one leg : and yet
Varro saith, that all the images of his making, be four square,
and all in manner after one pattern.

MYRON

This workman seemeth to have been the first that wrought not
his images after one sort, but altered his work after many
fashions, as being fuller of invention and given more to device in

his art, more curious also and precise in his symmetries and proportions, than *Polycletus*: And yet as exquisite as he was, he went no farther than to the outward lineaments of the body and members thereof; as for the inward affections of the mind, he did not express in any of his work: the hair also as well of head, beard, as share, he left after a gross manner, and wrought them no finer than the rude and inexpert workmen in old time, had either done or taught. No marvel therefore if *Pythagoras* (the imageur of Rhegium in Italy) went behind him in this feat, and namely in that piece of work of his which resembled a wrestler or Pancratiastes, which was dedicated in the temple of *Apollo* at Delphos. He came short also of *Leontius,* who expressed lively in brass, *Astylos,* the famous runner in a race; which image is showed for a rare piece of work in Olympia: also the boy *Libys,* which is to be seen in the same place, holding in his hand a little table, and withal carrying apples, stark naked. He made also the portraiture of one that seemed lame and to halt, upon some ulcer; but the same was so lively and naturally done, that as many as behold the same, seem to have a compassion and fellow-feeling with him of some pain and grievance of his sore; and this piece of work a man may see at Syracuse. Furthermore, the said, *Leontius* cast in brass one *Apollo* playing upon his harp: as also another *Apollo,* and the serpent killed with his arrows, which image he surnamed *Dicaeus,* i.e. Just; for that when the city of Thebes was won by *Alexander* the Great, the gold which he hid in the bosom thereof when he fled, was found there safe and not diminished, when the enemy was gone and he returned again. He was the first, that in his images expressed the sinews and veins lying under the skin: he it was also that couched and laid the hair of the head more handsomely, yea and wrought the same far more finely than any before him.

LYSIPPUS

As for *Lysippus* of Sicyone, *Duris* saith, that he learned the art by himself, and never was taught by other: but *Tullius* affirmeth, that he was apprentice unto it, and having been at first by occupation but a poor tinker or a plain brazier and coppersmith at the most, he began to take heart unto him, and to proceed further, by a speech or answer that *Eupompus* the painter gave him: for when he seemed to ask this painter's counsel, what pattern, and whom he were best to follow of all those workmen that were gone before him? he shewed unto him a multitude of people and said withal, that he should do best to imitate Nature herself, and no one artificer: and that was it (quoth he) which I meant by the former demonstration of so many men. And verily, so excellent a workman he proved in the end, that he left behind him the most pieces of any man, as I have said before, and those of all sorts, and fullest of art & good workmanship: and among the rest, an image of a man, currying, rubbing, and scraping the sweat and filth off his own body; which *M. Agrippa* caused to be set before his own bains: and the Emperor *Tiberius Caesar* took so great pleasure in it, that notwithstanding at his first coming to the crown, he knew well enough how to command and temper his own affections, yet he could not now rule himself, but would needs have the said image to be removed from thence into his own bed-chamber, and another to be set in the place of it: whereat the common people (see their contumacy and frowardness!) were so much offended and displeased at it, that they rested not with open mouth to exclaim upon him in all their theatres, when they met there together, and cried for to have their Apoxyomenos set again in the own place: Insomuch, as the Emperor was content for to do, notwithstanding he loved it so well. This *Lysippus* also won greater credit and commendation by another image that he made, representing a woman piping or playing upon the flute, and drunken withal: also by a kennel of hounds, together with the huntsman & all belonging to the game. But above all, he gat the greatest name for making in brass a chariot drawn with four steeds, together with the image of the Sun, so much honoured among the Rhodians. The personage of King *Alexander* the Great he likewise expressed in brass, and in many images he made of him, beginning at the very childhood of the said prince. And verily the Emperor *Nero* was so greatly enamoured upon one image of *Alexander,* that he commanded it to be gilded all over: but afterwards, seeing that the more cost was bestowed upon it by laying on gold, the less was the art seen of the first workman, so that it lost all the beauty and grace that it had by that means, he caused all the gold to be taken off again : and verily, the said image thus ungilded as it was, seemed far more precious than it was whiles it stood so enriched with gold, notwithstanding all the hacks, cuts, gashes, and rases all over the body wherein the gold did stick, remained still, which in some sort might disfigure it.

PRAXITELES

As for *Praxiteles,* his workmanship was more seen in cutting of marble, and making images thereof, wherein he had a singular grace and rare felicity, and in which regard, his name was the greater. Yet he shewed good proof of his skill in foundry also For there be most beautiful cast images of brass which he made, to wit, the ravishing of *Proserpina* by *Pluto,* a spinster spinning, which be called *Catagusa*: the image of drunkenness : god *Bacchus* attended with one of the Satyrs; a noble piece of work, and which, for the great voice and bruit that went of it, the Greeks surnamed *Periboetos.* The brassen images likewise which stood sometimes in the forefront of the temple at Rome dedicated to *Felicity,* were of his making : as also the goddess *Venus,* which when the chapel wherein she stood erected, was burnt (during the reign of *Claudius Caesar* the Emperor) was melted; an exquisite piece of work, and comparable to that *Venus* of his cutting in marble, which all the world speaketh so much of. He portrayed also in brass a woman making coronets and chaplets of flowers, which goeth under the name of *Stephusa*: a foul old trot and a nasty, bearing the title of *Spilumene*: a carrier also of flagons or wine-pots, known by the addition of *Oenophorus.* He expressed moreover in brass and that most lively, *Harmodius* and *Aristogiton,* massacring the tyrant *Pisistratus*: which images being with other pillage taken and carried away by *Xerxes* king of the Persians, and recovered by king *Alexander* the Great when he had conquered the kingdom of Persis, the said prince and conqueror restored to the Athenians, and sent them home to them again. Furthermore, he cast in brass a youth lying in wait with an arrow to kill a lizard, which was ready to creep close unto him and to sting; which piece of work he termed *Sauroctonus.* Two images there are besides in his making, which people take much pleasure to behold, and those in countenance shew divers affections; to wit, a sober matron weeping, and a light courtesan smirking: It is thought that this courtesan was his own sweet-heart *Phyrne,* for men do note both (in the curious workmanship of the artificer) the love of him which fancied her, and also (in the pleasant countenance of the harlot) the contentment that she took by receiving her hire. There is an image also of his making, which doth express his own benignity and bountiful mind; for to a coach of *Calamis* his doing, drawn with four horses, he set a coachman of his own handiwork: and why? because the posterity another day should not think, that *Calamis* having done so well in portraying the horses, failed of the like cunning in expressing the man: and to say a truth, *Calamis* was not altogether so perfect & ready in personages of men and women, as in the portraiture of horses.

IPHICRATES

Iphicrates likewise cast in brass a lioness, which is much praised, and goeth under the name of *Leaena,* and that upon this occasion: There was a certain strumpet named *Leaena,* who being familiarly acquainted with *Harmodius* and *Aristogiton* abovenamed, (for that she could play upon the harp, and withal sing so sweetly to it) and privy to their plots as projects as touching the murder of the tyrant *Pisistratus,* would never, to die for it, discover and reveal this intention and purpose of theirs unto the tyrant and his favourites, notwithstanding she was put to most exquisite and dolorous torments about it. The Athenians therefore desirous to honour this woman for her resolute constancy accordingly, and yet loth to be thought for to make so much of such an harlot as she was, devised to represent the memorial of her and her act by a beast of her name, and that was a lioness: yet for to express the particular motive and reason of this honour done unto this lioness, they gave order unto *Iphicrates,* the workman, to leave out the *tongue in the head of the said lioness.

* For this harlot Leaena fearing least she might for pain and torment let pass some words and bewray the thing, she bit out her own tongue, & spit it in the face of the tyrant and the tormentors.

CANACHUS

Canachus made one excellent image of *Apollo* all naked, which by the title and surname of *Philesius,* standeth in the temple called *Didymaeum.* And this *Apollo* was cast of the brass of Aeginetic temperature. There is with the said *Apollo* another most exquisite and curious piece of work by him devised and wrought, to wit, a stag standing so lightly upon his feet, that a man may draw a thread under them; and the same takes hold of the floor underneath, so daintily, that he seemeth to touch it with one foot by the clea, with another by the heel, and the same after such a winding manner twining and turning, as well with the one as the other, that a man would think one while he were about to bounce and spring forward, and another while to start and cast himself backward by turns.

DEMETRIUS

And this artisan made also the image of *Minerva,* surnamed *Musica,* upon this device, for that the dragon or serpents which serve instead of hairs upon her *Gorgon* or *Medusas* head, wrought in her targuet, would ring and resound again, if one struck the strings of an harp or citron near unto them.

LEOCRAS

Leocras made the eagle that ravished *Ganymedes* and flew away with him; but so artificially, as if she knowing what a fine and dainty boy she had in charge, and to whom she carried him, clasped the child so tenderly, that she forbare with her talons to pierce through his very clothes.

STIPAX AND SILANION

Stipax the Cyprian got himself a name by an image resembling one *Splanchnoptes*: This was a pretty boy or page belonging to *Pericles,* surnamed *Olympius,* whom *Stipax* made frying and roasting the inwards of a beast at the fire, puffing and blowing thereat with his mouth full of breath and wind, for to make it burn. *Silanion* did cast the similitude of *Apollodorus* in brass:

who likewise was himself a founder and imageur, but of all others most curious and precise in his art. He never thought a thing of his own making well done, and no man censured his works so hardly as himself : many a time when he had finished an excellent piece of work, he would in a mislike unto it, pash it in pieces, and never stood contented and satisfied with anything when it was all done, how full of art sovere it was, and therefore he was surnamed Mad : Which furious passion of his, when *Silanion* aforesaid would express, he made not the man himself alone of brass, but the very image of Anger and Wrath also with him, in habit of a woman.

THEODORUS

Theodorus, who made the maze or labyrinth at Samos, caused his own image to be cast in brass, which besides the wonderful near resemblance and likeness to himself, was contrived so artificially besides, and set out with other fine devices, that he was much renowned for the workmanship, and in the sight of all men it was admirable : he carrieth yet in his right hand a file, and in his left he bare sometime (with three fingers) a little pretty coach, and the same with four horses at it; which was afterwards taken from the rest, and had away to Praeneste : but both the coach, the team of horses, and the coachman were couched in so small a room, that a little fly (which also he devised to be made to the rest) covered all with her pretty wings.

EPIGONUS

Epigonus would have his hand in all those works in manner which I have rehearsed, and laboured to imitate those artificers; but he surpassed them all in a trumpeter of his own devising; and a little infant, who seeing the mother slain, made toward the dead corpse, and hung about it as if it would play and be played withal, full piteously to behold.

THE BRASSEN BULL

As for *Perillus*, there is no man commendeth him for his workmanship, but holdeth him more cruel than *Phalaris* the Tyrant, who set him awork, for that he devised a brassen bull, to roast and fry condemned persons in; assuring the tyrant, that after the fire was made under it, they would when they cried seem to bellow as a bull, and so rather make sport than move compassion : but this *Perillus* was the first himself that gave the hansell to the engine of his own invention, and although this was cruelty in the tyrant, yet surely such a workman deserved no better a reward, & justly he felt the smart of it : For why? The art and cunning of foundry, which of all others is most civil & agreeable to our nature, and which had been employed ordinarily in representing the personages of men and gods, this monster of man abused, and debased to this vile and unnatural ministry of tormenting man. Would one have ever thought, that after so many witty and worthy men who had travailed in this science to bring it to some perfection, all their labours should turn in the end to this proof, for to make instruments thereby of torture? And certes, there being many pieces of his workmanship, they be kept and saved for this cause only, that as many as see the same, may detest and abhor the wicked hand that made them.

CALLIMACHUS

But above all other, *Callimachus* is the workman of greatest note, in regard of a by-name given unto him, and that was *Cacizotechnos* : and well he might be so called, for he would always be finding fault with his own workmanship, and never could see when to make an end, thinking still that he had not bestowed art enough upon that he had under his hand. And so he brought forth little or nothing perfect in the end : A notable and memorable example to teach all men not to be over cautious and exquisite in anything, but to hold a measure in all. And there is a dance of Lacedemonian women of his making : a piece of work which he went about also to amend, and when he thought to make it better, he marred it clean, so that it lost all the grace it had before.

DOCTORS AND CHEMISTS

But our physicians in this age, when they are to make any

composition of simples, they have recourse straightways to their books to be directed by them, that is to say, they try experiments by the hazard of their poor patients; and there finding the names of this and that, they set down a receipt, and for the making thereto trust the apothecaries, as also for the ingredients; which commonly they do sophisticate and corrupt by all deceitful means that possibly they can devise; selling their emplasters and collyries that are old made, and such drugs as are past all goodness, serving the bills of the physicians with the very refuse of their shop. And thus the deceitful wares that they have, they rid their hands of, to the discredit of the physician, and danger of the sick.

VITRIOL

As concerning vitriol, which we call in Latin atramentum sutorium, that is to say, shoemaker's black, the Greeks have fitted it with a name respective unto brass, and by a near affinity thereunto call it chalcanthum : and verily there is not a mineral throughout all the mines, of so admirable a nature as it is. There have been found in Spain certain pits or standing pools, containing a water of the nature of vitriol : they used to seethe the same, putting thereto of other fresh water a like quantity, and pour it into certain troughs or broad keelers of wood : over those vessels, there be certain bars (of iron) or transoms overthwart, lying fast that they cannot stir, at which there hang down cords or ropes with stones at the end stretching them outright, that they reach to the bottom of the said decoction within those keelers, to the end that the viscous substance of the water may gather about those cords, which you shall see sticking fast thereto in drops, congealed in manner of glass, and it doth represent as it were the form of grapes; and that is vitriol. Being taken forth and separated from the cords aforesaid, they let it dry for the space of thirty days. In colour it is blue, and carrieth with it a most pleasant and lively lustre, so clear, as a man would take it to be transparent glass. Of this being infused in water, is made that black tincture which curriers and corviners occupy in colouring of their leather. This vitriol is engendered many ways of the copperesse vein within the mine, being hollowed into certain trenches: out of the sides whereof you shall see in the midst of winter when it is a frost, certain icicles depending, as the drops distilled and grew one to another; whereupon this kind of vitriol they call stalagmias, and a purer or clearer thing there is not.

*   *   *   *   *

A liniment made of vitriol alone, healeth up wounds, but it draweth the scar too near together: in regard of which astringency of vitriol, there hath been an invention devised of late, to cast the powder of vitriol into the mouths of bears and lions when they are to be baited: for so great a knitter & binder it is, that it will draw their jaws together in manner of a muzzle, that they shall not be able to bite.

BRASS

But before I depart from these brass mines and furnaces, I cannot conceal from you one miraculous thing as touching this metal. There is (you know) a noble family in Rome of the *Servilii,* well renowned, as it may appear by the Roman calendar and acts of record: and these have among them a certain piece of brass coin called a triens (i.e. the third part of a Roman ass) which they do keep and feed with silver and gold. For eat and consume it doth both the one and the other: from whence it came first, and what the reason in nature of this property is, I know not yet. But for my warrent, I will set down as touching this matter the very words of old *Messala*: The house (quoth he) of the *Servilii* hath a certain sacred trient, in the honour of which piece they do sacrifice yearly with great devotion and solemnity, omitting no magnificence nor ceremonies thereto belonging. And this trient the common speech is of them all, that is seemeth one while to grow bigger, and another while to diminish and be smaller: according to which increase or decrease, the said *Servilii* take presage, that their family should either rise to more honour, or decay in credit and reputation.

IRON

It remaineth now in the next place to discourse of the mines of iron, a metal which we may well say is both the best and the worst implement used now in the world: For with the help of iron we break up and ear the ground, we plant and plot our groves, we set our hortyards and range our fruitful trees in rows: we prune our vines, and by cutting off the superfluous branches and dead wood, we make them every year to look fresh and young again: by means of iron and steel we build houses, hew quarries, and cut in stone, yea and in one word, we use it to all other necessary uses of this life. Contrariwise, the same iron serveth for wars, murders, and robberies, not only to offend and strike therewith in hand, but also to reach and kill afar off, with divers sorts of darts and shot, one whiles discharged and sent out of engines, another while lanced and flung by force of the arm; yea and sometime let fly with wings: and this I take to be the wickedest invention* that ever was devised by the head of man: for to the end that death may speed away the faster to a man, and surprise him most suddenly, we make it to fly as a bird in the air, and to the arrow headed at one end with deadly iron, we set feathers at the other: whereby it is evident, that the mischief proceeding from iron, is not to be imputed to the nature of it, but to the unhappy wit of man.

*   *   *   *   *

Nevertheless men did not forbear and give over to do some honour unto iron, also in some other occasions of this life, tending to the entertaining of civility and humanity: for *Aristonidas* the cunning artificer, minding to represent in an image the furious rage of *Athamas,* beginning now to cool and be allayed, together with his repentance for the cruel murdering of his own son *Learchus,* whom he flung headlong against the hard stones, and thereby dashed out his brains, made a temperature of brass and iron together, to the end, that the rusty iron appearing before the bright lustre of the brass, might lively express a blushing red in the countenance, beseeming a man confused and dismayed for so unnatural a fact. This statue is at this day to be seen at Thebes.

* O *Plinie,* what wouldst thou say, if thou didst see and hear the pistols, muskets, culverines, & canons in these days?

NATURAL JUSTICE

But to come unto the nature of iron, herein appeareth still the same goodness of Nature, that this metal working such mischief as it doth, should be revenged of itself, and receive condign punishment by the own rust. See also the wonderful providence of Nature, who maketh nothing in the world more subject to death and corruption, than that which is most hurtful and deadly to mankind.

*　　*　　*　　*　　*

But wonderful it is above all, that man's blood should have such a virtue in it, as to be revenged of the iron blade that shed it; for being once imbrued therein, it is given ever after eftsoons to rust and canker.

MAGNETS

Concerning the load-stone, and the great concord or amity between iron and it, I mean to write more amply in the due place. Howbeit, for the present thus much I must needs say, that iron is the only metal which receiveth strength from that stone, yea, and keepeth the same a long time, insomuch as by virtue thereof, if it be once well touched and rubbed withal, it is able to take hold of other pieces of iron : and thus otherwhiles we may see a number of rings hanging together in manner of a chain, notwithstanding they be not linked and enclosed one within another. The ignorant people seeing these rings thus rubbed with the load-stone, and cleaving one to another, call it quick-iron. Certes, any wounds made by such a tool, are more eager and angry than by another. This stone is to be found in Biscay, scattered here and there in small pieces by way of bubbation (for this is the term they use !) but it is not that true magnet or loadstone indeed, which groweth in one continued rock. And I wot not whether these be so good for glassmakers, and serveth their turn so well in melting their glass, as the other : for no man yet hath made any experiment thereof. But sure I am, that if one do rub the edge, back, or blade of a knife therewith, it doth impart an attractive virtue of iron thereunto, as well as the right magnet. And here I cannot choose but acquaint you with the singular invention of that great architect and master deviser, of Alexandrian Egypt *Dinocrates,* who began to make the arched roof of the temple of *Arsinoe* all of magnet or this load-stone, to the end, that within that temple the statue of the said princess made of iron, might seem to hang in the air by nothing. But prevented he was by death before he could finish his work, like as king *Ptolomae* also, who ordained that temple to be built in the honour of the said *Arsinoe* his sister.

MEDICAL PROPERTIES OF IRON

As touching the use of iron and steel, in physic it serveth otherwise than for to lance cut and dismember withal : for take a knife or dagger and make an imaginary circle two or three times with the point thereof, upon a child, or an elder body, and then go round withal about the party as often, it is a singular preservative against all poisons, sorceries, or enchantments. Also to take any iron nail out of the coffin or sepulchre wherein man or woman lieth buried, and to stick the same fast to the lintel or side post of a door, leading either into the house or bed-chamber where any doth lie who is haunted with spirits in the night, he or she shall be delivered and secured from such fantastical illusions. Moreover, it is said, that if one be lightly pricked with the point of sword or dagger which hath been the death of a man, it is an excellent remedy against the pain of sides or breast, which come with sudden pricks and stitches. An actual cautery of iron red hot, cureth many diseases, and especially the biting of a mad dog; in which case it is so effectual, that if the poison inflicted by that wound, have prevailed so far, that the patient be fallen into an hydrophobia thereby, and cannot abide drink or water, let the sore be seared therewith, the party shall find help presently.

RUST

The very rust of iron also is counted midicinable : for so *Achilles* is said to have healed *Telephus* : but whether the head of his spear were iron or brass, of which he used the rust, I do not certainly know. Certes, he is painted thus: with his sword scraping and shaking off the rust into the wound. But if you would fetch off the rust from any old nails, scrape it with a knife wet before in water.

LEAD

Now ensueth the discourse of lead, and the nature of it; of which there be two principal kinds, the black, and the white. The richest of all, and that which carrieth the greatest price, is that which we in Latin name *plumbum candidum,* i.e. the white bright lead, and the Greeks *cassiteron*. But I hold it a mere fable and vain tale, that all of it is fetched as far as from the islands of the Atlantic sea, and that the inhabitants of those parts do convey it in little twiggen boats, covered all over with feathers. For the truth is, that there is found of it in these days within Portugal and Gallaecia, growing ebb upon the upmost face of the earth, being among the sands, of a black colour, and by the weight only is known from the rest of the soil; and here and there among, a man shall meet with small stones of the same stuff, most of all within the brooks that be dry sometimes of the year.

*   *   *   *   *

Blacklead or common lead is much used with us for sheets to make conduit pipes; also it is driven with the hammer into thin plates and leaves. This metal requireth much labour and toil in Spain and France, before it be gotten out of the mine, so deep it lieth; whereas in Britain it runneth ebb in the uppermost coat of the ground, and that in such abundance, that by an express act among the islanders themselves, it is not lawful to dig and gather ore above such a proportion, set down by stint.

*   *   *   *   *

To conclude, one marvellous quality lead hath besides, that no vessel made thereof, will melt over the fire, if there be water in it: and yet cast into the said water a little stone, or a small piece of brass coin, although it be no more than a quadrant, you shall see it melt, and a hole burnt through it by and by.

Great use there is in physic of lead applied by itself alone, and namely, to repress and keep down the scars and cicatrices that rise above the other skin : also by the refrigerative quality that it hath, to cool the heat of fleshly lust, if there be bound unto the loins and region of the reins, a thin plate or leaf thereof. And verily *Calvus* the orator (who by occasion of much dreaming in his sleep of venereous sports, fell into mighty pollutions, and so farther into the grievous malady of gonorrhoea or running of the reins) with wearing ordinarily these leaden plates, stayed (by report) all such vain and wanton fantasies and imaginations : by which means he preserved also his strength, and had a body able to endure the labour of much study and sitting at his book. And *Nero* the Emperor (since the gods would have it so) used ordinarily to wear a plate of lead to his breast, under which he would chant out lustily with a wide throat and strong voice, his filthy sonnets and beastly ballads; but he shewed thereby that lead was a singular means to maintain a good voice.

THE FIVE AND THIRTIETH BOOK

*discourseth of painting, colour,
and painters*

To BEGIN then with that which remaineth as touching picture
and painting, this would be known, that in times past it was
reputed a noble and excellent art : in those days I mean, when
Kings and whole States made account thereof; and when those
only were thought ennobled and immortalized, whom painters
vouchsafed to commend by their workmanship to posterity. But
now, the marble and porphyrit stones have put painting clean
down : the gold also laid upon them hath won all credit from
painters' colours : gold I say, wherewith not only plain and entire
walls are richly gilded over, but also the polished works of marble
engraven upon them after the manner of inlaid work and marquetage of divers pieces, resembling men, beasts, flowers, and all
things else : for in these days contented we are not with plain
squares and tables of marble, nor with the riches of mighty
mountains, couched under covert and laid within our bed-
chambers in that sort as they grew, but come we are now to paint
stones. Devised this was first in the days of *Claudius Caesar* : but
when *Nero* came to be Emperor, the invention was taken up, to
give those colours to stones in their superficial outside, which they
had not of their own; to make them spotted, which naturally
were of one simple colour : that by the help of man's hand, the
Numidian red porphyrit should be set out with white spots in
egg-fashion : the Sinadian grey marble distinguished with marks
and streaks of purple : as if our delicate wantons shewed thereby

how they could have wished the stones to grow. Thus would they seem to correct the works of Nature, to supply the want of mountains and quarries, and to make amends for the hills cloven in sunder for gold, and hewed in pieces for marble. And what is the end of all this prodigious prodigality and wasteful superfluity? but that the fire when it cometh, may consume in one hour a world of wealth.

WHY ARTISTS ARE OUT OF WORK

The manner was in ancient time, to continue and perpetuate the memorial of men, by drawing their portraitures in lively colours, as like to their proportion and shape as possible could be; but this custom is grown now altogether out of use: instead thereof we have shields and scutcheons set up of brass: we have faces of silver in them, without any lively distinction of one from another: and as for our statues, the heads upon them otherwhiles be changed one for another; which hath given occasion long since of many a jest and libel spread abroad in rhyme and sung in every street. In so much as all men nowadays are more desirous to have the rich matter seen that goeth to the making of images, than to be known by their own personage and visage as it is: and yet every man delighteth to have his cabinet and closet well furnished with antique painted tables: the statues and images of other men they think it enough to honour and adore; whiles they themselves, measuring worship by wealth, and thinking nothing honourable that is not sumptuous and costly, see not how by this means they give occasion to their heirs for to break open their counters and make spoil of all, or else before that day come, entice a thief to be hooking or twitching them away with gins and snares. Considering then, that no man careth for a lively picture, all the monuments that they leave unto their heirs, are images rather of their moneys, than resemblances of themselves. Howbeit, these great men take pleasure to have their own wrestling places and halls of exercise, yea and the rooms where they are anointed, beautified and adorned with the portraitures of noble champions: they delight also to have the face of *Epicurus* in every chamber of the house, yea and to carry the same about them upon their rings wheresoever they go: in the remembrance and honour of his nativity, they do offer sacrifice every twentieth day of the moon, and these month-minds they keep as holy days duly, which thereupon they call Icades: and none so much as they who will not abide to be known another day by any lively image drawn whiles they be alive. Thus it is come to pass, that whiles artificers play them and sit still for want of work, noble arts by the means are decayed and perished. But I marvel nothing hereat: for thus it is verily and no otherwise, when we have no respect or care in the world to leave good works behind us, as the images of our minds, we do neglect the lively portraitures and similitudes also of our bodies.

LIBRARIES

And seeing that I am so far entered into this theme, I must not pass over one new device and invention come up of late, namely, to dedicate and set up in libraries the statues in gold or silver, or at leastwise in brass, of those divine and heavenly men, whose immortal spirits do speak still and ever shall, in those places where their books are. And although it be impossible to recover the true and lively portraits of many of them, yet we forbear not for all that to devise one image or other to represent their face and personage, though we are sure it be nothing like them: and the want thereof doth breed and kindle in us a great desire and longing, to know what visage that might be indeed which was never delivered unto us: as it appeareth by the statue of *Homer*. Certes, in my opinion, there can be no greater argument of the felicity and happiness of any man, than to have all the world evermore desirous to know, what kind of person he was whiles he lived? This invention of erecting libraries, especially here at Rome, came from *Asinius Pollio*, who by dedicating his bibliotheque, containing all the books that ever were written, was the first that made the wits and works of learned men, a public matter and a benefit to a commonweal. But whether the kings of Alexandria in Aegypt, or of Pergamus, began this enterprise before (who upon a certain emulation and strife one with another, went in hand to make their stately and sumptuous libraries) I am not able to avouch for certain.

THE INVENTION OF PAINTING

Concerning pictures, and the first original of painter's art, I am not able to resolve and set down anything for certain : neither is it a question pertinent to my design and purpose. I am not ignorant, that the Aegyptians do vaunt thereof, avouching that it was devised among them, and practised five hundred years before there was any talk or knowledge thereof in Greece : a vain brag and ostentation of theirs, as all the world may see. As for the Greek writers, some ascribe the invention of painting to the Sicyonians, others, to the Corinthians. But they all do jointly agree in this, that the first portrait was nothing else but the bare pourfling and drawing only the shadow of a person unto his just proportion and lineaments. This first draught or ground, they began afterwards to lay with one simple colour, and no more : which kind of picture, after that they fell once to more curious workmanship, they called monochromaton, that is to say, a portrait of one colour, for distinction sake from other pictures of sundry colours : which notwithstanding, yet this plain manner of painting continueth at this day, and as much used. As for the lineary portraying or drawing shapes and proportions by lines only, it is said, that either *Philocles* the Egyptian, or else *Cleanthes* the Corinthian was the inventor thereof. But whosoever devised it, certes *Ardices* the Corinthian, and *Telephanes* the Sicyonian, were the first that practised it. Howbeit colours they used none, yet they proceeded thus far as to disperse their lines within, as well as to draw the pourfle, and all with a coal and nothing else. And therefore their manner and order was to write also the names of such as they thus painted, and always to set them close to the pictures. But the first that took upon him to paint with colour, was *Cleophantus* the Corinthian, who (as they say) took no more but a piece of red potsherd, which he ground into powder, and that was all the colour that he used. This *Cleophantus*, or some other of that name, was he, who by the testimony of *Cornelius Nepos*, as I will anon shew more at large, accompanied *Demetrius* the father of *Tarquinius Priscus* king of Rome, when he fled from Corinth to avoid the wrongs of *Cypsellus* the tyrant, who persecuted and oppressed him. But it cannot be so : for surely before this *Tarquine's* time, the art of painting was grown to some perfection, even in Italy: for proof whereof, extant there be at this day to be seen at Ardea within the temples there, antique pictures, and indeed more ancient than the city of Rome: and I assure you, no pictures came ever to my sight, which I wonder so much at, namely, that they should continue so long, fresh, and as if they were but newly made, considering the places where they be, so ruinate and uncovered over head. Semblably, at Lanuvium there remain yet two pictures of lady *Atlanta* and Queen *Helena*, close one to the other, painted naked, by one and the same hand: both of them are for beauty incomparable, and yet a man may discern the one of them to be a maiden by her modest and chaste countenance; which pictures, notwithstanding the ruins of the temple where they stand, are not a whit disfigured or defaced. Of late days, *Pontius* lieutenant under *C. Caligula* the Emperor, did what he could to have removed them out of the place, and carried them away whole and entire, upon a wanton affection and lustful fancy that he cast unto them: but the plaster or porget of the wall whereupon they were painted, was of that temper that would not abide to be stirred. At Caere also there continue certain pictures of greater antiquity than those which I have named. And verily, whosoever shall well view & peruse the rare workmanship therein, will confess, that no art in the world grew sooner to the height of absolute perfection than it, considering that during the state of Troy no man knew what painting was.

PICTURES FOR PUBLICITY

But the principal credit that painters attained unto at Rome, was, as I take it, by the means of *M. Valerius Maximus*, first surnamed *Messala*, who being one of the grand seigneurs of Rome, was the first that proposed to the view of all the world, and set up at a side of the stately hall or court Hostilia, one picture in a table, wherein he caused to be painted that battle in Sicily wherein himself had defeated the Carthaginians and king *Hiero*: which happened in the year from the foundation of Rome 490. The like also, I must needs say, did *L. Scipio*, and hung up a painted table in the Capitol temple, containing his victory and conquest of Asia, whereupon he was surnamed *Asiaticus*. But (as it is said) *Africanus* although he were his own brother, was highly displeased therewith : and good cause he had to be angry and offended, because in that battle his own son was taken prisoner by the enemy. The like offence was taken also by Scipio *Aemilianus*, against *Lucius Hostilius Mancinus*, who was the first that entered perforce the city of Carthage; for that he had caused to be set up in the market place of Rome a fair painted table, wherein was lively drawn the strong situation of Carthage, and the warlike means used to the assaulting and winning of it, together with all the particulars and circumstances thereof : which *Mancinus* himself in person sitting by the said picture, deciphered from point to point unto the people that came to behold it; by which courtesy of his he won the hearts of the people, insomuch, as at the next election of magistrates, his popularity gained him a Consulship. In the public plays which *Claudius Pulcher* exhibited at Rome, the painted cloths about the stage and theatre (which represented building) brought this art into great admiration : for the workmanship was so artificial and lively, that the very ravens in the air, deceived with the likeness of houses, flew thither apace for to settle thereupon, supposing verily there had been tiles and crests indeed.

TOO DEAR AT ANY PRICE

In the same forum or grand place at Rome there stood sometime the picture of an old shepherd leaning upon his crook, as touching which (for that is it should seem, it was very workmanlike made) when a certain Dutch ambassador who beheld it, was demanded, at what price he esteemed it, answered short and quick, What a question is that? I would not have such an one (were he alive, as I see he is but painted) though he were given me for nothing.

CERUSE

There is of white colours a third kind, and that is cerusa, or white lead, the reason and making whereof, I have shewed in my discourse of minerals : and yet there was found of it in the nature of a very earth by itself at Smyrna, within the land belonging to one *Theodotus,* wherewith in old time they used to colour & paint ships. But in these days we have no other ceruse or Spanish white but that which is artificial, made of lead and vinegar, in manner aforesaid. As touching ceruse burnt, the invention thereof came by mere chance, upon occasion of a scarefire happening in the harbour of Piraeum, which caught the pots and boxes wherein the Athenian dames that dwelt by the said harbour kept their blanch or ceruse for complexion, and this ceruse thus calcined, the first that used in picture was *Nicias,* of whom I have already spoken.

PAINTER'S BLACK

Painter's black (called in Latin atramentum) I count an artificial colour, although I know there is a vitriol or coperose going under that name, which is mineral, and is engendered two manner of ways : for either it issueth and oozeth out of the mine in manner of a salt humour or liquor; or else there groweth an earth itself of a brimstone colour, which serveth for it, that it may be drawn out thereof. Some painters have been known, who for to get black, have searched into sepulchres for the coals there, among the relics and ashes of the dead. But in mine opinion, all these be but new devices, and foolish irregular toys without any reason : for a man need seek no farther but to soot, and that made many ways, by burning either of rosin or pitch : in which regard, many have built places and forges of purpose to burn them in; without any emissaries, tunnels, or holes, that the said smoke or soot may not get forth. But the best black in that manner made, cometh of the smoke of torchwood. This fine soot is sophisticate with the gross soot that doth gather and engender in forges, furnaces, and stouphs : and this is that ink wherewith we use to write our books. Some there be who take the lees or dregs of wine, and when it is dried, boil it thoroughly : and they affirm, that if the wine were good whereof those lees came, the said ink or black will make a colour like indigo. And in truth, *Polygnotus* and *Mycon* (two as renowned painters as ever were) used no other black at all, but that which they made of the marre or refuse of grapes after they be pressed, & this they call tryginon. *Apelles* devised a way by himself, to make it of ivory or the elephant's tooth burnt, and this they named thereupon elephantinum. As touching the black called Indicum, it is brought out of India : but as yet I know not the manner either of the making or the engendering of it. A kind thereof I see the dyers do make, of that black florey which sticketh to their coppers. Also, there is a black made of torchwood burnt, and the coals that come of it punned to powder in a mortar. And here cometh to my mind that wonderful nature of the cuttle fishes, which do yield a black humour from them like unto ink : howbeit, I do not find that painters or writers make any use thereof.

PAINTED COFFINS

Of all colours, roset, indico, azure, tripoli or melinum, orpiment, white lead or ceruse, love not to be laid upon plaster-work, or any ground, while it is moist : & yet wax will take any of these colours abovesaid, to be employed in those kind of works which are wrought by fire (so it be not upon plaster, parget, and walls, for that is impossible) whether they be enamelled or damasked : yea and in their painting of ships at sea, as well hulks and hoys of burden, as galleys and ships of war : for now are we come (forsooth) to enamel and paint those things that are in danger to perish and be cast away every hour; so as we need not marvel any longer, that the coffin going with a dead corpse to a funeral fire, is richly painted : and we take a delight when we mind to fight at sea, to sail with our fleet gallantly dight & enriched with colours, which must carry us into dangers, either to our own death, or else to the carnage of others.

THE PORTRAIT OF NERO

And here I think it not amiss to set down the outrageous excess of this age, as touching pictures : *Nero* the Emperor commanded, that the portrait of himself should be painted in linen cloth, after the manner of a giantlike coloss, 120 foot high; a thing that never had been heard or seen before. But see what became of it? when this monstrous picture (which was drawn and made in the garden of *Marius*) was done and finished, the lightning and fire from heaven caught it, and not only consumed it, but also burnt withal the best part of the building about the garden. A slave of his enfranchising (as it is well known) when he was to exhibit an Antium certain solemnities, and namely a spectacle of sword-fencers fighting at sharp, caused all the scaffolds public galleries, and walking places of that city, to be hung and tapissed with painted cloths, wherein were represented the lively pictures of the sword-players themselves together with all the wiffle and servitors to them belonging. But to conclude, the best man and most magnanimous that for many a hundred years our country hath bred, have taken delight (I must needs say) in this art, and set their minds upon good pictures.

POLYGNOTUS

Furthermore, besides these painters above rehearsed, others there were of great name, and yet all of them before that nine-tieth Olympiad whereof they write; as namely, *Polygnotus* the Thasian, who was the first that painted women in gay and light apparel, with their hoods and other head attire of sundry colours: and in one word, passed all others before him in devices, for the bettering of this art. His invention it was to paint images with their mouths open, to make them show their teeth; and in one word, represented much variety of countenance, far different from the rigorous and heavy look of the visage beforetime. Of this *Polygnotus'* workmanship, is that picture in a table which now standeth in the stately gallery of *Pompeius*, and hung some-time before the Curia or Hall that beareth his name, in which table he painted one upon a scaling ladder, with a targuet in his hand; but so artificially it is done and with such dexterity, that whosoever looketh upon him, cannot tell whether he is climbing up or coming down.

ZEUXIS

He grew in process of time to such wealth by the means only of his excellent hand, that for to make show how rich he was, when he went to the solemnity of the games at Olympia, he caused his own name to be embroidered in golden letters, within the lozenge-work of his cloaks, whereof he had change, and which he brought thither to be seen. In the end, he resolved with himself to work no longer for money, but to give away all his pictures, saying, that he valued them above any price. Thus be bestowed upon the Agrigentines, one picture of queen *Alcmena*: and to king *Archelaus* he gave another of the rustical god *Pan*: there was also the portrait of lady *Penelope*, which he drew in colours; wherein he seemeth not only to have depainted the outward personage and feature of the body, but also to have expressed most lively the inward affections and qualities of her mind: and much speech there is of a wrestler or champion of his painting; in which picture he pleased himself so well, that he subscribed this verse under it, *Invisurus aliquis facilius quam imitaturus*: i.e. Sooner will a man envy me, than set such another by me. Which thereupon grew to be a byword in every man's mouth. One stately picture there is of his workmanship, *Iupiter* sitting upon a throne in his majesty, with all the other gods standing by and making court unto him. He portrayed *Hercules* also as a babe lying in the cradle, and strangling two fell serpents with his hand, together with his mother *Alcmena*, and her husband K. *Amphytrion* in place, affrighted both at the sight thereof. Howbeit, this *Zeuxis* as excellent a painter as he was, is noted for one fault and imperfection; namely, that the head and joints of his portraits, were in proportion to the rest somewhat with the biggest: for otherwise so curious and exquisite he was, that when he should make a table with a picture for the Agrigentines, to be set up in the temples of *Iuno Lacinia*, at the charges of the city, according to a vow that they had made, he would needs see all the maidens of the city, naked; and from all that company he chose five of the fairest to take out as from several patterns, whatsoever he liked best in any of them; and of all the lovely parts of those five, to make one body of incomparable beauty.

*   *   *   *   *

Of those four beforenamed, *Parasius* by report was so bold as to challenge *Zeuxis* openly and to enter the lists with him for the victory: in which contention and trial, *Zeuxis* for proof of his cunning, brought upon the scaffold a table, wherein were clusters of grapes so lively painted that the very birds of the air flew flocking thither for to be pecking at the grapes. *Parasius* again for his part to show his workmanship, came with another picture, wherein he had painted a linen sheet, so like unto a sheet indeed, that *Zeuxis* in a glorious bravery and pride of his heart, because the birds had approved of his handiwork, came unto *Parasius* with these words by way of a scorn and frump, Come on sir, away with your sheet once, that we may see your goodly picture: But taking himself with the manner, and perceiving his own error, he was mightily abashed, & like an honest minded man yielded the victory unto his adversary, saying withal, *Zeuxis* hath beguiled poor birds, but *Parasius* hath deceived *Zeuxis*, a professed artisan. This *Zeuxis*, as it is reported, painted afterwards another table, wherein he had made a boy carrying certain bunches of grapes in a flasket, and seeing again that the birds flew to the grapes, he shook the head, and coming to his picture, with the like ingenuous mind as before, brake out into these words, and said, Ah, I see well enough where I have failed, I have painted the grapes better than the boy, for if I had done him as naturally, the birds would have been afraid and never approached the grapes.

PARASIUS

As for *Parasius* beforenamed, born he was at Ephesus, and invented also diverse things of himself to the advancement of this art: for the first he was that gave the true symmetry to a portraiture, and observed the just proportions: he first exactly kept the sundry habits and gestures of the countenance: he it was, that first stood upon the curious workmanship of couching and laying the hairs of the head in order: the lovely grace and beauty about the mouth and lips, he first exactly expressed: and by the confession of all painters that saw his work, he won the prize and praise from them all in making up the pourfils and extenuities of his lineaments, which is the principal point and hardest matter belonging to the whole art: For to draw forth the bodily proportion of things, to hatch also, yea and to fill within, requireth (I confess) much labour and good workmanship : but many have been excellent in that behalf; marry to pourfil well, that is to say, to make the extremities of any part, to mark duly the divisions of parcels, and to give everyone their just compass and measure, is exceeding difficult, and few when come to the doing of it, have been found to attain unto that felicity. For the utmost edge of a work must fall round upon itself, and so knit up in the end, as if it shadowed somewhat behind, and yet showed that which it seemeth to hide. In this so curious and inexplicable point, *Antigonus* and *Xenocrates* both, who wrote as touching this art, have given him the honour of the best : not only confessing his singular gift herein, but also commending him for it. Many other plots and projects there do remain of his drawing, portrayed as well in tables as upon parchment, which serve as patterns (they say) for painters to learn much cunning by. And yet for inward works, and to express the middle parts of a portraiture, he seemeth not so perfect, nor answerable to himself otherwise. There is a notable picture of his making, which he called *Demon Atheniensium*, that is to say, the common people of the Athenians : the device whereof was passing full of wit and very inventive : for his intention was in one and the same portrait, and under one object of the eye to express the nature of the people, variable, wrathful, unjust, and uncontent; the same also he would have to appear exorable, mild, and pitiful, haughty, glorious & proud, and yet humble, lowly and submissive; fierce and furious, and the same coward, and ready to run away : all these properties, I say, he represented under one cast of the eye. This workman painted also *Theseus*, which stood sometimes in the Capitol of Rome : a certain Admiral likewise of a navy, armed with a corslet. In one table also which is at Rhodes, he depainted *Meleager*, *Hercules*, and *Perseus*. This table was thrice blasted with lightning; howbeit, the pictures were not defaced, but remained whole and entire as at the first : a miraculous thing, and that which maketh much for the credit of the picture.

*   *   *   *   *

An artisan full of work, and who evermore would be doing one thing or other; but so arrogant withal, as no man ever showed more insolence than he, in regard that he was cunning and well thought of : which he knew well enough, and no man need to tell him. In this proud spirit of his, he would take upon him divers titles and additions to his name : among others, he would call himself *Abrodiaetus* : and other words he used, whereby he would make himself known that he was the prince of painters, and the art by him made perfect and accomplished. But it exceedeth how vain-glorious he showed himself, in that he gave out, he was in right line descended from *Apollo* : also that the portrait of *Hercules*, which is in a table at Lindos, he drew from the very person of *Hercules* himself, answerable in all points to the proportion and lineaments of his body : who (by his saying) had appeared unto him oftentimes in his sleep of purpose, that he might paint him lively as he was. In this vein of vanity, being upon a time put down by *Timanthes* the painter at Samos, where, by the judgement of all that were present, his picture representing *Ajax*, and the awarding of the armour of *Achilles* from him to *Vlyxes*, was not thought comparable to another of *Timanthes'* making : I am ill apaid (quoth he) and sorry at the heart, for this noble knight and brave warrior *Ajax*, whose evil hap it is thus to be foiled once again by so unworthy a wight, and a far meaner person than himself. He delighted also to paint small pictures in pretty tables, and those representing wantonness and lechery : and this he did (as he was wont to say) for his recreation, and as it were to breathe himself when he had laboured hard at greater works.

TIMANTHES

As for *Timanthes*, an excellent fine wit he had of his own, & full he was of rare inventions. He it was that made the famous picture of *Iphigenia*, so highly commended by eloquent orators. And to say a truth, his conceit therein was admirable : for when he had devised that the poor innocent lady should stand hard at the altar ready to be slain for sacrifice, and had painted those that were present about her, with heavy and sad countenance, weeping and wailing all for the instant death of this young princess, and her uncle *Menelaus* above the rest, full of sorrow and lamentation, and showing the same as much as possibly might be : having by this time spent in them all the signs that might testify the heart's grief, and that he was come to portray her own father *Agamemnon*, he represented his visage covered with a veil, for that he was not able to express sufficiently the extraordinary sorrow above the rest which he had to see his own daughter sacrificed, and her guiltless blood spilt. Other pieces of work there be, patterns all of singular wit : among the rest, he devised within a very small table, a Cyclops lying asleep : and yet because he would seem even in that little compass to show his giant-like bigness, he devised withal to paint little elfish satyrs hard by, and those taking measure of one of his thumbs with long perches. In sum, so inventive he was, that in the works which passed through his hands, a man shall ever conceive & understand some hidden thing within more than is painted without : for albeit a man shall see in his pictures as much as art may be, yet his wit went always beyond his art.

APELLES

But what should I speak of these painters, when as *Apelles* surmounted all that either were before or came after. This *Apelles* flourished about the hundred and twelfth Olympias, by which time he became so consummate and accomplished in the art, that he alone did illustrate and enrich it as much, if not more, than all his predecessors besides : who compiled also divers books, wherein the rules and principles yea, and the very secrets of the art are comprised. The special gift that he had, was this, that he was able to give his pictures a certain lovely grace inimitable : and yet there were in his time most famous and worthy painters whom he admired, whose works when he beheld, he would praise them all, howbeit, not without a but : for his ordinary phrase was this : Here is an excellent picture, but that it wanteth one thing, and that is the *Venus* which it should have : which *Venus* the Greeks call *Charis*, as one would say, the grace : And in truth, he would confess, that other men's pictures had all things else that they should have, this only excepted, wherein he was persuaded, that he had not his peer or second. Moreover, he attributed unto himself another property, wherein he gloried not a little, and that was this, that he could see to make an end when a thing was well done. For beholding wistly upon a time a piece of work of *Protogenes* his doing, wherein he saw there was infinite pains taken, admiring also the exceeding curiosity of the man in each point beyond all measure, he confessed & said, that *Protogenes* in everything else had done as well as himself could have done, yea, and better too. But in one thing he surpassèd *Protogenes*, for that he could not skill of laying work out of his hand, when it was finished well enough : a memorable admonition, teaching us all, that double diligence and overmuch curiosity, doth hurt otherwhiles. This painter was not more renowned for his skill and excellence in art, that he was commended for his simplicity and singleness of heart : for as he gave place to *Amphion* in disposition, so he yielded to *Asclepiodorus* in measures and proportion, that is to say, in the just knowledge how far distant one thing ought to be from another. And to this purpose, impertinent it is not to report a pretty occurrent that fell between *Protogenes* and him : for being very desirous to be acquainted with *Protogenes*, a man whom he had never seen, and of his works, whereof there went so great a name, he embarked and sailed to Rhodes, where *Protogenes* dwelt : and no sooner was he landed, but he enquired where his shop was, and forthwith went directly thither : *Protogenes* himself was not at home, only there was an old woman in the house who had the keeping of a mighty large table set in a frame, and fitted ready for a picture. And when he enquired for *Protogenes*, she made answer that he was not within; and seeing him thereupon ready to depart, demanded what his name was, and who she should tell her master asked for him. *Apelles* then, seeing the foresaid table standing before him, took a pencil in hand and drew in colour a passing fine and small line through the said table, saying to the woman, Tell thy master, that he who made this line, enquired for him, and so he went his ways. Now when *Protogenes* was returned home, the old woman made relation unto him of this that happened in his absence. And, as it is reported, the artificer had no sooner seen and beheld the draught of this small line, but he knew who had been there, and said withal, Surely *Apelles* is come to town : for impossible it is, that any but he should make in colour so fine workmanship. With that he takes me the pencil, and with another colour drew within the same line a smaller than it : willing the woman when he went forth of doors, that if the party came again, she should show him what he had done, and say withal, that there was the man whom he enquired after. And so it fell out indeed, for *Apelles* made an errand again to the shop, and seeing the second line, was dismayed at first and blushed withal to see himself thus overcome : but taking his pencil, cut the foresaid lines throughout the length, with a third colour distinct from the rest, and left no room at all for a fourth to be drawn within it : Which when *Protogenes* saw, he confessed that he had met with his match and his master both, and made all the haste he could to the haven to seek for *Apelles* to bid him welcome and give him friendly entertainment. In memorial whereof it was thought good both by the one and the other, to leave unto posterity this table thus naked, without any more work in it, to the wonder of all men that ever saw it, but of cunning artisans and painters especially : for this table was kept a long time, and as it is well known, consumed to ashes in that first fire that caught *Caesar's* house within the Palatine hill. And verily, we took great pleasure before that, to see it many times, containing in that large and extraordinary capacity which it had, nothing in the world than certain lines, which were so fine and small, that unneath or hardly they could be discerned by the eye. And in truth, when it stood among the excellent painted tables of many other workmen, it seemed a very blank, having nothing in it : howbeit, as void and naked as it was, it drew many a one unto it even in that respect, being more looked upon and esteemed better than any other rich and curious work whatsoever. But to come again unto *Apelles*, this was his manner and custom besides, which he perpetually observed, that no day went over his head, but what business soever he had otherwise to call him away, he would make one draught or other, (and never miss) for to exercise his hand and keep it in ure, insomuch, as from him grew the proverb, *Nulla dies sine linea*, i.e. Be always doing somewhat, though you do but draw a line. His order was when he had finished a piece of work or painted table, and laid it out of his hand, to set it forth in some open gallery or thoroughfare to be seen of folk that passed by, and himself would lie close behind it to hearken what faults were found therewith; preferring the judgement of the common people before his own, and imagining they would spy more narrowly and censure his doings sooner than himself : and as the tale is told, it fell out upon a time, that a shoemaker as he went by seemed to control his workmanship about the shoe or pantophle that he had made to a picture, and namely, that there was one latchet fewer than there should be : *Apelles* acknowledging that the man said true indeed, mended that fault by the next morning, and set forth his table as his manner was. The same shoemaker coming again the morrow after, and finding the want supplied which he noted the day before, took some pride unto himself, that his former admonition had sped so well, and was so bold as to cavil at somewhat about the leg : *Apelles* could not endure that, but putting forth his head from behind the painted table, and scorning thus to be checked & reproved, Sirrah (quoth he) remember you are but a shoemaker, and therefore meddle no higher I advise you, than with shoes : which word also of his came afterwards to be a common proverb, *Ne sutor supra crepidam*. Over and besides, very courteous he was and fair spoken, in which regard king *Alexander* the Great accepted the better of him, and much frequented his shop in his own person : for, as I have beforesaid, he gave straight commandment, that no painter should be so hardy as to make his picture but only *Apelles*. Now when the king being in his shop, would seem to talk much and reason about his art, and many times let fall some words to little purpose, bewraying his ignorance; *Apelles* after his mild manner, would desire his grace to hold his peace, and say, Sir, no more words, for fear the apprentice boys there that are grinding of colours, do laugh you to scorn : So reverently thought the king of him, that being otherwise a choleric prince, yet he would take any word at his hands in that familiar sort spoken in the best part, and be never offended. And verily, what good reckoning *Alexander* made of him, he showed by one notable argument; for having among his concubines one named *Campaspe*, whom he fancied especially above the rest, in regard as well of that affection of his as her incomparable beauty, he gave commandment to *Apelles* for to draw her picture all naked : but perceiving *Apelles* at the same time to be wounded with the like dart of love as well as himself, he bestowed her upon him most frankly :

By which example he shewed moreover, that how great a commander and high minded a prince he was otherwise, yet in this mastering and commanding of his affections, his magnanimity was more seen : and in this act of his he won as much honour and glory as by any victory over his enemies, for now he had conquered himself, and not only made *Apelles* partner with him of his love, but also gave his affection clean away from her unto him, nothing moved with the respect of her whom before he so dearly loved, that being the concubine of a king, she should now become the bedfellow of a painter. Some are of opinion, that by the pattern of this *Campaspe*, *Apelles* made the picture of *Venus Anadyomene*. Moreover, *Apelles* was of a kind bountiful disposition even to other painters of his time, who commonly as concurrents, do envy one another. And the first he was that brought *Protogenes* into credit and estimation at Rhodes; for at the first, his own countrymen made no account at all of him (a thing ordinarily seen, that in our own country we are least regarded) but *Apelles*, for to countenance and credit the man, demanded of him what price he would set of all the pictures that he had ready made; *Protogenes* asked some small matter and trifle to speak of : howbeit, *Apelles* esteemed them at fifty talents, & promised to give so much for them : raising a bruit by this means abroad in the world, that he bought them to sell again as his own. The Rhodians hereat were moved and stirred up to take better knowledge of *Protogenes*, what an excellent workman they had of him : neither would *Protogenes* part with any of his pictures unto them, unless they would come off roundly and rise to a better price than beforetime. As for *Apelles*, he had such a dexterity in drawing portraits so lively, and so near resembling those for whom they were made, that hardly one could be known from the other; insomuch, as *Appion* the grammarian hath left in writing (a thing incredible to be spoken) that a certain physiognomist or teller of fortune, by looking only upon the face of men and women, such as the Greeks call Metoposcopos, judged truly by the portraits that *Apelles* had drawn, how many years they either had lived or were to live, for whom those pictures were made. But as gracious as he was otherwise with *Alexander* and his train, yet he could never win the love and favour of prince *Ptolomaeus*, who at that time followed

the court of K. *Alexander*, and was afterwards king of Egypt.
It fortuned, that after the decease of *Alexander*, and during the
reign of king *Ptolomae* aforesaid, this *Apelles* was by a tempest
at sea cast upon the coast of Egypt, and forced to land at
Alexandria : where, other painters that were no wellwishers of
his, practised with a juggler or jester of the kings, and suborned
him in the king's name to train *Apelles* to take his supper with
the king. To the court came *Apelles* accordingly, and showed
himself in the presence. *Ptolomae* having espied him, with a stern
and angry countenance demanded of him what he made there,
and who had sent for him? and with that showed unto him all
his servitors who ordinarily had the inviting of guests to the
king's table, commanding him to say which of them had bidden
him : whereat *Apelles*, not knowing the name of the party who
had brought him thither, and being thus put to his shifts, caught
up a dead coal of fire from the hearth thereby, and began therewith to delineate and draw upon the wall the proportion of that
cousener beforesaid. He had no sooner pourfiled a little about
the visage, but the king presently took knowledge thereby of the
party that had played this prank by him and wrought him this
displeasure. This *Apelles* drew the face of king *Antiochus* also,
who had but one eye to see withal : for to hide which deformity
and imperfection, he devised to paint him, turning his visage a
little away, and so he showed but the one side of his face, to
the end, that whatsoever was wanting in the picture, might be
imputed rather to the painter, than to the person whom he portrayed. And in truth, from him came this invention first to
conceal the defects and blemishes of the visage, and to make one
half face only, when it might be represented full and whole, if
it pleased the painter.

*   *   *   *   *

It is thought likewise, that the full portrait of *Hercules*, painted
in a table, standing now in the temple of *Antonia*, was of his
doing : an exquisite piece of work no doubt, for notwithstanding
that the back part stand toward them that look upon it, yet it
showeth the entire visage, which is an exceeding hard matter. A
man that beholdeth this *Hercules*, would think that the picture
itself turned the face to be seen, which the painter seemed by

the rest of the work to hide from the eye. Of his painting, there
is a prince or worthy knight all naked, in which picture he
seemed to challenge Nature: and have portrayed every part so
well, as she herself could not have framed the same better. There
is or was at leastwise, a horse of his painting: which he portrayed, to set against other horses painted by divers workmen,
with whom he was entered into contention for the victory: in
which trial, he appealed from the sentence of men to the judgement of fourfooted beasts, even living horses indeed: for perceiving that his concurrents were in favour too mighty for him,
and that they were like to carry away the prize by corrupting
the judges and umpires, he caused living horses to be brought
into the place; and when he had presented before them the
pictures of his concurrents' horses one by one they seemed not
to joy nor make toward them: but no sooner had he showed
that of his own portraying, but they fell all to neigh, as taking
it for one of their fellows; which experiment served ever after
for a rule, to know indeed a good piece of workmanship in that
kind.

*   *   *   *   *

What would you have more? he would seem to portray those
things which indeed cannot be portrayed, cracks of thunder,
leames or flashes of lightning, and thunderbolts; all of which
pictures go under the name of *Brontes*, *Astrape*, and *Cerauno-
bolos*: his inventions served as precedents and patterns for others
in that art to follow. One secret he had himself, which no man
was ever able to attain and reach unto, and that was a certain
black varnish which he used to lay upon his painted tables when
he had finished them; which was so finely tempered, and withal
driven upon the work so thin, that by the repercussion thereof it
gave an excellent gloss and pleasant lustre to the colours: the
same also preserved the picture from dust and filthiness: and
yet a man could not perceive any such thing at all, unless he
held the table close at hand, and looked very near. And great
reason he had besides to use this varnish, namely, least the
brightness of the colours without it, might offend and dazzle the
eyes, which now beheld them as it were afar off through a glass-
stone; and withal, the same gave a secret deeping and sadness

to those colours which were too gay and gallant. And thus much may suffice for *Apelles*.

ARISTIDES

In his time lived *Aristides,* the Theban, a famous painter. This *Aristides* was the first that would seem to paint the conceptions of the mind, and to express all the inward dispositions and actions thereof, which the Greeks call ethe : yea the very perturbations and passions of the soul he represented in picture : howbeit, his colours were unpleasant and somewhat too harsh. He represented in a table the winning of a town by force, wherein was portrayed most lively a little infant winding itself and making pretty means to creep unto the mother's pap, who lay a dying upon a mortal wound received in her breast : but it passed, how naturally the poor woman's affection was expressed in this picture; for a man might perceive in her, very sensibly, a certain sympathy and tender affection yet, under her babe, albeit she were now in her deadly pangs and going out of the world, fearing even then, least the child should meet with no milk when she was dead, but instead of sucking it fall to lick her blood, and do itself hurt and injury : This painted table *K. Alexander* the Great translated from Thebes to Pella, the city where himself was born.

* * * * *

He portrayed the running in a race of chariots drawn with four steeds, so lively, that a man would have thought he saw the wheels turning about. And as for an humble suitor or suppliant, he depainted him so naturally, making his petition and following it with such earnestness, that he seemed in manner to cry with an audible voice from the very picture.

PROTOGENES

About the same time, there flourished (as I have said before) *Protogenes* : born he was at Caunos a city in Cilicia, and subject to the Rhodians : he was so exceeding poor at the beginning, and withal so studious, intensive, and curious in his work without all end, that fewer pictures by that means came out of his hands, and himself never rise to any great wealth. Who it was that

2D

taught him his art, it is not known for certain; but some say that he painted ships until he was fifty years of age: which they collect by this argument, that when at Athens in the most conspicuous and frequented place of the city, he was to adorn with pictures the porch before the temple of *Minerva*; wherein he depainted that famous Paralus and Hemionis, which some call Nausicaa, he devised certain borders without: wherein he painted among those byworks (which painters call parerga) certain small galleys and little long barks, to show therby the small beginnings of his art, and to what height of perfection he was come to in the end, when his workmanship was thought worthy to be seen in the most eminent place of that city. But of all the painted tables that ever he wrought, that of *Ialysus* is accounted the principal, which is now dedicated at Rome within the temples of *Peace*: whiles he was in painting this *Ialysus*, it is said, that he lived only upon steeped lupins, which might serve him instead of meat and drink both, to satisfy his hunger and quench his thirst: and this he did, for fear least too much sweetness of other viands should cause him to feed over liberally, and so dull his spirit and senses. And to the end that this picture should be less subject to outward injuries, and last the longer, he charged it with four grounds of colour, which he laid one upon another; that ever as the upper coat went, that underneath might succeed in the place and show fresh again. In this table, the portraiture of a dog is admirable and miraculous; for not only art, but fortune also met together in the painting thereof: for when he had done the dog in all parts to the contentment of his own mind (and that ywis was a very hard and rare matter with him) he could not satisfy and please himself in expressing the froth which fell from his mouth as he panted and blowed almost windless with running; displeased he was with the very art itself: and albeit he thought that he had been long enough already about the said froth, and spent therein but too much art and curiosity, yet somewhat (he wist not what) was to be diminished or altered therein: the more workmanship and skill that went thereto, the farther off it was from the truth indeed and the nature of froth, (the only mark that he shot at:) for when he had done all that he could, it seemed still but painted froth, and not that which came out of the dog's mouth; whereas it should have been the very

same and no other, which had been there before. Hereat he was
troubled and vexed in his mind, as one who would not have anything seen in a picture of his, that might be said like, but the
very same indeed. Many a time he had changed his pencil and
colours; as often, he had wiped out that which was done, and
all to see if he could hit upon it : but it would not be, for yet it
was not to his fancy. At the last, falling clean out with his own
workmanship, because the art might be perceived in it, in a pelting chafe he flings me the sponge-ful of colours that he had
wiped out, full against that unhappy place of the table which
had put him to all this trouble. But see what came of it! The
sponge left the colours behind, in better order than he could have
laid them, and in truth, as well as his heart could wish. Thus
was the froth made to his full mind, and naturally indeed by
mere chance, which all the wit and cunning in his head could
not reach unto. (After whose example, *Nealces,* another painter
did like, and sped as well, in making the froth falling naturally
from a horse's mouth; namely, by throwing his sponge against
the table before him, at what time as he painted a horse rider
cheering and chirking up his horse, yet reining him hard as he
champed upon his bit.) Thus (I say) fortune taught *Protogenes*
to finish his dog. This picture of *Ialysus* and his dog, was of such
name and so highly esteemed, that K. *Demetrius* when he
might have forced the city of Rhodes, on that side only where
Protogenes dwelt, forbare to set it on fire, because he would not
burn it among other painted tables : and thus for to spare a picture, he lost the opportunity of winning a town. During this strait
siege and hot assault of Rhodes, it chanced that *Protogenes* himself was at work in a little garden that he had by the town's side,
even as a man would say within the compass of *Demetrius* his
camp. And for all the fury of war and the daily skirmishes within his sight and hearing, yet he went on still with his works that
he had in hand, and never discontinued one hour. But being
sent for by the king, and demanded, how he durst so confidently
abide without the walls of the city in that dangerous time? he
answered, that he knew full well that *Demetrius* warred against
the Rhodians, and had no quarrel to good arts and sciences.
The king then (glad in his heart that it lay now in his hand
to save those things, which he had spared before, and whereof

he had so good respect) bestowed a very strong guard about *Protogenes* for his better safety and security : and as great an enemy as he was to the Rhodians, yet he used otherwhiles to visit *Protogenes* of his own accord in proper person, because he would not eftsoons call him out of his shop from work : and setting aside the main point and occasion of lying before Rhodes, which was the winning thereof, the thing that he so much desired : even amid the assaults, skirmishes and battles, he would find times to come unto *Protogenes,* and took great pleasure to see his work. By occasion of this siege and hostility, arose this tale moreover of one table of his making, that all the whiles he painted it, the dagger (forsooth) was set to his heart, and a sword ready to cut his throat : and it was the picture of a satyr playing upon a pair of bagpipes, which he called *Anapauomenos* : by which name, as well as by the thing itself, he would seem to signify, that he took but little thought and care during those dangerous troubles. Moreover, he made the picture of lady *Cydippe,* and of *Tlepolemus* : he painted also *Philiscus,* a writer of tragedies, fitting close at his study meditating and musing. Also, there be of his making, a wrestler or champion, *Antigonus* the king, and the mother of *Aristotle,* the philosopher, who also was in hand with *Protogenes,* persuading him to busy himself in painting all the noble acts, victories, and whole life of king *Alexander* the Great, for everlasting memorial and perpetuity : but the vehement affection and inclination of his mind stood another way, and a certain itching desire to search into the secrets of the art, tickled him and drew him rather to these kinds of curious works whereof I have already spoken. Yet in the latter end of his days, he painted king *Alexander* himself, and god *Pan.* Over and besides this flat painting, he gave himself greatly to the practice of foundery, and to cast certain images in brass, according as I have already said.

ARISTIPPUS, PYREICUS AND SERAPION

This *Aristippus* portrayed a satyr crowned with a chaplet, and carrying a goblet or drinking cup : he taught *Antonides* and *Euphranor* his cunning; of whom I will write anon : for meet it is to annex unto the rest, such as have been famous with the pencil in smaller works and lesser pictures : among whom I may reckon *Pyreicus,* who for art and skill had not many that went before him : and verily of this man, I wot not well, whether he debased himself and bare a low sail, of purpose or no ? for surely his mind was wholly set upon painting of simple and base things : howbeit, in that humble and lowly carriage of himself, he attained to a name of glory in the highest degree : his delight was to paint shops, or barbers, shoemakers, cobblers, tailors, and seamsters : he had a good hand in portraying of poor asses with the victuals that they bring to market, and such homely stuff : whereby he got himself a by-name, and was called *Rhyparographus.* Howbeit, such rude and simple toys as these were so artificially wrought, that they pleased & contented the beholders, nothing so much. Many chapmen he had for these trifling pieces, and a greater price they yielded unto him, than the fairest and largest tables of many others. Whereas contraiwise, *Serapion* used to make such great and goodly pictures, that (as *M. Varro* writeth) they were able to take up and fill all the stalls, bulks, and shops, jutting forth into the street under the old market-place Rostra. This *Serapion* had an excellent grace in portraying tents, booths, stages, and theatres; but to paint a man or woman, he knew not which way to begin.

LUDIUS

By occasion of whose name, I must not defraud another *Ludius* of his due praise and commendation, who lived in the days of *Augustus Caesar* Emperor of happy memory : for this *Ludius* was he who first devised to beautify the walls of an house with the pleasantest painting that is in all variety; to wit, with the resemblance of manors, farms, and houses of pleasure in the country, havens, vinets, flower-work in knots, groves, woods, forests, hills, fishpools, conduits, and drains, rivers, riverets, with their banks, and whatsoever a man would wish for to see : wherein also he would represent sundry other shows of people, some walking and going to and fro on foot : others, sailing and rowing up and down the stream upon the water; or else riding by land to their farms, either mounted upon their mules and asses, or else in waggons and coaches : there a man should see folk, in this place fishing and angling, in that place hawking and fowling; some hunting here, the hare, the fox, or deer both red and fallow; others, busy there, in harvest or vintage. In this manner of painting a man should behold of his workmanship, fair houses standing among marshes, unto which all the ways that lead, be ticklish and full of bogs; where you should see the paths so slippery, that women as they go are afraid to set one foot afore another; some at every step ready to slide, others bending forward with their heads, as though they carried some burdens upon their neck and shoulders, and all for fear least (their feet failing under them) they should catch a fall : and a thousand more devices and pretty conceits as these, full of pleasure and delight. The same *Ludius* devised walls without-doors & abroad in the open air, to paint cities standing by the sea side. All which kind of painting pleaseth the eye exceeding well, and is besides of little or no cost. Howbeit, neither he nor any artificers in this kind (howsoever otherwise respected) grew ever to be famous and of great name; that felicity attained they only unto, who used to paint in tables : and therefore in this regard, venerable antiquity we have in greater admiration : for painters in old time loved not to garnish walls for to pleasure the master only of the house, ne yet to bedeck houses in that manner, which cannot stir out of the place nor shift and save themselves when fire cometh; as painted tables may, that are to be removed with ease. *Protogenes,* as excellent a painter as he was, contented himself to live within a little garden in a small cottage, and I warrant you no part thereof was painted. *Apelles* himself might well have the walls of his house rough-cast or finely plastered, but never a patch thereof had any painting. They took no pleasure, nay they had no lust at all to paint upon the whole walls, and to work upon them from one end to another : all their skill and cunning attended upon the public service of states and cities : and a painter was not for this or that place only, but employed for the good & benefit indifferently of all countries and nations.

TWO PAINTERS OF GODDESSES

But to return again to our particular painters : there flourished at Rome a little before *Augustus Caesar's* days, one *Arellius,* a renowned painter, but that he had one notable foul fault which marred all and discredited his art; given he was exceeding to wenching, and sure he would be to have one women or other all times in chase : which was the reason that he loved a-life to be painting of goddesses, and those were ever drawn by the pattern of his sweethearts whom he courted : A man might know by his pictures how many queans he kept, and which were the mistresses or goddesses rather, whom he served. Of late days we had among us here at Rome, one *Amulius,* a painter : he carried with him in his countenance and habit, gravity and severity; howbeit, he loved to make gay & gallant pictures, neither scorned he to paint the most trifling toys and meanest things that were : The picture of *Minerva* was of his making, which seemeth to have her eye full directly upon you, look which way soever you will upon her. He wrought but some few hours of the day, and then would he seem very grave and ancient; for you should never find him out of his gown and long robe, but very formal, though he were close set at work & even locked as it were to his frame.

A PRETTY JEST

Since I have proceeded so far in the discourse of painters and their art, I must not forget to set down a pretty jest, which hath been reported by many as touching *Lepidus* : It happened during the time of his triumvirate, that in a certain place where he was, the magistrates attended him to his lodging, environed as it were with woods on every side : the next morrow *Lepidus* took them up for it, and in bitter terms and minatory words chid them, for that they had laid him where he could not sleep a wink all night long, for the noise and singing that the birds made about him. They being thus checked and rebuked, devised against the next night, to paint in a piece of parchment of exceeding length, a long dragon or serpent, wherewith they compassed the place where *Lepidus* should take his repose : the sight of which serpent thus painted, so terrified the birds, that they had no mind to sing, but were altogether silent : by which experiment at that time, it was known afterwards that birds by this means might be stilled.

PAUSIAS

This *Pausias* was the son of *Brietes,* & apprentice also to his father at the beginning : he used also the plain pencil, wherewith he wrought upon the walls at Thespiae; which having been in times past painted by *Polygnotus,* were now to be refreshed and painted new again by his hand : howbeit, in comparison of the former work, he was thought to come a great way short of *Polygnotus* : and the reason was, because he dealt in that kind of work which was not indeed his proper profession. He it was that brought up first the device of painting vaulted roofs; for never was it the manner to adorn and garnish embowed ceiling overhead with colours, before his time. His delight naturally was to be painting of little tables, and therein he loved to portray little boys. Others painters his concurrents, and no well-wishers of his, gave out, that he made choice of this kind of work, because such painting went but slowly away, and required no quick and nimble hand. Whereupon *Pausias,* to disprove his adversaries, and withal to get himself a name as well for celerity and expedition, as for his art and skill otherwise in these small pieces, began and finished in a table the picture of a boy, within one day; and thereupon it was called *Hemeresios.* In his youthful days he fell in fancy with a woman in the same town where he dwelt, named *Glycera* : a fine wit she had of her own; and especially in making chaplets and garlands of flowers, she was full of invention. *Pausias,* by his acquaintance with her, and striving to imitate with his pencil her handiwork, and to express that variety of flowers which she gathered and couched together full artificially in her coronets, enriched his own pictures also with a number of colours, and brought the art to wonderful perfection in that point. In the end, he painted *Glycera* also his love sitting, with a chaplet of flowers in her hand : and certes, this is the most excellent piece of work that ever went out of his shop : this table with the picture was thereupon called by some, Stephanoplocos, i.e. (A woman) plaiting and twisting a garland : by others, Stephanopolis, i.e. Selling garlands : for that this *Glycera* got a poor living by making chaplets, and had no other good means to maintain herself. The counterfeit taken from this table and made by it (which kind of pattern the Greeks call apographon)

L. Lucullus bought of *Dionysius* a painter of Athens, and it cost him two talents of silver. Furthermore, this *Pausias* made fair and great pictures also; and namely, one of his making, which doth represent a solemn sacrifice of oxen, is to be seen at this day within the stately galleries of *Pompeius* : and verily, this manner of painting the solemnity of a sacrifice, he first invented : but no man ever after could attain to his dexterity in that kind : and notwithstanding many gave the attempt, and seemed to imitate him, yet they came all short of him. Above all, he had a singular gift to work by perspective : for when he was minded to paint a boeuf or ox, to show the full length, he would not portray him sidelong or aflank, but afront; by which means the beast is best represented, not only how long, but also how large and big he is every way. Again, whereas all other painters, whensoever they would raise their work, and make anything seem eminent and high, use to colour the same white and bright, and the better to make them perspective, do shadow or deep the same with black; this man in lieu thereof, would paint the ox all of a black colour, and cause the body as it were of the shadow to arise out of itself. And verily, so excellent he was in this perspective, that a man would say, his even, plain, and flat picture, were embossed and raised work, yea and imagine where fractures were, that all was sound and entire.

ANTIPHILUS

As for *Antiphilus*, he is much praised for painting a boy blowing hard at the coals; in which table, it is a pretty sight to see how all the house (which was fair enough besides) shineth by the fire than he maketh, as also what a mouth the boy makes : likewise for the picture of a company of spinsters, so lively, that one would imagine he saw every woman making haste to spin off her distaff, striving avie who shall have done her task first.

CLESIDES AND STRATONICE

Clesides, was notorious for one picture which he made in despite of queen *Stratonice,* wife of king *Antiochus,* and to be revenged of her for a disgrace that he had received at her hands :

For being in the court, and perceiving that the queen did him no honour at all, nor gave him any countenance, he made no more ado, but painted her in her colours, tumbling and wallowing along full unseemly with an odd base fisherman, whom as the voice went, she was enamoured upon; and when he had done, set it up in the very haven of Ephesus, recovered a bark presently, and away he went under sail as fast as wind and tide would carry him. When the queen heard of it, she made but a jest and mock of it; neither would she suffer the picture to be taken away, in regard of the wonderful workmanship, which expressed both her and him so like and lively.

NEALCES

Nealces made one picture of *Venus* most curiously : for passing witty he was, full of invention, and exquisite in his art. When he painted the naval battle between the Egyptians and the Persians, which was fought upon the river Milus, the water whereof is rough and like the sea; because he would have it known, that the fight was upon the said river, he devised another by-work to express the same, which all the art of painting otherwise could not perform : for he painted an ass upon the bank, drinking at the river, and a crocodile lying in wait to catch him : whereby any man might soon know it was the river Nilus, and no other water.

WOMEN PAINTERS

Moreover, women there were also, excellent paintresses, to wit, *Timarete,* the daughter of *Nicon,* who made that excellent portraiture of *Diana* at Ephesus, a most antique picture : *Irene* the daughter of *Cratinus* the painter, who learned under her father, & drew the picture of a young damosel, which is at Eleusine : *Calypso,* of whose workmanship there is the picture of an old man, and of *Theodorus* the juggler : *Alcisthene* painted a dancer : and *Aristarete,* both daughter and apprentice to *Nearchus,* made proof how well she had profited by the picture of *Aesculapius.* And *Marcus Varro* saith, that when he was a young man, there was at Rome one *Laela,* a Cyzecene born, who passed her whole life in virginity; and she was skilful both in painting with the pencil, and also in enamelling with hot steel in ivory : her delight was principally in drawing women; and yet there is a Neapolitan of her portraying in a fair long table : last of all, she took out her own counterfeit at a mirror or looking glass. This one thing is reported of her, that no painter had a quicker hand or went faster away with his work than she : and look what pictures soever came out of her hands, they were so artificially done, that they did outsell a great deal the works of *Sopylos* and *Dionysius* (the most famous painters in that age) notwithstanding their pictures and tables were so fair, as that they take up whole cabinets; and well was he (before that her pictures came abroad) who could be furnished out of their two shops.

A REMARKABLE PROCESS

Moreover, in Egypt they have a device to stain cloths after a strange and wonderful manner : They take white cloths, as sails or curtains when they have been worn, which they besmear not with colours but with certain drugs that are apt to drink and take colour : when they have so done, there is no appearance in them at all of any dye or tincture. These clothes they cast into a lead or cauldron of some colour that is seething and scalding hot : where, after they have remained a pretty while, they take them forth again, all stained and painted in sundry colours. An admirable thing, that there being in the said cauldron but only one kind of tincture, yet out of it the cloth should be stained with this and that colour, and the foresaid boiling liquor change so as it doth, according to the quality and nature of the drugs which were laid upon the white at first. And verily, these stains or colours are set so sure, as they can never be washed off afterwards. Thus the scalding liquor, which no doubt if it had diverse tinctures and colours in it, would have confounded them all into one : now out of one doth dispense and digest them accordingly, and in boiling the drugs of the clothes, setteth the colour and staineth surely. And verily, this good moreover have the cloths by this scalding, that they be always more firm and durable, than if they had not come into the boiling cauldron.

THE INVENTION OF CLAY-MODELLING

Now that I have discoursed of painting enough, if not too much, it were good to annex and join thereto the craft of pottery, and working out of clay. And to begin with the original and invention of making the image or likeness of anything in clay, it is said, that *Dibutades,* a Sicyonian born and a potter, was the first that devised at Corinth to form an image in the same clay whereof he made his pots, by the occasion and means of a daughter which he had : who being in love with a certain young man, whensoever he was to take a long journey far from home, used ordinarily to mark upon the wall the shadow of her lover's face by candlelight and to pourfil the same afterwards deeper, that so she might enjoy his visage yet in his absence. This her father perceiving, followed those tracts, and by clapping clay thereupon, perceived that it took a print, and made a sensible form of a face : which when he saw, he put it into the furnace to bake among other vessels, and when it was hardened, showed it abroad. And it is said, that this very piece remained in the bains of Corinth safe, until *Mummius* destroyed the city.

LYSISTRATUS

But *Lysistratus* of Sicyone, and brother to *Lysippus,* of whom I have written before, was the first that in plaster or alabaster represented the shape of a man's visage in a mould from the lively face indeed; and when he had taken the image in wax, which the foresaid mould of plaster had given, used to form and fashion the same more exactly. This man stayed not there, but began to make images to the likeness and resemblance of the person : for before him every man studied only to make the fairest faces, and never regarded whether they were like or no. *Lysistratus* also invented to make counterfeits in clay, according to the images and statues in brass, already made. And in the end, this feat of working in clay grew to such height, that no images or statues were made without moulds of clay : Whereby it may appear, that the skill and knowledge of pottery is more ancient than foundry or casting brass.

THE GOODNESS OF THE EARTH

If a man consider these things aright, and weigh them duly in particular, he shall find the bounty and goodness of the Earth to be inenarrable, though he should not reckon her benefits that she hath bestowed upon mankind, in yielding us so many sorts of corn, wine, apples, and such like fruits, herbs, shrubs, bushes, trees, medicinable drugs, metal, and minerals, which I have already treated of: for even in these works of earth and pottery, which we are glutted with (they be so usual and ordinary) how beneficial is the Earth unto us, in yielding us conduit pipes for to convey water into our bains, tiles flat yet hooked and made with crotchets at one end to hang upon the sides of the roof, chamfered for to lie in gutters to shoot off water, curbed for crests to clasp the ridge on both sides; bricks to lie in walls afront for building, and those otherwhiles to serve as binders in parpine work with a face on both sides; to say nothing of the vessels that be turned with the wheel and wrought round; yea and great tuns and pipes of earth devised to contain wine and water also?

MENS SANA IN CORPORE SANA?

There is found also in Nilus a certain sand, whereof the finest part differeth not much from that of Puteoli beforesaid: not in regard that it is so strong as to break the force of the sea water and to beat back the waves, but to subdue and crush the bodies of our young gentlemen, and therefore serveth well in the public place of wrestling for those that be given to such exercises: And for this purpose verily was it brought from thence by sea unto *Patrobius*, a slave lately enfranchised by *Nero* the Emperor. I read also, that *Leonatus, Cratus, & Meleager,* who were great captains under *Alexander* the Great and followed his court, were wont to have this sand carried with them, with other baggage belonging to the camp. But I mean not to write any more of this argument, no more verily than of the use of earth in those places where our youth anoint their bodies against they should wrestle; wherein our youths addict themselves so much to the exercise of the body, that they have spoiled themselves otherwise, and lost the vigour of the mind.

A PARLOUR-TRICK

As touching the nature of brimstone, so forcible it is, that if it be cast into the fire, the very smell and steam thereof will drive those in the place into a fit of the falling sickness, if they be subject thereunto. As for *Anaxilaus,* he would commonly make sport withal at a feast, and set all the guests into a merriment: for his manner was to set it a-burning within a cup of new earth over a chafing-dish of coals, and to carry it about the table where they were at supper: and in very truth the reverberation of the flame would make all that were near it to look pale and wan after a most fearful manner, like as if there were as many grisly ghosts or dead men's faces.

THE SIX AND THIRTIETH BOOK

treateth of marble and stone for building.

PREFACE

IT REMAINETH now to write of the nature of stones, that is to say, the principal point of all enormous abuses, and the very height of wasteful superfluities, yea though we should keep silence, and say nothing either of precious stones and amber, or of crystal and cassidony. For, all things else which we have handled heretofore even to this book, may seem in some sort to have been made for man; but as for mountains, Nature had framed them for her own self; partly to strengthen (as it were) certain joints within the veins and bowels of the earth; partly to tame the violence of great rivers, and to break the force of surging waves and inundations of the sea: and in one word, by that substance and matter whereof they stand, which of all others is most hard, to restrain and keep within bounds that unruly element of the water. And yet notwithstanding, for our wanton pleasures and nothing else, we cut and hew, we load and carry away those huge hills and inaccessible rocks, which otherwise to pass only over, was thought a wonder. Our ancestors in times past reputed it a miracle, and in manner prodigious, that first *Anniball,* and afterwards the Cimbrians, surmounted the Alps: but now, even the same mountains we pierce through with pick-axe and mattock, for to get out thereof a thousand sorts of marble; we cleave the capes and promontories; we lay them open for the sea, to let it in; down we go with their heads, as if we would lay the whole world even, and make all level. The mighty mountains set as limits to bound the frontiers of diverse countries, and to separate one nation from another, those we transport and carry from their native seat : ships we build of purpose for to fraught with marble; the cliffs and tops of high hills they carry to and fro, amid the waves and billows of the sea, and never fear the danger of that most fell and cruel element : wherein verily we surpass the madness and vanity of those, who search as high as the clouds for a cup to drink our water cold; and hollow the rocks that in manner touch the heaven, & all to drink out of ice. Now let every man think with himself what excessive prices of these stones he shall hear anon, and what monstrous pieces and masses he seeth drawn and carried both by land and sea; let him consider withal, how much more fair and happy a life many a man should have without all this, and how many cannot choose but die for it, whensoever they go about to do, or, if I should speak more truly, to suffer this enterprise : Also, for what use, or pleasure rather, but only that they might lie in beds and chambers of stones that forsooth are spotted, as if they never regarded how the darkness of the night bereaveth the one half of each man's life of these delights and joys. When I ponder and weigh these things in my mind, I must needs think great shame, and impute a great fault to our forefathers that lived long since, & blush in their behalf. Laws were enacted, and prohibitions published by the Censors, and those remaining upon record forbidding expressly, that neither the kernelly part of a boar's neck, nor dormice, and other smaller matters than these to be spoken of, should be served up to the board at great feasts : but as touching the restraint of bringing in marble, or of sailing into foreign parts for the same, there was no act or statute ordained.

BUPALUS AND ANTHERMUS

Long time before *Dipoenus* and *Scyllis,* there had been in the island Chios one *Melas,* a cutter and graver in marble : after whom, his son *Micciades* succeeded, and he likewise left a son behind him, named *Anthermus,* of the said isle, a cunning workman : whose two sons *Bupalus* and *Anthermus,* proved also most skilful imageurs. These flourished in the days of *Hipponax* the poet, who (as it is well known) lived in the 60 Olympias. Now, if a man will calculate the times, according to the genealogy of these two last named, and count backward in ascent no higher than to their grandsire, he shall find by the ordinary course of Nature, that the art of cutting and graving in stone, is equal in antiquity to the original and beginning of the Olympiades. But to prove that these two, *Bupalus* and *Anthermus*, lived in the days of *Hipponax* abovenamed, recorded it is, that the said poet had a passing foul and illfavoured face of his own : and these imageurs could find no better sport, than to counterfeit both him and his visage, as lively as possible might be in stone; and in a knavery to set the same up in open place where merry youths met in knots together, and so to propose him a laughing stock to the whole world. *Hipponax* could not endure this indignity, but for to be revenged upon these companions sharpened his style open against them, and so coursed them with bitter rhymes and biting libels, that as some do think and verily believe, being weary of their lives, they knit their necks in halters, and so hanged themselves. But surely this cannot be true : for they lived many a fair day after, yea and wrought a number of images in the islands adjacent to Chios, and namely in Delos : under which pieces of their work, they subscribed certain arrogant verses to this effect, that the island Chios was not only ennobled for the vines there growing which yielded so good wine, but renowned as well for *Anthermus* his two sons, who made so many fine and curious images.

A STRANGE THING

But here cometh to my remembrance a strange thing that is recorded of the quarries in the island Paros; namely, that in one quarter thereof there was a vein of marble found, which when it was cloven in twain with wedges, showed naturally within, the true image and perfect portraiture of a Silenus imprinted in it.

PHIDIAS

As touching *Phidias*, no man doubteth but he was the most excellent graver that ever was, as all nations will confess who

2E

ever have heard of that statue of *Iupiter Olympius,* which his own hands wrought: but that all others also may know (who never saw his work nor the statues that he made), that he well deserved the name which went of him: I will lay abroad some small pieces as arguments of his handiwork, and those only that may testify his fine head and rare invention: neither will I allege for proof hereof, either the beautiful image of *Iupiter Olympius,* which he made at Olympia, or the stately statue of *Minerva,* that he wrought at Athens, which carried in height six and twenty cubits, and was all made of ivory and gold: but I will take the shield or targuet that the said goddess is protrayed with; in the embossed and swelling compass whereof, he engraved the battle wherein the Amazons were defeated (by Theseus;) within the hollow part and concavity, he enchased the conflict between the gods and the giants: upon the shoes or pantofles that she weareth, he portrayed the fight between the Lapithae and the Centaurs; so full compact of art was everything about her, and so curiously and artificially contrived. Now in the base or pedestal under the statue, the work that was cut, he called the Genealogy of *Pandora*: there a man might see the nativity (as it were) of the gods, to the numbei of thirty; and among them the goddess *Victory,* of most admirable workmanship. Moreover, artificers that are seen and skilful in these matters, do greatly admire the fell serpent; as also the monster *Sphinx* made in brass, under the very spear that *Minerva* holdeth in her hand. This may serve by the way in a word or two touching that famous and renowned artisan *Phidias* (whom no man is able to praise and commend sufficiently) that it may be known likewise that the magnificence of his workmanship was the same still, even in small matters as well as great.

PRAXITELES

To come now to *Praxiteles*: what time he lived, I have declared already in my catalogue of founders and imageurs in brass: who, albeit he was singular in that kind, yet in marble he went beyond himself: his works are to be seen at Athens, in that conspicuous street called Ceraumicum: but of all the images that ever were made (I say not by *Praxiteles* only, but by all the workmen that were in the world) his *Venus* passeth, which he wrought for them of Gnidos : and in truth, so exquisite and singular it was, that many a man hath embarked, taken sea, and sailed to Gnidos for no other business, but only to see and behold it : he had made two of them, and sold them both together; the one with a veil and arrayed decently in apparel, which in that regard the men of Cos bought; for being put to their choice, they like honest men preferred it before the other which was naked (notwithstanding *Praxiteles* tendered them both at one and the same price) in a good mind that they carried, and having respect and regard unto their gravity and modest carriage of themselves : that which they refused and rejected, the Gnidians bargained for, and indeed (to speak of workmanship) it was infinitely better, and there was no comparison between them, by the general fame and opinion of all men : and verily king *Nicodemes* afterwards would gladly have bought it again of the Gnidians, and offered them enough; for he promised in consideration thereof, to discharge all debts that their city was engaged in, which were very great sums; but they would not give ear nor hearken unto him : content they were to live in debt and danger still, yea and to abide and endure any forfeitures, exegents, executions, and extents whatsoever, than to part with their *Venus*. And to say a truth, good reason they had so to do; for that one image of *Praxiteles* his making, was their chief credit, ennobled their city, and drew resort from all parts thither. This *Venus* was shrined in a little chapel by herself within a tabernacle; but of purpose so devised, that it might be set open on all sides for to be seen and viewed all and whole on every part : wherewith the goddess herself (as men were verily persuaded) was well enough pleased, and showed her contentment therein to all comers; for look upon her as one would, amiable she was and admirable every way. It is reported, that a wretched fellow was enamoured of this *Venus,* and having lurked one night secretly within the chapel, behaved himself so and came so near unto the image, that he left behind him a mark of his lewd love and beastly lust; the spot of which pollution, appeared afterwards upon the body.

THE MAUSOLEUM

This mausoleum was the renowned tomb or sepulchre of *Mausolus,* a petty king of Caria, which the worthy lady *Artemisia,* (sometime his queen, and now his widow) caused to be erected for the said prince her husband, who died in the second year of the hundredth Olympias: and verily so sumptuous a thing it was, & so curiously wrought, by these artificers especially, that it is reckoned one of those matchless monuments which are called the seven wonders of the world. From north to south it carrieth in length, sixty three foot; the two fronts east and west, make the breadth, which is not all out so large; so as the whole circuit about, may contain four hundred and eleven foot: it is raised in height five and twenty cubits, and environed with six and thirty columns: one the east side, *Scopas* did cut; *Bryaxes* chose the north end; that side which regardeth the south, fell to *Timotheus;* and *Leochares* engraved at the west end: but Queen *Artemisia,* (who caused this rich sepulchre to be made for the honour and in the memorial of her husband late deceased) happened herself to depart this life before it was fully finished: howbeit these noble artificers whom she had set a-work, would not give over when she was dead and gone, but followed on still and brought it to a final end, as making this account, that it would be a glorious monument to all posterity, both of themselves and also of their cunning: and in truth at this day, it is hard to judge by their handiwork who did best. There was a fifth workman also came in unto them; for above the side wall or wing of the tomb, there was a pyramis founded, which from the very battlements of the said wall was carried to the height of the building underneath it: the same grew smaller still as the work arose higher, & from that height at every degree (which in the whole were four and twenty) was narrowed and taken in, until at last it ended in a pointed broch: in the top whereof, there is pitched a coach with four horsees wrought curiously in marble; and this was the work of *Pythis* for his part. So that reckoning this chariot with the sharp spire, the pyramis under it unto the battlements, and the body of the sepulchre founded upon the first ground, the whole work arose to an hundred and forty foot in height.

MENESTRATUS

As touching *Menestratus,* men have in high admiration *Hercules* of his making; as also *Hecate,* which standeth in a chapel at Ephesus behind the great temple of *Diana* : the sextons or wardens of which chapel, give warning unto those that come to see it, that they look not too long upon it for dazzling and hurting their eyes, the lustre of the marble is so radiant and resplendent.

A NARROW ESCAPE

This *Iunius* was born in the marches and coasts of Italy called Graecia, and together with the towns of that tract, was made a Roman free-denizen; being himself also a good cutter in stone, he made that image of *Iupiter* in ivory which standeth in the chapel of *Metellus,* in the way which leadeth into (*Mars'*) field. It happened upon a time, that being about the Arsenal, where certain wild beasts were, newly brought out of Affrick, he looked in at a grate to behold a lion and to take out the counterfeit of him : but as he was engraving in stone according to the pattern, behold, out of another cage a panther brake loose, to no small danger of that most curious and painful workman.

A PRETTY THING

Moreover, I cannot conceal from you one pretty thing to be observed, and which we all know to be true, that in one chapel of *Iupiter* all the pictures, therein, as also all the ceremonial service thereto belonging, are respective altogether to the feminine sex : the which happening at first by mere chance, continued afterwards : for when the temple of *Iuno* was finished, the porters who had the carriage of the images ordained there to stand, mistook their marks and carried thither those which were appointed for the chapel of *Iupiter,* and contrariwise those for *Iuno,* into the chapel of *Iupiter* : which being once done, was not altered again, but taken for a presage, and religiously ever after kept, as if the very gods themselves had so ordered and appointed it, and made a counterchange : which is the reason also, that in the foresaid chapel of *Iuno,* there is that kind of service which was meant for *Iupiter.*

MICROSCOPIC SCULPTURE

To conclude, there have been certain workmen that have grown to a great name, by cutting and graving in small pieces of marble; and namely, *Myrmecides* devised to inchase in marble, a chariot with four horses, and a man to drive the same, in so small a room, that a poor fly might cover all with her little wings. As for *Callicrates,* he cut in stone the similitude and proportion of prismires in so narrow a compass, that a man cannot easily discern the feet and other parts of the body.

SLICING MARBLE

But surely, whosoever devised that invention, to saw marble stone and to slit it into leaves for to serve the turn of riotous and wasteful persons, had a perilous head of his own, and a shrewd. But would you know the cast of slitting marble? it is done with a kind of sand, and yet a man would think that it were the saw alone that doth the deed; for when there is an entry once made by a very small line or trace, they strew the said sand aloft all the length thereof : then they set the saw to it, and by drawing it to and fro, the sand under the teeth thereof, maketh way downwards still and so the stone, as hard as it is, they cut through in a trice : Now for this purpose the Aethyopian sand hath no fellow. And to this path forsooth we are come, that we cannot have marble to serve our turns, unless we send as far as into Aethyopia; nay, we must be provided of sand to slit our marble with, out of India; from whence in times past, during the ancient discipline of Rome, it was thought too much and a shameful thing, to fetch rich pearls. And yet this Indian sand is commended in a second degree : but the Aethyopian is the softer and better simply; for that sand cutteth smooth and clean as it goeth, and leaves no race at all in the work; the Indian maketh not so even and neat plates, howbeit, they that polish marble, fit themselves with this sand when it is burnt and calcined; for if they rub their leaves and plates therewith, it will make them slick and fair; for otherwise, if it be not calcined to a fine powder, of itself it is churlish and rugged: which is the fault likewise of the sand that cometh from Naxos and Coptis, which commonly is called the Aegyptian sand: for these sands verily were used in old time to the cutting of marbles. Afterwards they met with a sand as good as the best, and went no farther than to a certain bay or creek in the Adriatic sea or Venice gulf, which being left bare when the tide is gone, they may at a low water easily discern to have been cast up by the flood. And nowadays our sawers of marble, make no more ado, but take the first sand they come by (it makes no matter out of what river it be) this serves their turn well enough; and thus they abuse & deceive the world, although few chapmen there be that know what loss there is by their marble leaves sawn in that sort: howbeit, such gross sand as that, first maketh a wider slit in the main stone, and by consequence spendeth and consumeth more of the marble: again, there is more work and labour about the polishing thereof, the saw and sand beforesaid leaveth the faces of the stone so rugged and uneven: and by this means the plates become slight and thin before they can be employed.

OBELISKS

It is said, that *Ramises* abovenamed, kept twenty thousand men at work about this obelisk: The king himself in person when it should be reared on end, fearing least the engines devised for to raise it, and hold the head thereof between heaven and earth, in the rearing should fail and not be able to bear that monstrous weight; because he would lay the heavier charge upon the artificers that were about this enterprise, upon their uttermost peril, caused his own son to be bound unto the top thereof, imagining also, that the care of the engineers who undertook the weighing up of this obelisk, over the young prince, for fear of hurting him, would induce them also to be more heedful to preserve the stone. Certes, this obelisk was a piece of work so admirable, that when king *Cambyses* had won the city where it stood, by assault, and put all within to fire and sword, having burnt all before him, as far to the very foundation and underpinning of the obelisk, commanded expressly to quench the fire:

and so in a kind of reverence yet unto a mass and pile of stone, spared it, who had no regard at all of the city besides.

*   *   *   *   *

And as for that obelisk which standeth in *Mars* field, *Augustus Caesar* the emperor devised a wonderful means that it should serve to mark out the noontide, with the length of day and night, according to the shadows that the sun doth yield by it : for he placed underneath at the foot of the said obelisk, according to the bigness and length thereof, a pavement of broad stone; wherein a man might know the sixth hour or the mid-day at Rome, when the shadow was equal to the obelisk, and how by little and little, according to certain rules (which are lines of brass, inlaid within the said stone) the days do increase or decrease : A thing no doubt worth the knowledge, and an invention proceeding from a pregnant wit. *Manlius*, a renowned mathematician and astronomer, put unto the top of the said obelisk a gilded ball, in such sort, that all the shadow which it gave fell upon the obelisk, and this cast other shadows more or less, different from the head or top of the obelisk aforesaid. The reason whereof (they say) was understood from the sundry shadows that a man's head doth yield. But surely for these thirty years past or thereabout, the use of this quadrant aforesaid hath not been found true; and what the reason thereof should be, I know not, whether the course of the sun in itself be not the same that heretofore, or be altered by some disposition of the heavens; or whether the whole earth be somewhat removed from the true centre in the midst of the world (which I hear say is found to be so in other places :) or that it proceed by occasion of the earthquakes which have shaken the city of Rome, and so haply wrested the gnomon from the old place; or last of all, whether by reason of many inundations of Tiberis, this huge and weighty obelisk hath settled and sunk down lower (and yet it is said that the foundation was laid as deep under ground, as the obelisk itself is above the ground).

PYRAMIDS

Having thus discoursed of the obelisks, it were good to say

somewhat of the pyramids also in Egypt : a thing I assure you that bewrayeth the foolish vain-glory of the kings in that country, who abounding in wealth, could not tell what to do with their money, but spent it in such idle and needless vanities. And verily most writers do report, that the principal motives which induced them to build these pyramids, was partly to keep the common people from idleness, partly also because they would not have much treasure lying by them, least either their heirs apparent, or other ambitious persons who aspired to be highest, should take occasion thereby to play false and practise treasons. Certes, a man may observe the great follies of those princes herein, that they began many of these pyramids, and left them unfinished; as may appear by the tokens remaining thereof.

* * * * *

Over against the said pyramids there is a monstrous rock called Sphinx, much more admirable than the pyramids, and forsooth the peasants that inhabit the country esteemed it no less than some divine power and god of the fields and forests : within it, the opinion groweth, that the body of king *Amasis* was entombed; & they would bear us in hand, that the rock was brought thither, all and whole as it is : but surely it is a mere crag growing naturally out of the ground; howbeit wrought also with man's hand, polished and very smooth and slippery. The compass of this rock's head (resembling thus a monster) taken about the front, or as it were the forehead, containeth one hundred and two foot, the length or height 143 foot; the height from the belly to the top of the crown in the head, ariseth to three score and two foot. But all of these pyramids, the biggest doth consist of the stone hewed out of the Arabic quarries : it is said, that in the building of it there were 366,000 men kept at work twenty years together : and all three were in making three score and eighteen years and four months. The writers who have made mention of these pyramids, were *Herodotus, Euhemerus, Duris* the Samian, *Aristagoras, Dionysius, Artemidorus, Alexander Polyhistor, Butorides, Antisthenes, Demetrius, Demotelles, & Apion* : but (as many as have written hereof) yet a man cannot know certainly and say, This pyramid was built by this king : a most just punishment, that the name and authors of so monstrous vanity, should be buried in perpetual oblivion: but some of these historiographers have reported, that there were a thousand and eight hundred talents laid out only for radish, garlic, and onions, during the building of these pyramids. The largest of them taketh up eight acres of ground at the foot, four square it is made, and every face or side thereof equal, containing from angle to angle eight hundred four score and three foot, and at the top five and twenty: the second made likewise four cornered, is on every side even, and comprehendeth from corner to corner seven hundred thirty and seven foot: the third is less than the former two, but far more beautiful to behold, built of Aethyopian stones; it carrieth at the foot in each face between four angles, three hundred three score and three foot. And yet of all these huge monuments, there remain no tokens of any houses built, no appearance of frames and engines requisite for such monstrous buildings: a man shall find all about them far and near, fair said and small red gravel, much like unto lentil seed, such as is to be found in the most part of Africa. A man seeing all so clean and even, would wonder at them how they came thither: but the greatest difficulty moving question and marvel is this, what means were used to carry so high as well such mighty masses of hewn squared stone, as the filling, rubbish, and mortar that went thereto? for some are of opinion, that there were devised mounts of salt and nitre heaped up together higher and higher as the work arose and was brought up; which being finished, were demolished, and so washed away by the inundation of the river Nilus: others think, that there were bridges reared with bricks made of clay, which after the work was brought to an end, were distributed abroad and employed in building of private houses; for they hold, that Nilus could never reach thither, lying as it doth so low under them when it is at the highest, for to wash away the heaps and mounts abovesaid.

THE LIGHTHOUSE ON PHAROS

Over and above the pyramids aforesaid, a great name there is of a tower built by one of the kings of Aegypt within the island Pharos, and it keepeth and commandeth the haven of

Alexandria, which tower (they say) cost eight hundred talents the building. And here, because I would omit nothing worth the writing, I cannot but note the singular magnanimity of king *Ptolome,* who permitted *Sostratus* of Gnidos (the master workman and architect) to grave his own name in this building. The use of this watch-tower, is to show light as a lantern, and give direction in the night season to ships, for to enter the haven, and where they shall avoid bars and shelves : like to which there be many beacons burning to the same purpose, and namely at Puteoli and Ravenna. This is the danger only, least when many lights in this lantern meet together, they should be taken for a star in the sky; for that afar off such light appear unto sailors in manner of a star.

LABYRINTHS

Since we have finished our obelisks and pyramids, let us enter also into the labyrinths; which we may truly say, are the most monstrous works that ever were devised by the hand of man : neither are they incredible and fabulous, as peradventure it may be supposed, for one of them remaineth to be seen at this day within the jurisdiction of Heracleopolis, the first that ever was made, to wit, three thousand and six hundred years ago, by a king named *Petesuccas,* or as some think *Tithoes* : and yet *Herodotus* saith, it was the whole work of many kings one after another, and that *Psammerichus* was the last that put his hand to it and made an end thereof. The reason that moved these princes to make this labyrinth, is not resolved by writers, but divers causes are by them alleged : *Demoteles* saith, that this labyrinth, was the royal palace and seat of king *Motherudes* : *Lycias* affirmeth it to be the sepulchre of king *Moeris* : the greater part are of opinion, that it was an edifice dedicated expressly and consecrated unto the Sun, which in my conceit cometh nearest to the truth. Certes, there is no doubt made that *Daedalus* took from hence the pattern and platform of his labyrinth which he made in Crete; but surely he expressed not above the hundredth part thereof, choosing only that corner of the labyrinth which containeth a number of ways and passages, meeting and encountering one another, winding and turning in and out every way, after so intricate manner and so inexplicable, that when a man is once in, he cannot possibly get out again : neither must we think that these turnings and returnings were after the manner of mazes which are drawn upon the pavement and plain floor of a field, such as we commonly see serve to make sport and pastime among boys, that is to say, which within a little compass and round border comprehend many miles; but here were many doors contrived, which might trouble and confound the memory, for seeing such variety of entries, alleys, and ways, some crossed and encountered, others flanked on either side, a man wandered still and knew not whether he went forward or backward, nor in truth where he was.

*   *   *   *   *

The labyrinth in Lemnos was much like to them, only in this respect more admirable, for that it had a hundred and forty columns of marble more than the other, all wrought round by turners' craft, but with such dexterity, that a very child was able to wield the wheel that turned them, the pins and poles whereby they hung were so artificially poised. The master devisers and architects of this labyrinth, were *Zmilus*, *Rholus*, and a third unto them, one *Theodorus* who was born in the same island. Of this, there remain some relics to be seen at this day; whereas a man shall not find one small remnant either of the Italian or Candian labyrinths : for meet it is that I should write somewhat also of our labyrinth here in Italy, which *Porsena* K. of Tuscany caused to be made for his own sepulchre; and the rather, because you may know that foreign kings were not so vain in expenses, but our princes in Italy surpassed them in vanity : but for that there go so many tales and fables of it which are incredible, I think it good in the description thereof to use the very words of my author *M. Varro* : King *Porsena* (quoth he) was interred under the city Clusium in Tuscany, in which very place he left a sumptuous monument or tomb built all of square stone; thirty foot it carried in breadth on every side, and fifty in height; within the base or foot whereof (which likewise was four square) he made a labyrinth so intricate, that if a man were entered into it without a bottom or clue of thread in his hand, and leaving the one end thereof fastened to the entry or door, it was impossible that ever he should find the way out again. Upon this quadrant there stood five pyramids or steeples, four at the four corners, and one in the midst, which at the foot or foundation carried 75 foot every way in breadth, & were brought up to the height of 150 : these grew sharp spired toward the top, but in the very head so contrived, that they met all in one great roundle of brass which raught from one to the other, and covered them all in manner of a cap, and the same rising up in the midst with a crest most stately : from this cover there hung round about at little chains, a number of bells or cymbals, which being shaken with the wind, made a jangling noise that might be heard a great way off, much like unto that ring of bells which was devised in times past over the temple of *Iupiter* at Dodona : and yet are we not come to an end of this building mounted aloft in the air, for this cover overhead served but for a foundation of four other pyramids, and every one of them arose a hundred foot high above the other work : upon the tops whereof there was yet one terrace more to sustain five pyramids, and those shot up to such a monstrous height, that *Varro* was ashamed to report it : but if we may give credit to the tales that go current in Tuscany, it was equal to the whole building underneath. O the outrageous madness of a foolish prince, seeking thus in a vainglorious mind to be immortalized by a superfluous expense which could bring no good at all to any creature, but contrariwise weakened the state of his kingdom. And when all was done, the artificer that enterprised and finished the work, went away with the greater part of the praise and glory.

THE TEMPLE OF DIANA AT EPHESUS

But to speak of a stately and magnificent work indeed, the temple of *Diana* in Ephesus is admirable, which at the common charges of all the princes in Asia was two hundred and twenty years a building. First and foremost, they chose a marrish ground to set it upon, because it might not be subject to the danger of earthquakes, or fear the chinks and opening of the ground : again, to the end that so mighty and huge building of stone-work should stand upon a sure and firm foundation (notwithstanding the nature of the soil given to be slippery and unsteadfast) they laid the first couch and course of the ground-work with charcoal well rammed in manner of a pavement, and upon it a bed of wool-packs: this temple carried in length throughout, four hundred twenty and five foot, in breadth two hundred and twenty: in it were a hundred and seven & twenty pillars, made by so many kings, and every one of them threescore foot high; of which, six and thirty were curiously wrought and engraven, whereof one was the handiwork of *Scopas*: *Chersiphron* the famous architect was the chief deviser or master of the works, and who undertook the rearing thereof: the greatest wonder belonging thereto was this, how those huge chapters of pillars, together with their friezes and architraves, being brought up and raised so high, should be fitted to the sockets of their shafts: but as it is said, he compassed this enterprise and brought it to effect, by the means of certain bags or sacks filled with sand; for of these he made a soft bed as it were raised above the head of the pillars, upon which bed rested the chapters, and ever as he emptied the nethermost, the foresaid chapters settled downward by little and little, and so at his pleasure he might place them where they should stand: but the greatest difficulty in this kind of work, was about the very frontispiece and main lintle-tree which lay over the jambs or cheeks of the great door of the said temple; for so huge and mighty it was, that he could not wield it to lay and bestow the same as it ought, for when he had done what he could, it was not to his mind, nor couched and settled in the right place: whereupon the workman *Chersiphron* was much perplexed in his mind, and so weary of his life, that he purposed to make himself away: but as he lay in bed in the night season, and fell asleep all weary upon these dumpish and desperate cogitations, the goddess *Diana* (in whose honour this temple was framed, and now at the point to be reared) appeared sensibly unto him in person, willing him to be of good cheer and resolve to live still, assuring him that she herself had laid the said stone of the frontispiece, and couched it accordingly: which appeared true indeed the morrow morning, for it seemed that the very weight thereof had caused it to settle just into the place, and made a joint as *Chersiphron* would have wished it.

CYZICUM

There is at this day a temple standing at Cyzicum, wherein the mason had bestowed threads of gold in all the joints under every stone throughout, and those were all fair polished : within this temple, prince *Cyzicus* (who caused it to be built) minded to dedicate the image of *Iupiter* in ivory, and of *Apollo* in marble, setting a crown upon his head. Certes, these joints thus interlaced with most fine and dainty threads, gave a wonderful grace and beauty to the whole church, by sending and breathing (as it were) from them certain rays, which by reverberation cause all the images therein to have a glittering lustre : in such sort, that over and above the device and witty invention of the workman, the very matter also (although it be close couched and hidden between each stone) commendeth the price and riches of the work.

*   *   *   *   *

Within the said town there is a stone called the Fugitive or Runaway : The brave knights of Greece called Argonauts, who accompanied prince *Iason* in his voyage for the golden fleece, after they had used it for an anchor, left it there : but for that this stone was ready many times to run away and be gone out of their Prytaneum (for so they called their public hall) soudred it fast with lead. In the same city, near unto that gate which is called Thracia, there stand seven turrets, which do multiply a voice, and send back many again for one : this miraculous rebounding of the voice, the Greeks have a pretty name for, and call it echo. True it is, that this repercussion and redoubling of the voice, proceedeth otherwhiles from the nature of the place, and most of all in valleys lying between hills; but at Cyzicum it cometh by fortune, and no such reason can be given thereof. At Olympia the like is wrought by art, for there is a gallery there made of purpose, which after a wonderful manner delivereth the same voice which it receiveth, seven times back, whereupon they call it Heptaphonon. Moreover, in Cyzicum there is a fair and large building, which (because they keep courts and sit in council there) is named Buleuterion : the same is built in such sort, as there goeth not one pin or nail to all the carpentry thereof : and the stories are so laid, that a man may take away the beams and rafter without any prop or shore to support them, yea and bestow them again fast enough without laces to bind them. After which manner, the modern bridge at Rome was so framed over the river Tyberis; and a matter of religion and conscience was made thereof, to maintain it so, in remembrance of the difficulty in taking it a pieces and breaking it down, at what time as *Horatius Cocles* made the place good against the power of K. *Porsena*.

ROME

And now since the coherence of matters hath brought me to Rome, me thinks I should not do amiss to proceed unto the miraculous buildings of this our city, to show the docility of our people, and what proof there is of their progress in all things, during the space of nine hundred years; that it may appear how not only in magnanimity and prowess they have conquered the world, but in magnificence also of stately and sumptuous buildings surmounted all nations of the earth : and as a man shall find this singularity and excellence of theirs, in the particular survey of every one of their stately and wonderful edifices as they have been reared from time to time, so if he put them all together and take a general view of them at once, he shall conceive no otherwise of their greatness, than of another world assembled (as it were) to make show in one place.

*   *   *   *   *

But old men marvelled even in those days at the mighty thick rampiers that K. *Tarquinius Priscus* caused to be made, the huge foundations also of the Capitol that he laid, the vaulted sinks also and draughts (to speak of a piece of work the greatest of all others) which he devised, by undermining and cutting through the seven hills whereupon Rome is seated, and making the city hanging as it were in the air between heaven and earth, like unto Thebes in Aegypt, whereof erewhile I made mention; so as a man might pass under the streets and houses with boats. But how would they be astonished now, to see how *M. Agrippa* in his Aedileship, after he had been Consul, caused seven rivers to meet together under the city in one main charnel, and to run with such a swift stream and current, that they take all afore them whatsoever is in the way, and carry it down into Tyber: and being otherwise increased with sudden showers and landfloods, they shake the paving under them, they flank the sides of the walls about them: sometimes also they receive the Tyber water into them when he riseth extraordinarily, so as a man shall perceive the stream of two contrary waters affront and charge one another with great force and violence within under the ground: And yet for all this, these waterworks aforesaid yield not a jot, but abide firm and fast, without any sensible decay occasioned thereby. Moreover, these streams carry down eftsoons huge and heavy pieces of stones within them, mighty loads are drawn over them continually, yet these arched conduits neither settle & stoop under the one, nor be once shaken with the other; down many a house falleth of itself, and the ruins beat against these vaults: to say nothing of those that tumble upon them with the violent force of scarefires, ne yet of the terrible earthquakes which shake the whole earth about them: yet for all these injuries, they have continued since *Tarquinius Priscus*, almost eight hundred years, inexpugnable. And here by the way I will not conceal from you a memorable example which is come into my mind by occasion of this discourse, and the rather, for that even the best and most renowned chroniclers who have taken upon them to pen our Roman history, have passed it over in silence: When this K. *Tarquinius* surnamed *Priscus,* caused these vaults under the ground to be made, and forced the common people to labour hard thereat with their own hands, it happened that many a good Roman citizen being now over-toiled in this kind of work (which whether it was more dangerous or tedious it is hard to say) chose rather to kill themselves for to be rid of this irksome and painful life; in such sort, that daily there were people missing, and their bodies found after they were perished. This king therefore, to prevent farther mischief, and to provide that his works begun might be brought to an end, devised a remedy which never was invented before, nor practised afterwards, and that was this, that the bodies of as many as were thus found dead, should be hung upon gibbets, exposed not only to the view of all their fellow citizens to be despised as cursed creatures, but also to the wild and ravenous fowls of the air to be torn and devoured. The Romans (as they are the only nation under heaven impatient of any dishonour) seeing this object presented before their eyes, were mightily abashed; and as this mind of their had gained them victory many a time in desperate battles, so at this present also it guided and directed them : and being (as they were) dismayed at this disgrace, they made account no less to be ashamed of such an ignominy after death, than they now blushed thereat in their life.

THE THEATRE OF SCAURUS

And in truth, this *Scaurus* when he was Aedile, caused a wonderful piece of work to be made, and exceeding all that ever had been known wrought by man's hand, not only those that have been erected for a month or such a thing, but even those that have been destined for perpetuity; and a theatre it was : the stage had three lofts one above another, wherein were three hundred and threescore columns of marble; (a strange and admirable sight in that city, which in times past could not endure six small pillars of marble, hewed out of the quarry in mount Hymettus, in the house of a most honourable personage, without a great reproach and rebuke given unto him for it;) the base or nethermost part of the stage, was all of marble; the middle of glass (an excessible superfluity, never heard of before or after;) as for the uppermost, the boards, planks, and floors were gilded; the columns beneath, were (as I have said before) forty foot high, wanting twain : and between these columns (as I have showed before) there stood of statues and images in brass to the number of three thousand. The theatre itself was able to receive fourscore thousand persons to sit well, and at ease. Whereas the compass of *Pompeie's* amphitheatre (notwithstanding the city of Rome so much enlarged, and more peopled in his time) was devised for to contain no greater number than forty thousand seats at large. As touching the other furniture of this theatre of *Scaurus* in rich hangings, which were cloth of gold; painted tables, the most exquisite that could be found : players' apparel and other stuff meet for to adorn the stage, there was such abundance thereof, that there being carried back to his house of pleasure at Tusculum the surplusage thereof, over and above the daintiest part, whereof he had daily use at Rome, his servants and slaves there, upon indignation for this waste and monstrous superfluity of their master, set the said country house on fire and burnt as much as came to a hundred millions of sesterces.

THE HANGING THEATRES

To come then to *C. Curio*, and his cunning device, he caused two theatres to be framed of timber, and those exceeding big, howbeit so, as they might be turned about as a man would have them, approach near one to the other, or be removed farther asunder as one would desire, and all by the means of one hook apiece that they hung by, which bare the weight of the whole frame, the counterpoise was so even, and all the whole therefore sure and firm. Now he ordered the matter thus, that to behold the several stage plays and shows in the forenoon before dinner, they should be set back to back, to the end, that the stages should not trouble one another : and when the people had taken their pleasure that way, he turned the theatres about in a trice against the afternoon, that they affronted one another : and toward the latter end of the day, and namely, when the fencers and sword-players were to come in place, he brought both the theatres nearer together (and yet every man sat still and kept his place, according to his rank and order) insomuch, as by the meeting of the horns or corners of them both together in compass, he made a fair round amphitheatre of it : and there in the midst between, he exhibited indeed unto them all jointly, a sight and spectacle of sword-fencers fighting at sharp, whom he had hired for that purpose : but in truth, a man may say more truly, that he carried the whole people of Rome round about at his pleasure, bound sure enough for stirring and removing. Now let us come to the point, and consider a little better of this thing. What should a man wonder at most therein, the deviser or the device itself ? The workman of this fabric, or the master that set him on work ? Whether of the twain is more admirable, either the venturous head of him that devised it, or the bold heart of him that undertook it ? to command such a thing to be done, or to obey and yield to go in hand with it? But when we have said all that we can, the folly of the blind and bold people of Rome went beyond all; who trusted such a ticklish frame, and durst sit there in a seat so movable. Lo where a man might have seen the body of that people, which is commander and ruler of the whole earth, the conqueror of the whole world, the disposer of kingdoms and realms at their pleasure, the divider of countries and nations at their will, the giver of laws to foreign states, the vicegerent of the immortal gods under heaven and representing their image unto all mankind: hanging in the air within a frame at the mercy of one only hook, rejoicing and ready to clap hands at their own danger. What a cheap market of men's lives was here toward! What was the loss at Cannae to this hazard, that they should complain so much as they do of Cannae? How near unto a mischief were they, which might have happened hereby in the turning of a hand? Certes, when there is news come of a city swallowed up by a wide chink and opening of the earth, all men generally in a public commiseration do grieve thereat, and there is not one but his heart doth earne; and yet, behold the universal state and people of Rome, as if they were put into a couple of barks, supported between heaven and earth, and sitting at the devotion only of two pins or hooks. And what spectacle do they behold, a number of fencers trying it out with unrebated swords? nay ywis, but even themselves rather entered into a most desperate fight, and at the point to break their necks every mother's son, if the scaffold failed never so little, & the frame went out of joint: Now surely by this proof, *Curio* had gotten a good hand over the people of Rome, and no Tribunes of the Commons with all their orations could do more: from that time forward he might make account to be so gracious, as to lead all the tribes after him in any suits; and have them hanging in the air at his pleasure.

FEATS OF ENGINEERING

But of all the conduits that ever were before this time, that which was last begun by *C. Caligula Caesar*, and finished by *Claudius Caesar* his successor, passeth for sumptuousness: for they commanded the waters from the two fountains, Curius and

Caeruleus, whose heads were 40 miles of : and these they carried before them with such a force and to such a height, that they mounted up to the top of the highest hills of Rome, and served them that dwelt thereupon. This work cost three hundred millions of sesterces. Certes, if a man would well and truly consider the abundance of water that is brought thereby, and how many places it serveth, as well public as private, in bains, stews and fishpools, for kitchens and other houses of office, for pipes and little riverets to water gardens, as well about the city, as in manors and houses of pleasure in the fields near unto the city; over & besides, what a mighty way these waters be brought; the number of arches that of necessity must be built of purpose for to convey them; the mountains that be pierced and mined through to give way together, with the valleys that are raised and made even and level with other ground : he will confess, that there was never any design in the whole world enterprised and effected, more admirable than this. In the rank of these most memorable works of man, I may well range the mountain that was digged through by the same *Claudius Caesar,* for to void away the water out of the loch or mere Fucinus, although this work was left unfinished for hatred of his successor : which I assure you cost an incredible and inenarrable sum of money, besides the infinite toil and labour of a multitude of workmen and labourers so many years together, as well to force the water which came upon the pioneers from under the ground with device of engines and windles up to the top of the hill, whereas it stood upon mere earth; as to cut and hew through hard rags and rocks of flint : and all this by candlelight within the earth, in such sort, as unless a man had been there to have seen the manner of it, impossible it is either to conceive in mind or express in tongue the difficulty of the enterprise. As for the pier and haven at Ostia (because I would make an end once of these matters) I will not say a word thereof, nor of the ways and passages cut through the mountains, nor yet of the mighty piles and dams to exclude the Tuscan sea, from the Lucrine lake, with so many rampiers and bridges made of such infinite cost. Howbeit, among many other miraculous things in Egypt, one thing more I will relate out of mine author *Papyrius Fabianus,* a great learned naturalist, namely, that marble doth grow daily in the quarries: and in very truth, the farmers of those quarries, and such as ordinarily do labour and dig out stone, do affirm no less; who upon their experience do assure us, that look what holes and caves be made in those rocks and mountains, the same will gather again and fill up in time: which if it be true, good hope there is, that so long as marbles do live, excess in building will never die.

TALC

There hath been devised another use also of talc in smaller pieces, namely, to pave therewith the floor of the great show-place of cirque in Rome, during the running of chariots and other feats of activity there performed, to the end that their whiteness might give a more lovely gloss to commend the place.

MOSAIC PAVING

The device of paved floors arose first from the Greeks, who made them with great art, and curiously, in regard of the painting in sundry colours which they bestowed thereupon. But these brave painted floors were put down, when pavements made of stone and quarrels came in place: The most famous workman in this kind, was one *Sosus*, who at Pergamus wrought that rich pavement in the common hall, which they call Asaroton oecon, garnished with bricks or small tiles enealed with sundry colours: and he devised, that the work upon this pavement should resemble the crumbs and scraps that fell from the table, and such like stuff as commonly is swept away, as if they were left still by negligence upon the pavement. Among the rest, wonderful was his handiwork there, in portraying a dove drinking, which was so lively represented as if the shadow of her head had dimmed the brightness of the water: there, should a man have seen other pigeons sitting upon the brim of the water-tankard, pruning themselves with their bills, and disporting in the sunshine.

THE INVENTION OF GLASS

The coast along this river which showeth this kind of sand,

is not above half a mile in all, and yet for many a hundred year it hath furnished all places with matter sufficient to make glass. As touching which device, the common voice and fame runneth, that there arrived sometimes certain merchants in a ship laden with nitre, in the mouth of this river, and being landed, minded to seethe their victuals upon the shore and the very sands : but for that they wanted other stones, to serve as trivets to bear up their pans and cauldrons over the fire, they made shift with certain pieces of sal-nitre out of the ship, to support the said pans, and so made fire underneath : which being once afire among the sand and gravel of the shore, they might perceive a certain clear liquor run from under the fire in very streams, and hereupon they say came the first invention of making glass.

UNBREAKABLE GLASS

Moreover, it is said, that during the reign of Tiberius the Emperor, there was devised a certain temper of glass, which made it pliable and flexible to wind and turn without breaking : but the artificer who devised this, was put down, and his work house, for fear least vessels made of such glass should take away the credit from the rich plate of brass, silver, and gold, and make them of no price : and verily, this bruit hath run current a long time (but how true, it is not so certain). But what booted the abolishing of glass-makers, seeing that in the days of the Emperor *Nero* the art was grown to such perfection, that two drinking cups of glass (and those not big, which they called pterotos) were sold for 6000 sesterces.

THE SON OF FIRE

But before I make an end of fire, and the hearth where it burneth, I will not overpass an admirable example commended unto us by the Roman chronicles : in which we read, that during the reign of *Tarquinius Priscus,* king of Rome, there appeared all on a sudden upon the hearth where he kept fire, out of the very ashes, the genital member of a man : by virtue whereof, a wench belonging unto *Tanaquil* the queen as she sat before the said fire, conceived and arose from the fire with child. And of this conception came *Servius Tullus,* who succeeded *Tarquin* in the kingdom. And afterwards, whiles he was a young child and lay asleep within the court, his head was seen on a light fire, and thereupon he was taken to be the son of the domestical spirits of the chimney. Which was the reason, that when he was come to the crown, he first instituted the Compitalia, and the solemn games in the honour of such house-gods or familiar spirits.

THE SEVEN AND THIRTIETH BOOK

concludeth with precious stones.

PREFACE

To THE end that nothing might be wanting to this history of mine concerning Nature's works, there remain behind nothing but precious stones, wherein appeareth her majesty, brought into a narrow and strait room: and to say a truth, in no part of the world is she more wonderful, in many respects: whether you regard their variety, colours, matter, or beauty; which are so rich and precious, that many make conscience to seal with them, thinking it unlawful to engrave any print in them, or to diminish their honour and estimation by that means. Some of them are reckoned inestimable, or valued at all the goods of the world besides, insomuch as many men think some one precious stone or gem sufficient, to behold therein the very perfection of Nature and her absolute work. Touching the first invention of wearing such stones in jewels, and how it took first root and grew afterwards to that height as all the world is in admiration thereof, I have already shewed in some sort in my treatise of gold and rings. And yet I will not conceal from you that which poets do fable of this matter, who would bear us in hand, that all began at the rock Caucasus, whereunto *Prometheus* was bound fast, who was the first that set a little fragment of this rock within a piece of iron, which being done about his finger, was the ring, and the foresaid stone the gem: whereof the poets make much foolish moralization.

POLYCRATES

Prometheus having given this precedent, brought other stones into great price and credit, insomuch as men were mightily enamoured upon them : and *Polycrates* of Samos, the puissant prince and mighty monarch over all the islands and coasts thereabout, in the height of his felicity & happy estate, which himself confessed to be excessive; being troubled in his mind that he had tasted of no misfortune, and willing after a sort to play at Fortune's game, one while to win and another while to lose, & in some measure to satisfy her inconstancy, was persuaded in his mind that he should content her sufficiently by the voluntary loss of one gem that he had, and which he set so great store by : thinking verily, that this one heart's grief for parting from so precious a jewel was sufficient to excuse & redeem him from the spiteful envy of that mutable goddess. Seeing therefore the world to come upon him still, and no sore sorrows intermingled with his sweet delights, in a weariness of this continual blessedness : he embarked himself and sailed into the deep where wilfully he flung into the sea a ring from his finger, together with the said stone so precious, set therein. But see what ensued? A mighty fish, even made as a man would say for the king, chanced to swallow it down as if it had been some bait; which being afterwards caught by fishers, & thought to be of an extraordinary bigness, was brought as a present into the king's palace, and so sent into the kitchen; where the cook found within the belly thereof the foresaid ring of his lords and masters. Oh the subtlety of sly Fortune, who all this while twisted the cord that another day should hang *Polycrates*!

AN AWKWARD CUSTOMER

Setting aside these two gems above-named, we do not read in authors, of any great reckoning made of such jewels; unless we speak of one *Ismenias* a famous minstrel, who had the name to wear many of them ordinarily about him, and those very gay and glittering : and surely his vanity that way was such, that there goeth a notable tale of him; for meeting upon a time in a merchant's hand with an emerald in the island Cyprus, wherein lady *Amymone* was engraven, and whereof the price was at first held at six deniers in gold, he made no more ado but caused the money to be paid presently : but the merchant being a man of some conscience, and thinking the price indeed too high, gave two of them back again unto *Ismenias* : whereat being ill apaid, I beshrew you, (qd.he) for this bating of the money hath much impaired the worth of the stone.

THE SPHINX AND THE FROG

Augustus late Emperor of worthy memory, used at the beginning to seal with the image Sphinx upon his signet : and verily in the casket of his mother's jewels, two of these he found so like one unto the other, that one could not be known and discerned from the other : and as he was wont to wear one of them about him wheresoever he went, so in his absence (during the civil wars which he levied against *M. Antonius*) his friends who managed his affairs at Rome, signed with the other Sphinx, all those letters and edicts which passed in his name, for the performance of some demands which those times did require. And from hence it came, that those who received any such letters or edicts, containing some matter of difficulty, were wont pleasantly & merrily to say, that the said Sphinx came ever with some hard riddle or other that could not be expounded. Moreover, the Frog, wherewith *Maecenas* used to seal, was always terrible unto those who received any letters signed therewith; for evermore they were sure upon the receipt of it to make some payment of impost or taxes levied upon them. But *Augustus Caesar,* to avoid the obloquy that arose by his Sphinx, gave over sealing therewith, and signed ever after with the image of K. *Alexander* the Great.

THE TRIUMPHS OF POMPEY

To the end that it may appear more evidently, what the triumph of *Pompey* wrought in this respect, I will put down word for word what I find upon record in the registers that bear witness of the acts which passed during those triumphs. In the third triumph therefore which was decreed unto him (for that he had scoured the seas of pirates and rovers, reduced Natolia and the kingdom of Pontus under the domination of the Romans, defeated kings and nations, according as I have declared in the seventh book of this my history) he entered Rome the last day of September, in the year when *M. Piso and M. Messala* were Consuls, on which day there was carried before him in show, a chess board with all the men, and the same board was made of two precious stones, and yet it was two foot broad and four foot long : and lest any man should doubt hereof and think it incredible, considering that no gems at this day come near thereto in bigness, know he, that in this triumph he showed a golden moon weighing thirty pounds, three dining tables also of gold, other vessel likewise of massy gold and precious stones as much as would garnish nine cupboards; three images of beaten gold representing *Minerva, Mars,* and *Apollo;* coronets made of stones to the number of three and thirty; a mountain made of gold four square, wherein a man might see red deer, lions, fruit-trees of all sorts, and the whole mountain environed and compassed all about with a vine of gold : moreover, an oratory or closet consisting of pearl, in the top or louvre whereof there was a clock or horologe : He caused also to be borne before him in a pompous show, his own image made of pearls; the portraiture (I say) of that *Cn. Pompeius,* whom regal majesty and ornaments would have better beseemed; and that good face and venerable visage so highly honoured among all nations, was now all of pearls; as if that manly countenance and severity of his had been vanquished, and riotous excess and superfluity had triumphed over him, rather than he over it. *O Pompey, O Magnus,* how could this title and surname *Le-grand,* have continued among those nations, if thou hadst in thy first victory triumphed after this manner ! What, *Magnus,* were there no means else but to seak out pearls, (things so prodigal, superfluous, and devised for women, and which it had not beseemed *Pompey* once to wear about him) and therewith to portray and counterfeit thy manly visage !

"OR LEAVE A KISS BUT IN THE CUP"

And verily, from day to day the excess herein hath so far overgrown, that one great cassidoine cup hath been sold for four-score sesterces, but a fair and large one it was, and would contain well three sextars (*id est*, half a wine gallon). There are not many years past, since that a noble man who had been Consul of Rome, used to drink out of this cup; and notwithstanding that in pledging upon a time a lady whom he fancied, he bit out a piece of the brim thereof (which her sweet lips touched) yet this injury done unto it, rather made it more esteemed and valued at a higher price; neither is there at this day a cup of cassidoine more precious or dearer than the same.

CRYSTAL

But will you hear of another notorious example of folly and madness in these crystals as well as in cassidoins? There are not many years since a dame of Rome, and she none of the richest, who bought one bowl or drinking cup of crystal, and paid 150,000 sesterces for it. As for *Nero* the Emperor (of whom I spake erewhile) when unhappy news was brought unto him of a great overthrow and a field lost to the danger of his own state and the commonwealth, in the height of his rage and a most furious fit of anger, caught up two crystal drinking cups and pashed them all to pieces: his spite was belike at all the men living in that age, & better means he could not devise to plague and punish them, than to prevent that no man else should drink out of those glasses: and in very truth, a crystal being once broken, cannot by any device whatsoever he reunited and made whole again as before. We have at this day cups and vessels of glass that come passing near unto crystal, but wonderful it is, that notwithstanding our glasses be so like, yet they have not abated and brought down the price of crystal, but rather caused it to be far dearer.

AMBER

And here I must beseech the readers to bear with me in this my discourse as touching the first original of amber; for I think it not impertinent to deliver what marvels and wonders the

Greeks have broached as touching this thing, that the age and posterity ensuing may yet be acquainted with their fabulosities: first and foremost therefore, many of their poets, yea, and I suppose, the chief and principal of them, to wit, *Aeschylus, Philoxenus, Nicander, Euripides,* and *Satyrus,* tell us a tale of the sisters of young prince *Phaëton,* who weeping piteously for the miserable death of their brother who was smitten with lightning, were turned into poplar trees, which instead of tears yielded every year a certain liquor called electrum (*id est,* amber) which issued from them where they grew along the river Eridanus, which we call Padus, *id est,* the Po: and the reason why the same was named electrum, is this, because the sun in old time was usually called elector in Greek. But that this is one of their loud lies, it appeareth evidently by the testimony of all Italy. But some of these Greek writers and such as would seem to be more speculative and better seen in the works of Nature than their fellows, have told us of certain islands that should lie along the coast within the Venice gulf, called Electrides, forsooth because that amber is there gathered, by reason that the foresaid river Po falleth into the sea and among them: howbeit well known it is, that there were never yet islands so named within that tract; no nor any islands at all near to that place, into which the river Padus could possibly bring anything at all down his stream. As for *Aeschylus* the foresaid poet, who saith that the river Eridanus is in Iberia, that is to say, Spain, and otherwise that is called Rhodanus: as also for *Euripides* and *Apollonius,* who say that Rhosne and Po both meet in one, and discharge themselves together into the said Venice gulf, they show their gross ignorance in cosmography and description of the world; and therefore they would be rather pardoned if they knew not what amber was.

*   *   *   *   *

But I wonder most at *Sophocles* the tragical poet (a man, who wrote his poesies with so grave & lofty a style, and lived besides in so good reputation; being otherwise born at Athens, and descended from a noble house, employed also in the managing of state affairs, as who had the charge and conduct of an army) that he should go beyond all others in fabulous reports, as touch-

ing amber: for he sticketh not to avouch, that beyond India it
proceedeth from the tears that fall from the eyes of the birds
Meleagrides, wailing and weeping for the death of *Meleager*.
Who would not marvel, that either himself should be of that
belief, or hope to persuade others to his opinion? For what child
is there to be found so simple and ignorant, who will believe,
that birds should keep their times to shed tears every year so
duly, and especially so great drops and in such quantity, sufficient to engender amber in that abundance? Besides, what congruity is there, that birds should depart as far as to the Indians
and beyond, for to mourn and lament the death of *Meleager,*
when he died in Greece? What should a man say to this? Are
there not many more as goodly tales as these, which poets have
sent abroad into the world? And their profession of poetry, that
is to say, of feigning and devising fables, may in some sort excuse
them. But that any man should seriously and by way of history
deliver such stuff, as touching a thing so rife and common,
brought in every day in abundance by merchants which were
enough to convince such impudent lies, is a mere mockery of
the world in the highest degree; a contempt offered unto all men,
and argueth an habit of lying, and an impunity of that vice
intolerable.

* * * * *

That it doth distill and drop at the first very clear and liquid,
it is evident by this argument, for that a man may see divers
things within, to wit, pismires, gnats, and lizards, which were no
doubt entangled and stuck within it when it was green
and fresh, and so remained enclosed within as it waxed
harder.

* * * * *

As for this Amber, I see nothing in the world to commend it;
only it is a mind that folk have to take an affection to it, they
know not wherefore, even of a delicate and foolish wantonness.
And in truth, *Nero Domitius*, among many other fooleries and
gauds wherein he showed what a monster he was in his life,
proceeded so far, that he made a sonnet in praise of the hair of
the Empress *Poppaea*, his wife, which he compared to amber,

and as I remember, in one stave of his ditty he termed them succina, i.e. amber : and from that time our dainty dames and fine ladies have begun to set their mind upon this colour, and have placed it in the third rank of rich tincture : whereby we may see there is no superfluity and disorder in the world, but it hath a pretence and cloak of some precious name or other. And yet I will not disgrace amber too much : for why? there is some good use thereof in physic.

GOATS AND DIAMONDS

Moreover, as touching the concord and discord that is between things natural, which the Greeks call Sympathia and Antipathia (whereof I have so much written in all my books, and endeavoured to acquaint the readers therewith) in nothing throughout the world may we observe both the one & the other more evidently, than in the diamond : for this invincible mineral (against which neither fire nor steel, the two most violent and puissant creatures of Nature's making, have any power, but that it checketh and despiseth both the one and the other) is forced to yield the gauntlet and give place unto the blood of a goat, this only thing is the means to break it in sunder, howbeit, care must be had, that the diamond be steeped therein whiles it is fresh drawn from the beast before it be cold : and yet when you have made all the steeping you can, you must have many a blow at the diamond with hammer upon the anvil : for even then also, unless they be of excellent proof & good indeed, it will put them to it, and break both the one and the other : But I would gladly know what invention this might be to soak the diamond in goat's blood, whose head devised it first, or rather by what chance was it found out and known? What conjecture should lead a man to make an experiment of such a singular & admirable secret, especially in a goat, the filthiest beast one of them in the whole world? Certes I must ascribe both this invention and all such like to the might and beneficence together of the divine powers : neither are we to argue and reason how and why Nature hath done this or that? Sufficient it is that her will was so, and thus she would have it.

EMERALD

Emeralds for many causes deserve the third place : for there is not a colour more pleasing to the eye. True it is, that we take great delight to behold green herbs and leaves of trees, but this is nothing to the pleasure we have in looking upon the emerald, for compare it with other things, be they never so green, it surpasseth them all in pleasant verdure. Besides, there is not a gem or precious stone that so fully possesseth the eye, and yet never contenteth it with satiety. Nay, if the sight hath been wearied and dimmed by intentive poring upon anything else, the beholding of this stone doth refresh and restore it again, which lapidaries well know, that cut and engrave fine stones; for they have not a better means to refresh their eyes than the emerald, the mild green that it hath doth so comfort and revive their weariness and lassitude.

THE LION AND THE TUNNIES

It is reported, that in the same isle Cyprus, about the sepulchre of *Hermias* a petty king there, and near unto the sea sides where were pools and stews of great fishes kept to be salted, there stood in the old time a lion of marble, in the head of which lion were set certain fair emeralds instead of eyes, looking opposite into the sea : but they glittered and pierced so deep into the water, that the tunnies upon that coast were afraid thereat, and fled from the nets and other instruments that the fishers laid to take them withal : who marvelled a long time at this strange incident : but in the end knowing what the matter was, they changed the eyes of the foresaid lion, and removed the emeralds.

RUBY

Archelaus writeth, that the Carchedonian rubies be blacker than others to see to; but if they be quickened as it were with fire or sun, or be held bowing forward, they are more ardent and fiery than any other : the same in a shady house, seem purple; in the open air, flaming; against the rays of the sun, sparkling : he avoucheth moreover, that the fiery heat thereof

is so actual, that if a man seal with them, though it be in a
shadowy and cool place, they will melt the very wax that is
stamped therewith.

TURQUOISE

This stone in regard of colour may be accompanied with the
turquoise called Gallais, for a certain green it hath inclining
to a yellow. It is found beyond the farthest parts of India among
the inhabitants of the mountain Caucasus, to wit, the Phicarians
and Asdates; they grow unto a very great bigness, but the same
is fistulous and full of filth. The purest and richest of this kind
be those of Carmania. But in both countries they be found in icy
cliffs hardly accessible, where you shall see them bearing out
after the manner of bosses like unto eyes : they stick unto those
crags and rocks so lightly, that a man would say that saw them,
how they grew not naturally out of the rock, but were only
set to by man's hand. And for that the place where they do
grow, is so steep that a horseman is not able to ride up to them,
and because the people of that country be loth to climb so high
with their feet, being otherwise acquainted ordinarily to the
horseback, besides, in regard of the danger in venturing to climb
for them, therefore they reach them afar off with slings, and so
drive them down, withal the hard moss about them : And in
very deed, a commodity this is of great revenue, and besides, the
rich men know not the like jewel to wear about their necks.

AMETHYST

The magicians, as vain herein as in all other things, seem to
bear us in hand that they have a special virtue to withstand
drunkenness, whereupon they should be called amethysts :
Neither stay they so, but tell us, that if the name of the moon
and the sun, be engraven in them and so worn about the neck
hanging, either with the hairs of a cynocephalus head, or else
swallow's feathers, they are a sovereign remedy against charms
and sorceries that be practised, with poisoning. Nay they would
make us believe that there is a way to use them, which will
cause men to be gracious with princes who have any negotiation

with them, and by that means thereof they shall find easy access to their presence, and favour in their eyes. Also, by their saying, they arc of force to avert hail and such like distemperature of the weather, yea, and to turn away locusts, so there be a charm in manner of a prayer said withal, the form whereof they also do prescribe and show : & no marvel : for they have promised the like of emeralds, if there were enchased in them the form either of eagles, or the flies named beetles. In setting down which toys and vanities, they show well enough in what contempt they have mankind, and how they are disposed for to mock the world.

BRONTIA

Brontia is shaped in manner of a tortoise head : it falleth with a crack of thunder (as it is thought) from heaven; and if we will believe it, quencheth the fire of lightning.

DRACONITES

Draconites or Dracontia, is a stone engendered in the brains of serpents, but unless it be cut out whiles they be alive, namely after their heads be chopped off, it never groweth to the nature of a precious stone; for of an inbred malice and envy that that this creature hath to man, if perceiving itself to languish and draw on toward death, it killeth the virtue of the said stone : and therefore they take these serpents while they be asleep, and off with their heads. *Sotacus* (who wrote that he saw one of these stones in a king's hand) reporteth, that they who go to seek these stones used to ride in a coach drawn with two steeds, & when they have espied a dragon or serpent, cast in their way certain medicinable drugs to bring them asleep, and so have the means and leisure to cut off their heads : white they are & naturally transparent, for impossible it is by any art to polish them, neither doth the lapidary lay his hand upon them.

GLOSSI-PETRA

Glossi-petra resembleth a man's tongue, and groweth not upon the ground, but in the eclipse of the moon falleth from heaven, and is thought by the magicians to be very necessary for panders and those that court fair women : but we have no reason to believe it, considering what vain promises they have made otherwise of it; for they bear us in hand, that it doth appease winds.

HELIOTROPIUM

The precious stone heliotropium, is found in Aethyopia, Africa, and Cyprus : the ground thereof is a deep green in manner of a leek, but the same is garnished with veins of blood : the reason of the name heliotropium is this, for that if it be thrown into a pail of water, it changeth the rays of the sun by way of reverberation into a bloody colour, especially that which cometh out of Aethyopia : the same being without the water, doth represent the body of the sun, like unto a mirror : and if there be an eclipse of the sun, a man may perceive easily in this tone how the moon goeth under it, and obscureth the light : but most impudent and palpable is the vanity of magicians in their reports of this stone; for they let not to say, that if a man carry it about him, together with the herb heliotropium, and besides mumble certain charms or prayers, he shall go invisible.

POLYTRIX

Polytrix is a green stone, bedecked with fine veins in manner of the hair of one's head : but (by report) it will make the hair to shed of as many as carry it about them.

HOW TO TELL IF JEWELS ARE GENUINE

Moreover, there be in my hands certain books of authors extant, whom I will not nominate for all the good in the world, wherein is deciphered the manner and means how to give the tincture of an emerald to a crystal, and how to sophisticate other transparent gems; namely, how to make a sardonyx of a Cornalline, and in one word, to transform one stone into another. And to say a truth, there is not any fraud and deceit in the world turneth to greater gain and profit than this.

Let other writers teach how to deceive the world by counterfeit gems, for mine own part I will take a contrary course, and show the means how to find out false stones that be thus sophisticat: for surely, wanton and prodigal though men and women be in the excessive wearing of these jewels, yet meet it is they should be armed and instructed against such couseners. And albeit I have already touched somewhat respectively as I treated of the chief and principal gems, yet I will add somewhat more to the rest: First and foremost therefore this is observed, that all stones which be transparent, ought to have their trial in a morning betimes, or at the farthest (if need so require) within four hours after morning light, but in no wise later. Now there be diverse experiments that serve for this purpose, to wit, the weight of a stone, for commonly the fine gem indeed is heavier than the other: Secondly, the very body and substances is to be considered: for it is an ordinary matter to see in the ground and bottom of falsified stones certain little pushes as it were rising out; to feel them rough in hand outwardly; also to perceive their filaments not to continue their lustre surely, and to bear it out to the very eye, but commonly in the way to vanish and be spent. But the most effectual proof of all, is to take a little fragment, for to be ground afterward upon a plate of iron: but lapidaries will not endure this trial; they refuse also the experiment made by the file. Furthermore, the fragments of the black agate or geat, will not rase or scarify true gems. *Item*, False stones if they be pierced or engraven, will show no white.

THE MOST BEAUTIFUL COUNTRY ON EARTH

And now having discoursed sufficiently of all the works of Nature, it were meet to conclude with a certain general difference between the things themselves, and especially between country and country. For a final conclusion therefore, go through the whole earth and all the lands lying under the cope of heaven, Italy will be found the most beautiful & goodliest region under the sun, surpassing all other whatsoever, and worthily to be counted the chief and principal in every respect: Italy (I say) the very lady and queen, yea, a second mother next to dame Nature of the world: Chief for hardy men, chief for fair and beautiful women, enriched with captains, soldiers, and slaves; flourishing in all arts and excellent sciences, abounding with noble wits and men of singular spirits; situat under a climate most wholesome and temperate, seated also commodiously (by reason of the coasts so full of convenient havens) for traffic with all nations, wherein the winds are most comfortable (for it extendeth itself and lieth to the best quarter of the heaven, even the midst just between East and West:) having waters at command, large forests and fair, and those yielding most healthful air; bounded with mighty rampiers of high mountains, stored with wild beasts and those harmless: finally, the ground so fertile for corn, the soil so battle for herbage, as none to it comparable. In sum, whatsoever is necessary & requisite for the maintenance of this life is there to be had, in no place better: all kind of corn and grain, wines, oil, wool, linen, woollen and excellent boeufes; as for horseflesh, I have always heard, even from the mouth of those that be professed runners in the race with horse and chariot, that the breed of Italy passeth all others: for mines of gold, silver, brass, and iron, it gave place to no country whatsoever, so long as it pleased the state to employ it that way; and in lieu of those rich commodities which it hath still within her womb, she yieldeth unto us variety of good liquors, plenty of all sorts of corn, and abundance of pleasant fruits of all kinds. But if I should speak of a land after Italy (setting aside the monstrous and fabulous reports that go of India) in my conceit Spain is next in all respects, I mean those coasts which are environed with the sea.

FINIS

GLOSSARY

ABSIDES, n.pl. Orbits.

ACCOMMODAT, p.p. Adapted (to), fitted, suitable (for).

ACETABLE, n. A liquid measure (about 2½ fluid ounces); cup-shaped cavity, sucker.

ACTUS, n. A Roman measure (120 ft.).

ADDITION, n. Title, name.

ADUST, a. Brown, sunburnt.

ADVERTISE, v. Warn, advise; inform.

AFFINE, v. Refine.

AFFRONT, v. Encounter, attack; prep. Straight towards.

AFRONT, adv. From the front.

AGILITY, n. Activity, versatility.

AGNEL, n. Corn.

A-LIFE, adv. Dearly.

AMPHORE, n. A liquid measure (about 7 gallons).

AMUSED, p.p. Absorbed, fascinated.

AMYGDALES, n. Tonsils.

AND, conj. If, even if, though.

ANGLE-ROD, n. Fishing-rod.

ANTICHTHONES, n.pl. Antipodes.

APAID, p.p. Pleased.

APOSTEME, n. Abscess.

APPALLED, a. Flat, stale (of wine).

APPOINT, v. Prescribe.

AQUOSITY, n. Moisture, humour.

ARREST, n. Decree, order, sentence.

ARTIFICIALLY, adv. Artistically, cleverly.

ASAROTON OECON, a. & n. Greek name for a type of mosaic pavement, meaning "Unswept room".

ASS, n. A Roman copper coin (worth about ½d.).

ASSAUT, phr. *to go assaut*, to rut, be on-heat.

ASSOILLE, v. Absolve, pardon.
ASSURANCE, n. Betrothal, engagement.
ASTONIED, p.p. Astonished.
ATO-SIDE, adv. On one side.
AUTHOR, n. Authority, informant.
AVIE, adv. In competition.
AVISE, v. refl. Take thought, ponder, deliberate.
AWAY, phr. *can(not) away with*, can(not) put up with, tolerate.

B

BAGD, a. Pregnant.
BAIN, n. Bath.
BALLAISE, v. Ballast, steady.
BALTERED, p.p. Clotted, clogged.
BARBS, n. Wattles of cock.
BARM, n. Froth.
BASE-COURT, n. Courtyard.
BASH, v. Be ashamed (to do something), shrink (from doing it).
BATTLE, a. Fertile.
BEAR IN HAND, phr. Deceive, assure falsely, delude into believing.
BEETIL, n. A heavy tool for ramming or hammering.
BELLYGOD, n. Glutton.
BENTY, a. Rush-like, grass-like.
BERAYED, p.p. Dirtied, disfigured.
BESTRAUGHT, a. Distracted, distraught.
BIAS, adv. Obliquely.
BIBLIOTHEQUE, n. Library.
BILE, n. Boil.
BLABD, a. Swollen.
BLANCH, n. White paint.
BLUE-BLAW, n. Cornflower.
BOUEF(E), n. Ox, bull, cow.
BONGRACE, n. A sort of curtain attached to the front of a bonnet to keep the sun off the face.
BORDER, n. A plait or braid of hair worn round the forehead.
BOTCH, n. Ulcer.
BOTTOM, n. Ball of thread.
BOUGE, v. Stave in (a ship), make it spring a leak.
BRAKED, p.p. Beaten & crushed.
BRASSEN, a. Made of brass, brazen.

BRAVERY, n. Act of bravado; ostentatious ornament.

BROCH, n. Skewer, spit, pin.

BRUIT, n. Noise, fame, rumour.

BUBBATION, n. Bubbling, formation of pebbles (an Anglicized version of Pliny's *bullatio* or *bulbatio*, a term used to describe stone found in small, detached fragments).

BUCKLERS, phr. *give the bucklers to*, yield to, own oneself beaten by.

BULK, n. Stall, shop.

BULKIN, n. Bull-calf.

BUNCH-BACKED, a. Hunch-backed.

BURGADE, n. Village.

BURRET. A kind of shell-fish used for dyeing, murex.

BURSE, n. Purse-like sac.

BUTT, n. Trunk (of tree).

BY-CORNER, n. Out-of-the-way corner.

BY-NAME, n. Surname, nickname.

C

CADE, a. Pet (lamb).

CANEL, n. Pipe, tube.

CANICULAR, a. Of, or pertaining to the dog-star.

CAPILLARE, a. Hair-like.

CAPTIVATE, p.p. Captivated, subjugated.

CARCANET, CARKANET, n. Necklace.

CARQUAN, n. Necklace.

CARREFOUR, n. Crossroads.

CARRY, v. Measure, have the dimensions of.

CART-JADE, n. Cart-horse.

CASSIDOINE, n. A precious stone, chalcedony.

CAST, n. Contrivance, device.
　　　 v. Warp.

CATAPLASM, n. Plaster, poultice.

CATAPLASTER, n. Plaster, poultice.

CATCH, n. Round or canon in music.

CAUTELOUS, a. Crafty, cautious.

CAUTION, n. Security, bail, guarantee.

CAVALLERIE, n. Knighthood, knights.

CAWLE, n. Netted cap or head-dress.

CERE-CLOTH, n. Waxed cloth.

CEREOUS, a. Wax-like, waxy.

CERUSE, n. White lead, used as cosmetic or paint.

CHAFE, n. Rage, fury.

CHAFED, p.p. Heated.

CHAFER, n. Saucepan.

CHALLENGE, v. Claim.

CHAMBERLIE, n. Urine.

CHAMPION, a. Level, open (country).

CHAPE, n. Metal mounting of sword-sheath.

CHAPMAN, n. Customer, buyer.

CHAPTER, n. Capital of pillar.

CHAUFED, p.p. Rubbed.

CHEEK, n. Sidepost of door.

CHEER, v. Incite.

CHIEVANCE, u. Wealth, fortune, estate.

CHINE, n. Back.

CHINK, n. & v. Crack.

CHIRK, v. Encourage (a horse) by making a noise with the lips like a bird's chirp.

CHIRURGERY, n. Surgery.

CHIRURGIAN, n. Surgeon.

CITRON, n. Cithern, lute, guitar.

CLEA, n. Hoof.

CLEAN, a. Pure.

CLOISTURE, n. Lock, bolt, bar.

CLOT-BUR, n. Burdock.

CLYSTER, n. Enema.

CLYSTERIZED, p.p. Injected as an enema.

COAL, COALS, n. Charcoal.

CODS, n. Pods, husks; testicles.

COLLECT, v. Conclude, deduce.

COLLUTION, n. Mouth-wash.

COLLYRIE, n. Eye-wash.

COLOUR, n. Pretence.

COMMODITY, n. Advantage, benefit.

COMPLEXION, n. Colouring preparation for the face, rouge.

CONCENT, n. Harmony.

CONCOCTION, n. Digestion.

CONCURRENT, n. Rival, competitor.

CONDITE, a. Preserved, pickled.

CONFINE, v. Border (upon), be adjacent (to).

CONGLUTINATE, v. Unite (wounds), heal.

CONGRUITY, n. Sense, point, reason.

CONSUMMATE, p.p. Completed, brought to perfection.

CONTROL, v. Criticize, find fault with.

CONVENIENCE, n. Sympathy (cf. REPUGNANCE).

CONVINCE, v. Refute.

COPEROSE, COPPERESSE, n. Sulphate of iron.

CORNALLINE, n. Cornelian.

CORVINER, n. Shoemaker.

COSTUS, n. An oriental aromatic plant.

COUNTER, n. Counting-house, treasury.

COURSE, v. Pursue, persecute.

     n. Menstrual discharge; (one's) turn (to do something).

COUSEN, v. Cheat, deceive.

COUSENAGE, n. Fraud, deception.

COUSENER, n. Deceiver, cheat.

COVERT, n. Cover, shelter. phr. *under covert*, indoors.

CRAFTSMASTER, phr. *his craftsmaster*, master of his craft, expert.

CRAZY, a. Feeble, infirm.

CREST, n. Stone finishing on roof-ridge.

CROCHET, n. Hook.

CRUDITIES, n. Undigested humours, indigestion.

CUBIT, n. A measure of length (about 18″).

CUIRIE, n. (Royal) stable.

CUIT, a. (Wine) boiled down to a certain thickness, and sweetened.

CULLIONS, n. Testicles.

CULVERINE, n. Gun, cannon.

CURB, v. Curve.

CURRIER, n. Dresser of leather.

CURSED, a. Fierce, savage, vicious.

CUTANEAN, a. Of the skin, cutaneous.

CYATH, n. Wine-glassful.

CYPRIN, a. (Oil) made from seeds of Egyptian tree called cypros.

D

DEBASE, v. Depreciate, speak slightingly of.

DEEP, v. Deepen the colour of, darken.

DEEPING, n. Darkening.

DELFE, n. Layer or stratum of earth.

DELICATE, a. Self-indulgent, luxurious.

     n. Fastidious, luxurious person, sybarite.

DEMERIT, n. Merit, desert.

DENIER, n. A Roman coin, denarius (worth about 8d.).

DEVOTION, phr. *at the devotion of*, at the mercy of.

DEW-BLOWN, a. (Of cattle) swollen from over-feeding on fresh moist grass or clover.

DIAPHORETICAL, a. Causing or pertaining to perspiration.

DIFFERENCE, n. Judgement between, discrimination.

DIGEST, v. Dispose, distribute, arrange, classify.

DISCUSS, v. Dispel, disperse, dissipate.

DISSEIZE, v. Dispossess.

DISTEMPERATURE, n. Disturbance of mind or temper.

DIVISION, n. Rapid melodic passage of music, run, descant.

DOMAIN, n. Property, estate.

DOOR-SELL, n. Threshold.

DOUBT, n. Fear.

DRAUGHT, n. Drink; sewer, cesspool; traction, pulling.

DRIVE THE HIVES, phr. drive bees out of hives, e.g. with smoke, in order to take the honey.

DUMPISH, a. Depressed, dejected.

E

EAGER, a. Sharp, acute, severe; fierce, savage.

EAR, v. Plough.

EARNE, v. Feel grief.

EBB, a. Shallow, near the surface.

ECSTASY, n. Withdrawal of soul from body, trance.

EFTSOONS, adv. Again, afterwards, repeatedly.

ELEPHANTIE, n. Elephantiasis.

EMBOWED, a. Arched, vaulted.

EMISSARY, n. Outlet.

EMMANTLED, p.p. Covered, wrapped.

EMPLASTER, n. Plaster.

EMUNCTORY, n. Excretory duct.

ENCHASE, v. Enclose; engrave.

ENDUMENT, phr. *have an endument of*, be endowed with.

ENEAL, v. Burn in colours, enamel by an encaustic process.

ENGRAFF, v. Insert, implant.

ENHUILED, p.p. Oiled.

ENORMOUS, a. Outrageous.

ERE, v. Plough.

ERVIL, n. Bitter vetch.

ESPIAL, phr. *in espial*, on the watch.

EVERY FOOT, phr. Constantly, incessantly.

EXCHANGE, phr. *of exchange*, in exchange, on the other hand.

EXEGENT, n. Writ summoning a defendant to appear in court on pain of outlawry.

EXECUTION, n. Legal seizure of goods or person of debtor in default of payment.

EXORABLE, a. Capable of being moved by entreaty.

EXTENUITY, n. (Drawing of) extreme fineness or subtlety.

EXTENT, n. Writ to recover a debt.

EXULCERAT, p.p. Ulcerated.

F

FACT, n. Deed, crime.

FADOME, v. Encircle with extended arms.

FALLING EVIL, phr. Epilepsy.

FATHOM, v. Encircle with extended arms.

FESTUE, n. Straw, rush, twig.

FET, p.p. Fetched.

FISTULOUS, a. Tubular, honeycombed with small tubes.

FIVE-LEAF, n. Cinquefoil.

FLAGGY, a. Drooping, pendulous, flabby.

FLASKET, n. Long, shallow basket.

FLATUOSITY, n. Quantity of wind, air or gas; (also, flatulence).

FLEAME, n. Phlegm.

FLEURES, FLEURS, n. Menstruation, menstrual discharge.

FLIGHT, a. Swift, fleet.

FLOAT, n. Flux or flood of the tide.

FLOREY, n. Scum collected from vat in dyeing with woad or indigo.

FOALFOOT, n. Coltsfoot.

FOIST, n. A light galley.

FORELAY, v. Lie in wait for, waylay.

FORE-LET, a. Desolate, uncultivated.

FORE-WIND, n. Wind that blows ship forward on course, favourable wind.

FORTH-COMING, n. Appearance, production in court.

FOUNTAINER, n. Man in charge of fountain or water-supply.

FRANCHISE, n. (Place of) asylum, sanctuary.

FRANK-FED, p.p. Fed in a frank, a sty for fattening pigs in.

FRAUGHT, v. Load (ship) with cargo.

FROBISH, v. Furbish, polish, remove rust from (sword or other weapon).

FRONTAL, n. Medicament applied to forehead as cure for headache.

FRONTISPIECE, n. Pediment over door.

FRUMP, n. Sneer, jeer.

FRUSTRAT, p.p. Disappointed (of).

G

GALLIACE, n. Heavy, low-built warship, bigger than a galley.

GARDENAGE, n. Horticulture; garden produce.

GAUD, n. Trick, prank.

GEASON, a. Rare, scarce.

GEAST, n. Deed, exploit.

GEAT, n. Jet.

GENETOIRS, GENITOIRS, n. Testicles, genitals.

GESTATION, n. Riding (for exercise) on horseback or in carriage.

GLADER, n. Iris.

GLASS-STONE, n. A kind of transparent stone, perhaps mica.

GLEANE, n. Placenta, afterbirth.

GNOMON, n. Pillar, rod or other object that casts a shadow on sundial.

GODSPENIE, n. Small sum paid as earnest to confirm bargain or contract.

GOLDENIE, n. A fish, perhaps the golden wrasse.

GOMBE, n. Gum.

GRAIN, phr. *in grain*, dyed scarlet or crimson.

GREIMILE, GREMIL, n. A plant, gromwell.

GRINDING, n. Excruciating pain.

GROVELONG, a. Prone, face downward.

GRUDGING, n. Slight symptom, recurrence of ailment.

GUILT, n. Young sow.

GURRIE, n. Diarrhoea.

H

HAND, phr. *at best hand*, most cheaply, as cheaply as possible.
phr. *go in hand* (to), proceed to.

HAND OVER HEAD, phr. Hastily, rashly, without deliberation.

HANSELL, n. First trial or test.

HARDLY, adv. Boldly.

HARPOCRATES, n. Egyptian god of silence.

HASTY, a. Early-flowering.

HATCH, v. Draw parallel lines, for shading, etc.

HEAD, n. Source, fountain-head; body of water kept at a height to provide pressure for a water-supply.

HEMINE, n. A liquid measure (about ½ pint).

HICCOUGH, n. Hiccup.

HICKWAY, n. Green woodpecker.

HIPPED, p.p. Lamed in the hip.

HIPPOMANES, n. Mucous fluid produced by mares when on heat.

HORTYARD, n. Orchard, garden.

HOT-HOUSE, n. Turkish bath.

HOULET, n. Owl, owlet.

HOUND-FISH, n. Dog-fish, shark.

HOY, n. A small boat.

HUCK, v. Haggle, bargain.

HUGGLE, v. Hug.

HULVER-TREE, n. Holly.

HUMBLE-HEEL, n. A heel chapped, or with an ulcerated chilblain.

I

IDES, n. pl. 15th of March, May, July or October; 13th of other ·months.

ID EST, phr. That is, i.e.

IMAGEUR, n. Sculptor, carver.

IMAGINATE, a. Imaginative.

IMPALE, v. Fence in, enclose with stakes.

IMPEACH, v. Impede, hinder, prevent.

IMPEACHMENT, n. Hindrance.

IMPORTUNE, a. Troublesome, tiresome.

IMPOSTUMATE, v. Fester, gather into an abscess.

IMPOSTUMATION, n. Abscess, ulcer.

IMPOSTUME, n. Abscess, ulcer.

INCONTINENTLY, adv. Immediately, at once.

INCORPORAT, p.p. Mixed, combined.

INDICO, n. Indigo.

INDURATE, a. Hardened.

INENARRABLE, a. Indescribable, unspeakable.

INEXPUGNABLE, a. Incapable of being overthrown.
INSIGHT, n. Sight, inspection.
IN SUM, phr. In short.
INTERMEDLED, p.p. Mixed, intermingled.
INTERTAINMENT, n. Interlocking grip.
INUNCTION, n. Ointment; act of anointing.
ITEM, adv. Also.
      n. Intimation, hint.

J

JOB, v. Peck.

K

K. Abbreviation for *King*.
KEELER, n. Shallow tub.
KEL, n. Enclosing membrane, caul.
KEMBE, v. Comb, remove by combing.
KENNEL, n. Pack (of hounds).
KERNEL, n. Gland, or morbid swelling.
KERNELLY, a. Glandular, fleshy.

L

LANCE, v. Hurl, throw, shoot.
LASK, n. Diarrhoea.
LAP, v. Wrap, bind up.
LARG, n. The longest note in early music.
LATCH, v. Catch.
LATON, n. A yellow mixed metal, like brass.
LAY FOR, phr. Plan for, contrive to get.
LEAD, n. Pot, kettle, cauldron.
LEAGUER, phr. *in leaguer,* in camp, engaged in a siege.
LEAME, n. Flash, ray or gleam of light.
LEAP, n. Basket, for catching fish.
LEESE, v. Lose.
LEIRE, n. Clay, mire, mud.
LET, v. Omit, forbear, cease; hinder, prevent.

LEUCE, n. White leprosy.

LEWD, a. Ignorant.

LIB, v. Castrate, geld.

LIBARD, n. Leopard.

LIBEL, n. Defamatory leaflet, bill or pamphlet.

LIE, n. Alkalized water used for washing; any such detergent liquid.

LIGHTLY, adv. Probably; easily, readily.

LIMBER, LIMMER, a. Soft, flexible, pliant.

LIMIT, n. Cross-path or boundary-line between fields.

LINE, n. Flax.

LINTLE-TREE, n. Horizontal piece of stone or timber over door or window.

LIVELODE, n. Landed property.

LONG OF, phr. Because of, owing to.

LONG ROBE, phr. *of the long Robe,* wearing a toga, i,e, a Roman citizen.

LOOSE, v. Weigh anchor, set sail.

LUSTY-GALLANT, n. A shade of light red.

LUTED, p.p. Coated with clay or cement.

LUZERNE, n. Lynx.

M

MAIN, n. Mainland.

MANDELLION, n. Loose coat worn by soldiers and menservents.

MANDRAGE, n. Mandrake, mandragora.

MANNER, n. Custom, usual procedure.

        phr. *in manner,* almost entirely, very nearly.

        phr. *taking himself with the manner,* catching himself in the act.

        phr. *taken in the manner,* caught in the act.

MARCHES, n. Frontier regions.

MARK, n. Boundary.

MARQUETAGE, n. Inlaid work.

MARRE, n. Refuse remaining after grapes or other fruit have been pressed.

MARRISH, n. & a. March, marshy.

MASCELLIN, n. A kind of brass.

MASH, n. Mesh.

MASTERIES, phr. *try masteries,* try conclusions, compete.

MATRICE, n. Uterus, womb.

MATURE, n. Female sexual organs (perhaps a misprint for NATURE).

MAUGRE, prep. In spite of.

MEAN, n. A middle part in harmony (e.g. tenor or alto).

MELINUM, n. A colour, Melian white.

MERIDIONAL, a. Southern.

MEUTE, v. Excrete.

MIDDES, MIDS, n. Midst.

MILCH, a. Giving milk, kept for milking.

MILT, n. Spleen.

MINATORY, a. Threatening.

MINDING, n. Reminder.

MISLIKE, v. Grow sickly or unhealthy.

MONGER, n. Trader, dealer.

MONTH-MIND, n. Commemoration of a dead person by celebration of masses, etc, one month from the date of death.

MONUMENTS, n.pl. Written documents, records.

MOORY, a. Marshy, fenny.

MORION, n. A kind of helmet.

MORPHEW, n. Leprous or scrufy eruption on skin.

MOTHER, phr. *rising of the mother,* hysteria.

MOVEABLE, n. Article of furniture.

MUFFLE, n. Thick part of upper lip & nose of ruminants & rodents; proboscis.

MULLET, n. Young mule.

MUNDIFY, v. Cleanse, purify.

MUR, MURRE, n. Severe catarrh.

MURE, n. Wall.

MUTTON, n. Sheep.

N

NAMELY, adv. Particularly, especially.

NATHELESS, adv. Nevertheless.

NATURE, n. Female sexual organs.

NAUGHT, n. Nothing.

a. Bad, injurious, worthless.

NE, conj. Nor.

NEAT, a. Pure.

NERVE, n. Sinew, tendon, muscle.

NIGHT-WALKER, n. Someone who prowls about at night, especially with criminal intentions.

NOBLE, a. (Of parts of the body) those which are essential to life, e.g. heart, lungs, etc.

NODOSITY, n. Knotty swelling or protuberance.

NONCE, phr. *for the nonce*, for the time being.

NOONSTEAD, n. (Position of the sun at) noon.

NOURCE, n. Nourisher, nurse (Holland's translation of *alumna*, which in late Latin can mean "nourisher, educator", but here probably means "nurseling".)

O

OASE, n. Ooze.

OCCUPY, v. Make use of, use.

OCCURRENT, a. Presenting itself.
　　　　　n. Occurrence, event, episode.

OF, prep. From.

OLEOUS, a. Oily.

OLYMPIAD, OLYMPIAD, n. Period of 4 years between one celebration of the Olympic Games and the next, by which the Greeks computed time (First Olympiad began 776 B.C.).

OPIET, n. Guelder rose.

OPILATION, n. Obstruction.

ORDER, n. Custom, regular procedure.

ORDNANCE, n. Engines and implements of war (catapults, slings etc).

ORPIMENT, n. A colour, King's Yellow.

OTHERWHILES, adv. Sometimes, occasionally; at other times.

OVERCAST, v. Coat (brick, stone etc) with plaster.

P

PAGEANT, n. Stage, platform, piece of stage-machinery.

PANICKE, n. A kind of grass or graminaceous plant.

PANNICLE, n. Membrane.

PAPYR, a. Made of papyrus.

PARCEL, n. Part, portion.

PARGET, n. Plaster, ornamental work in plaster.

PAROLE, a. Expressed or given by word of mouth, orally.

PARPINE, n. In masonry, a stone which passes through a wall from side to side, having two smooth vertical faces.

PANTOPHLE, PANTOFLE, n. Shoe, slipper.

PASH, v. Hurl, dash, smash.

PASS, v. Surpass, excel, exceed.

    adv. Surpassingly, very.

PASSION, n. Bodily disorder, disease.

PEARL, n. Cataract.

PELTING, a. Petty.

PENCIL, n. Artist's paint-brush.

PENNACHE, n. Plume.

PENT, a. Constricted, unable to urinate.

PERCEIVANCE, n. Perception.

PERCH, n. Measuring-rod ($5\frac{1}{2}$ yards).

PERILOUS, a. Dreadful, terrible, awful.

PERTUISANE, n. Partisan, long-handled spear.

PERVINCLE, n. Periwinkle (the plant).

PHRENSIE, n. Mental derangement, delirium, insanity.

PIED-STALL, n. Pedestal.

PILL, v. Peel (of skin).

PIN AND WEB, phr. An eye disease.

PISMIRE, n. Ant.

PIZZLE, n. Penis of animal.

PLATFORM, n. Plan.

PLOT, n. Plan, sketch.

PLUCK, v. Strain, dislocate, sprain.

POISE, n. Weight.

    v. Weigh.

PORCELLANE, n. A kind of shell-fish, the cowrie.

PORGET, n. Plaster, ornamental work in plaster.

PORTWAY, n. Road, highway.

POSE, n. Cold in the head, catarrh.

POTENTIAL CAUTERY, phr. Medical agent producing same effects on skin as an *Actual Cautery,* or red-hot iron.

POUN, v. Pound, crush, pulverise.

POURCUTTLE, n. Octopus.

POURFIL, POURFLE, v. Draw in outline.

    n. Representation or drawing in outline.

POURPRISE, n. Enclosure, circuit.

PRACTISE, v. Conspire, plot, intrigue.

PREMEDITAT, p.p. Planned beforehand.

PRESENTLY, adv. Immediately, instantly, promptly.

PREST, v. Enlist, conscript for military service.

    a. Ready, prepared.

PREVENT, v. Anticipate.

PRINCIPAL, n. Main rafter, post or brace in framework of a building.

PRO CERTO, phr. For certain.

PROFFER, n. Attempt.

PROJECT, n. Plan, design, sketch.

PROKE, v. Poke, thrust.

PROPER, a. Own, belonging to oneself.

PROUD, a. (Of female animal) on heat.

PROVOCATION, n. Impulse, urge.

PRUNE, v. (Of birds) preen, dress feathers with beak.

PUN, v. Pound, crush, pulverize.

PUNAISE, PUNICE, PUNIE, n. Bed-bug or similar insect.

PUNCHEON, n. A piercing weapon, dagger.

PURPOSEDLY, phr. *purposedly of the Trojan war*, on the subject of the Trojan war.

PUSH, n. Pimple, boil, pustule.

PYRRIE, n. Pear-tree.

Q

QUADRANT, n. Small Roman coin, worth $\frac{1}{4}$ *as*; farthing.

QUARREL, *n.* Square tile.

QD. v. Abbreviation for *quoth,* said.

QUAVER, v. Use trills or shakes in singing.

QUICK, a. Alive.

R

RACE, n. Narrow channel; cut, mark, scratch.

RAG, n. Piece or mass of hard, rough stone.

RAMPIAR, RAMPIER, n. Rampart.

RASE, n. & v. Scratch, cut.

RAUGHT, v. past tense. Reached.

REACH (UP), v. Bring up, vomit, spit.

RECEIPT, n. Prescription, remedy; capacity, size, reservoir.

RECORD, v. Practise a song, sing.

RECOVER, v. Make for, betake oneself to.

RECULE, v. Go backwards, retreat.

REDUCE, v. Refer (e.g. to origin), relate.

REGRATER, n. Trader who buys up goods in order to establish a monopoly, and sell at an inflated price.

REINS, n. Kidneys.

RELIGION, n. Member of a religious order.

RENDLES, n. Rennet.

REPERCUSSION, n. Reflection.

REPUGNANCE, n. Antipathy (cf CONVENIENCE).

RESERVING HONOUR, phr. Saying "Saving your honour", "By your leave".

RESIANT, a. Resident, dwelling, abiding.

RESOLVE, v. Melt, dissolve.

RETAIN, v. Conceive.

REVERBERATION, n. Reflection.

RIVEL, n. Wrinkle.

RIVELED, a. Wrinkled.

RIVERET, n. Small stream, rivulet.

ROAD, n. Raid, invasion, foray.

ROBE, phr. *of the long Robe,* see LONG ROBE.

ROSAT, a. Rose-coloured.
 phr. *oil rosat,* oil of roses.

ROSET, n. A rose-coloured paint.

ROUND, v. Whisper.

ROUNDLE, n. Round plate, disk, or globe.

RUFFE, phr. *in his ruffe,* in his pride.

RULE, n. Graduated mark, as on ruler, sundial, etc.

S

SACRE, v. Consecrate, bless.

SADNESS, phr. *in sadness,* seriously, in earnest.

SAL-NITRE, n. Saltpetre.

SALVE, v. Salute, greet, wish health to.

SAMPIER SAVAGE, phr. Wild samphire.

SCALD, a. Affected with scaly or scabby skin disease.

SCANTLING, n. Prescribed size.

SCAREFIRE, n. Sudden conflagration.

SCLISE, n. Fire-shovel.

SCORCH, v. Shrivel up (skin) as if by heat.

SEAZE, v. Assess, impose a tax or fine on.

SECOND, v. Support, assist.

SECURE OF, phr. Free from fear of.

SEEGE, n. Excretion.

SEEL, v. Overlay (walls) with gold or marble; line a roof; provide with a ceiling.

SEELY, a. Innocent, harmless.

SEEN, phr. (*well*) *seen in,* (well) versed in, an expert in.

SEMBLABLE, phr. *the semblable,* the same thing; a similar thing.

SEMBLABLY, adv. Similarly.

SENSIBLE, a. Perceptible by the senses; (of pain) acute.

SENSIBLY, adv. Perceptibly, visibly and audibly.

SENTENCE, n. Judgement, verdict.

SEPTENTRIONAL, a. Northern.

SERCE-WISE, adv. In the manner of a sieve.

SESTERCE, SESTERTIUS, n. (pl. SESTERTII). Roman coin, worth about 2d.

SET CASE, phr. Suppose, assume.

SEXTAR, n. Roman liquid measure (about 1 pint).

SEY, n. A cloth of fine texture.

SHADOW, n. Reflection.

SHAFTMENT, n. Distance from end of extended thumb to opposite side of hand, reckoned as 6″.

SHAP, n. Female sexual organs.

SHARE, n. Groin, fork, pubic region.

SHARP, phr. *at* or *with the sharp,* with unbated swords (as opposed to mere fencing).

SHENT, p.p. Blamed, reproached, put to shame.

SHERNE, n. Dung.

SHIFT, n. Series.

SHIVE, n. Slice (of bread).

SHREWD, a. Spiteful, mischievous.

SIGHT, n. Pupil of the eye.

SIGNIFER SPHERE, phr. Zodiac.

SIGNORY, n. Rule, domination.

SILLY, a. Poor; helpless; weak; simple; humble.

SINK, n. Sewer, drain, cesspool; bilge, bilge-water.

SIR, n. Gentleman.

SITUAT, p.p. Situated.

SKALLING, verbal, n. Scaling.

SKILL, v. Have knowledge of, know of; make a difference, be important, matter.

SKIN, phr. *sleep in a whole skin,* avoid wound or injury (by not fighting).

SKUT, n. Female sexual organs.

SLAVE-COURSER, n. Slave-dealer.

SLICK, a. Smooth, glossy, sleek.

SLIVE, v. Split, cut, slice.

SLOW-BACK, n. Sluggard, drone.

SODDEN, p.p. Boiled.

SOPHISTICATE, v. Adulterate, make impure, add inferior substance to; offer substitute or imitation instead of genuine article.

SOPHISTICAT, p.p. Adulterated, made impure, etc.

SORANCE, n. Sore.

SOUDER, SOUDRE, v. Unite, stick together; (of wounds) cause to close up, heal.
　　　　　　　n. Solder; any binding or uniting substance.

SPAN, n. Greatest distance from tip of thumb to tip of little finger (reckoned as 9″).

SPARIE, a. Sparing (a word used only by Holland).

SPART, n. Coarse, rushy grass, esparto.

SPEIGHT, n. Green woodpecker.

SPIALL, phr. *in spiall*, on the watch.

SPONGEOUS, a. Spongy.

SPITTER, n. Young deer with simple, unbranched horns.

SQUARE, v. Strut, swagger.

SQUINANCIE, n. Quinsy, inflammation of throat and tonsils.

STADIUM, (pl. STADIA), n. Ancient measure of length (606¾ feet).

STALE, n. Urine.

STANDARD, n. An upright timber, bar, or rod.

STAND UPON, phr. Consist of; attach importance to, set store by.

STARTOP, n. High boot or legging.

STATIONS, phr. *Walk his stations,* go through his paces.

STELE, n. Stalk, stem.

STELLION, n. (A kind of) lizard.

STEW, n. Pond or tank in which fish were kept until needed to eat; brothel.

STINT, n. Prescribed limit, allotted amount of work.

STOCK, STORKE, v. Root up, pull up by roots, fell (a tree) by digging round and cutting roots.

STOCK-GILLOFRE, n. Stock-gillyflower.

STONE-HORSE, n. Stallion.

STONES, n. Testicles.

STOPPLE, n. Stopper.

STORKE, v. (see STOCK).

STOUPH, STOVE, n. Hot-air, steam, or vapour bath; stove.

STRAIT, a. Close, small, narrow.

STRAIT-WINDED, a. Short of breath, asthmatic.
STRENGTH, n. Stronghold, fortress.
STRIKE, v. Rub, smear, anoint.
STUT, v. Stutter.
STYLE, n. Ancient writing instrument, pen.
SUBSISTENCE, n. Substance, consistency.
SUBTILE, n. Thin (so, of a worn mirror, slightly concave).
SUM, phr. *in sum,* in short.
SUPPURAT, p.p. Formed by suppuration, having suppurated.
SURD, a. Insensate, unintelligent.
SWAYED, p.p. Strained in the back (of a horse).
SWERT, a. Dark, black.

T

TABLE, n. Board, or other flat surface on which picture is painted; hence, the picture itself; tablet, slab for inscription.
TAKE, v. Consider, regard as.
> phr. *taking himself with the manner, taken in the manner,* see MANNER.
TANKARD, n. Large, open, tub-like vessel used for carrying water.
TAPISSED, p.p. Hung, covered with tapestry.
TARGUET, n. Light, round shield.
TEMPER, n. Mixture, composition, constitution.
> v. Regulate, control, govern; mix.
TEMPERATURE, n. Middle condition, mean between opposites; mixture, composition; climate.
TENDRON, n. Young shoot or sprout of a plant.
TENT, n. Probe; roll of soft absorbent material, often medicated, used to search and cleanse a wound.
TERMS, n. pl. Menstrual discharge.
TETTAR, n. Skin-disease (e.g. eczema).
TEWED, p.p. (Of a skin) steeped and beaten.
TEW-TAWED, p.p. (Of hemp or flax) beaten or dressed.
TICKLISH, a. Sensitive, brittle; precarious, unstable.
TINE, n. One of the teeth or prongs on agricultural implement (e.g. harrow); pointed prow or beak of ancient warship.
TINESME, n. Continual urge to excrete, with no discharge; tenesmus.
TIWILL, n. Anus, rectum, lower bowel.
TO-BEHANGED, p.p. Hang all over.

To-beperfumed, p.p. Liberally perfumed.

Tonus, n. Tone.

To-rate, v. Scold severely.

Tornsoll, n. A violet-blue or purple colouring matter.

Torrify, v. Roast, deprive of all moisture by heating.

To-shake, v. Shake violently.

Train, v. Induce, entice, persuade.

Treatable, a. Deliberate, at a slow tempo.

Treddle, n. Pellet of sheep's or goat's dung.

Treen, a. Wooden.

Tribunal, n. Raised platform or mound.

Trifoly, n. Trefoil.

Tripoli, n. A dark purple colour.

Trochiske, Trosche, n. Medicated pastille, tablet or lozenge.

Trot, n. Old woman, hag.

Truchman, no. Interpreter.

Trunk, n. Pipe, tube.

Tune, n. Scale or mode in ancient Greek music.

Tunicle, n. Membrane enclosing a bodily organ.

Twiggen, a. Made of twigs or wickerwork.

Twine, v. (Of timber) be contorted or irregular in formation.

Twist, n. The junction of the thighs, fork.

Tympanie, n. Swelling, especially with reference to pregnancy.

U

Uncessant, a. Incessant, ceaseless.

Uncessantly, adv. Incessantly, ceaselessly.

Uncom, n. Ulcerous swelling, boil.

Uncouth, a. Unknown, unfamiliar, strange.

Undergrown, a. Showing signs of puberty, pubescent.

Unneath, Unneth, adv. Not easily, with difficulty; scarcely, hardly.

Unpointed, a. Not wearing tags or laces.

Unrebated, a. Unblunted, unbated.

Untowardly, adv. Awkwardly, clumsily.

Unwitch, v. Unbewitch, free from enchantment.

Ure, phr. *in ure*, in practice.

Utmost, n. Outermost limit or boundary.

Utterance, phr. *at* (*the*) *utterance*, to the death, to the bitter end, with the utmost violence.

V

VAN, n. Winnowing basket or shovel.

VANTCOURRIER, n. Forerunner.

VAUT, n. Cistern.

VENDITATE, v. Set out as if for sale, display speciously.

VENEREOUS, a. Sexual, erotic.

VENGIBLE, a. Grievous, severe.

VENTOSE, n. A kind of cupping-glass.

VENTOSITY, n. Flatulence, wind.

VENTRICLE, n. Stomach : cavity in the brain.

VICE, n. Mechanical contrivance, especially one incorporating the principle of the screw.

VINET, n. Ornament or design imitating branches, leaves and tendrils of vine.

VOLUBILITY, n. Revolution, rotation.

VOLUNTARY, phr. *sing voluntary,* sing a cadenza, or spontaneous improvisation.

VULNERARY, a. Skilled in treatment of wounds.

            n. Preparation, herb or drug used in treatment of wounds.

W

WALM, WAULME, v. (Of water) well up, gush out; boil, bubble.
             (Of smoke, vapour) Swirl, billow forth.

WARISH, v. Heal, cure.

WARRANTIZE, n. Authorization, permission; assurance; guarantee of safety.

WEIGH UP, phr. Hoist up.

WEIRE, n. Fence or enclosure of stakes made in river or harbour to catch fish.

WHERVE, n. Whorl or flywheel of spindle.

WHILE, WHILES, n. Time, period of time.

WHILES, conj. While, whilst.

WHIRLPUFF, n. Whirlwind.

WHITLED, a. Drunk, intoxicated.

WIFFLER, n. Attendant employed to keep way clear for procession or public show.

WINDER, v. Wither, pine.

Windles, n. Windlasses.
Wistly, adv. Intently, with close attention.
Within-forth, adv. Within, inside.
Without-doors, adv. Out of doors, in the open air.
Without-forth, adv. Outside; outwards.
Woe Worth, phr. Woe betide.
Wood, a. Mad, insane.
Worm-stall, n. Outdoor shelter for cattle in warm weather.
Wraule, v. Bawl, squall.
Wring, n. Sharp griping pain.

Y

Yard, n. Penis.
Yeeles, n. Eels.
Yex, Yox, n. & v. Hiccup.
Ywis, adv. Certainly, assuredly, indeed, truly.

INDEX